THE *Natural History* OF *Mammals*

THE *Natural History*

TRANSLATED FROM THE FRENCH
by H. M. Parshley

WITH REVISIONS IN ENGLISH
BY THE AUTHOR

NEW YORK: 1970
Alfred A. Knopf

by François Bourlière

OF *Mammals*

THIRD EDITION, REVISED

Preface

to the American Edition

THIS translation into English of my book on mammals (*Vie et mœurs des mammifères*, Paris, 1951) has been revised and brought up to date to make it a more comprehensive and more nearly worldwide introduction to field mammalogy. New drawings and photographs have been added, and I hope that they will increase the usefulness of the book.

The bibliography has been enlarged, but it is not intended to be exhaustive. I have selected titles by authors in various countries, wishing to avoid scientific provincialism, and at the same time I have chosen studies representative of the main trends of modern zoological research in the field.

It is a privilege to express my thanks to the many persons who have helped me in the preparation of this edition in English. Among them I may name my friend Richard Pough, Curator of Conservation and Preservation of Natural Resources in the American Museum of Natural History, without whose assistance this book would probably never have been published, and the late Professor H. M. Parshley of Smith College, who undertook the task of translating the original French text and of working out with me the numerous additions and revisions. I gratefully acknowledge also my indebtedness to the individuals and institutions that have aided me in gathering the supplementary drawings and photographs: namely, P. Barruel (Paris), Dr. M. Eisentraut (Frankfurt), Prof. P. P. Grassé (Paris), Robert Hainard (Geneva), Prof. H. Hediger (Basel), Dr. R. Verheyen (Brussels), the New York Zoological Society, and the Marine Studios, Marineland, Florida. Finally, I wish to express my thanks to Alfred A. Knopf, Inc., and to Mr. Philip Vaudrin in particular, for the courteous consideration they have shown me and for the care they have bestowed on the book.

FRANÇOIS BOURLIÈRE

NOTE TO THE THIRD EDITION

MAMMALOGISTS have been particularly active during the last decade, and their field and experimental work has, in many cases, shed new light on numerous problems of mammalian ecology and behavior. Therefore, it has been necessary, in order to keep this volume up to date, to undertake extensive revisions. Large portions of Chapters 1 to 9 and all of Chapter 10 have been rewritten. In addition, some important physiological problems have been reviewed in an appendix. The bibliography has been completely reorganized and indexed in a new way to make it more useful for the field worker. The author expresses his thanks to his publishers, and to Mr. Angus Cameron in particular, for their understanding and their help. He hopes that *The Natural History of Mammals*, thus rejuvenated, will continue to be of value to those who wish to have a better understanding of the life of our close relatives.

F. B.

Paris
January 1964

Introduction

OF all animals the mammals are probably the most familiar to us. Among them we find the earliest and most valued auxiliaries of man, those domesticated hoofed animals which have played a determining role in the history of civilization and still remain of great importance in the world economy of today. Other species have become our daily companions, and still others have made themselves uninvited guests in our homes and cities. Certain species are prized game animals, whereas others, often labeled "injurious," may be hunted down to the point of extinction.

Besides, since the rise of the experimental sciences, it is the mammals that have furnished the majority of laboratory animals; most of the researches in physiology, experimental medicine, and comparative psychology during the last fifty years have been carried out mainly on a few species of rodents and carnivores.

It might then be supposed that this multiplicity of contacts between the mammals and man would have brought with it a better knowledge of their biology; it would indeed be logical for the various aspects of their life to be better known to us than those of birds, fishes, or certain groups of insects. Unfortunately this is true only in part. Certainly the domesticated species and the laboratory rodents have been studied in great detail, and that biological reagent *par excellence*, the white rat, for example, has served as the subject matter of thousands of publications. This, however, has not much advanced our knowledge of the life of wild mammals—all those which live outside the artificial conditions of domestication or captivity. Moreover, many laboratory biologists have a regrettable tendency to apply to mammals in general, including the primates to which we ourselves belong, the conclusions drawn from their observations on the cat, the dog, the guinea pig, the white rat, or the mouse. Has not, for example, a whole school of experimental psychologists somewhat confused animal psychology with the study of the behavior of the white rat? Such excesses were inevitable once the biologist ceased to be a naturalist, and laboratory experimentation was no longer accompanied by observation in the field. They are no less dangerous to the progress of our knowledge than they are for the conclusions, practical or philosophical, that some will draw from them.

The study of *ethology* (the habits) and of *ecology* (the relations of individuals and of populations with their environment) is therefore of great theoretical and practical importance. It alone will inform us regarding the normal modes of life of the various species, their reactions throughout their vital cycles, and their numerous and remarkable adaptations. It allows us to take account of the great differences, at once morphological, physiological, and psychological, that exist between the different groups, and in some measure serves as an antidote against oversimplification and premature generalization.

Unfortunately the observation of mammals in nature is a delicate matter; most small species are nocturnal, and all display caution and shyness toward the observer. To obtain results of interest requires much ingenuity and patience—and sometimes luck. The study of birds in the field is much easier, and here probably lies one of the major causes of the neglect of the mammals by many naturalists.

During the last twenty years, however, the enthusiasm of a few outdoor mammalogists has increased our knowledge considerably. Thanks to them, many problems have been solved and others—formerly unsuspected—have been posed to challenge the sagacity of research workers. Most of their works, unfortunately, have been published in specialist journals of difficult accessibility and many of them have thus remained unknown to the average naturalist. It is not uncommon even today, therefore, to see articles on mammals which, from the ethological and ecological point of view, could have been written a half century ago.

In the absence of a general synthesis of mammalian ethology and ecology—which would be at present as premature as unwise—the lack of any broad survey of the existing state of our knowledge constitutes an evident gap. It is this gap that I have attempted to fill with this book, limiting myself to the chief problems and to the best known aspects of this vast subject. I have not endeavored to write a manual, still less a treatise on the biology of mammals, but rather a plain introduction to the comparative ethology and ecology of wild mammals. I am quite aware of the imperfections and shortcomings of this work, the aim of which is rather to furnish basic information than to give answers to problems whose solutions depend largely upon future researches. Yet I hope that, such as it is, it will be of service and will guide the beginner through the existing maze of the literature.

I have not considered it necessary to rehearse here the

fundamental concepts of anatomy, taxonomy, and physiology, which, I assume, are familiar to the reader. If, however, he should feel the need of refreshing his memory in these matters, he will find all the essential information in certain of the works cited at the end of this volume. Nor have I considered it necessary to grapple with the problems of genetics, speciation, and geographical distribution. These questions have formed the subject, during the last ten years, of several excellent books.[1]

I have asked my friend Paul Barruel—whose artistic talent is in every way equal to his competence as a naturalist —to make a series of drawings that have freed my text from much arid descriptive matter. I wish to express my sincere gratitude to him. In addition I have been able to reproduce a number of photographs owing to the kindness of Professor Hediger and of the following institutions: the American Museum of Natural History (New York); the United States Fish and Wildlife Service (Washington); *l'Institut des Parcs nationaux du Congo Belge* (Brussels); and *les Expéditions polaires françaises* (Paris). It is my pleasant duty to express here my thanks to them.

[1] Especially: E. Mayr, *Animal Species and Evolution* (Cambridge, Mass.: Harvard University Press; 1963).

Contents

Chapter 1   *Locomotion*   3

2   *Food and Feeding Habits*   37

3   *Home, Territory, and Home Range*   66

4   *Defense and Protection*   108

5   *Sexual Life and Reproduction*   138

6   *Development and Longevity*   170

7   *Migrations*   203

8   *The Social Life of Mammals*   220

9   *Mammals and Their Environment*   250

10   *The Structure and Dynamics of Natural Populations*   281

Appendix   321

Taxonomic List of Species   337

Bibliography   349

Subject Index to Bibliographical References   385

Index   *following page* 387

Illustrations

facing page

I   *Storing of food.*   8

II   *Breathing-hole of a Weddell's seal.*   **9**

III   *Resting and sleeping position of a lesser horseshoe bat.*   **9**

IV   *Topography of the home range. A red-deer wallow.*   40

V   *Topography of the home range of Burchell's zebra. Rubbing-post.*   40

VI   *Topography of the home range. Hippopotamus trails.*   41

VII   *Topography of the home range of the West African civet. Heap of dung.*   41

VIII   *A gorilla "nest."*   72

IX   *Nest and eggs of the duckbilled platypus.*   73

X   *Beaver dam in Oregon.*   104

XI   *An American beaver house.*   105

XII   *Beaver canal in state of Washington.*   105

XIII   *Defensive attitude of the southern elephant seal.*   136

XIV   *Llama giving birth.*   137

XV   *American bison giving birth.*   137

XVI   *Birth of a bottlenosed dolphin: early stage.*   168

XVII   *Birth of a bottlenosed dolphin: late stage.*   168

XVIII   *Mother bottlenosed dolphin and newborn young asleep.*   169

XIX   *Female marmosa carrying her young.*   232

XX   *Female opossum carrying her young.*   232

XXI   *Eastern chipmunk hibernating.*   233

XXII   *Young long-eared bat, three days old.*   264

XXIII   *Adult long-eared bat.*   264

XXIV   *A harem of Alaska fur seals.*   265

Illustrations in the Text

FIG. 1: *Typical "diagonal" gait of fox.*   4

FIG. 2: *A giraffe ambling.*   5

FIG. 3: *Gallop of the hare.*   5

FIG. 4: *Gallop of the deer.*   6

FIG. 5: *Successive stages in the progress of an adult earless seal.*   8

FIG. 6: *Erect bipedal posture of Waller's gazelle.*   10

FIG. 7: *Bipedal walking in an armadillo.*   11

FIG. 8: *Bipedal walk of the black gibbon.*   12

FIG. 9: *Bipedal walk of the chimpanzee.*   13

FIG. 10: *Bipedal walk of the northern three-toed jerboa.*   14

FIG. 11: *Rapid bipedal locomotion of the Merriam kangaroo rat.*   14

FIG. 12: *The leap of the tarsier at the outset.*   16

FIG. 13: *Scales on the underside of the tail of a flying squirrel.*   17

FIG. 14: *A squirrel descending a tree trunk.*   18

FIG. 15: *Brachiation as performed by the lar gibbon.*   19

FIG. 16: *Swimming position of the American beaver.*   22

FIG. 17: *Successive stages in gliding flight in the North American flying squirrel.*   28

FIG. 18: *A gliding Australian marsupial.*   29

FIG. 19: *Path of wingtip during ordinary flight of a lesser horseshoe bat.* 31

FIG. 20: *Upstroke of the wing of the little brown bat.* 32

FIG. 21: *Record of ultrasonic sounds emitted by a bat.* 34

FIG. 22: *Fat dormouse eating a grape.* 43

FIG. 23: *The fish-eating bat with a fish just caught.* 50

FIG. 24: *The giant anteater.* 50

FIG. 25: *Diagram of plankton strainer of a* Balænoptera. 53

FIG. 26: *Sea otter sleeping "moored" to a float of* Nereocystis. 68

FIG. 27: *Sea otter sleeping "wrapped up" in an alga.* 68

FIG. 28: *Sleeping position of a potto.* 71

FIG. 29: *Shelter of the bat* Artibeus watsoni. 73

FIG. 30: *Polar bear's den for giving birth to young.* 75

FIG. 31: *The two types of wild rabbit burrows.* 77

FIG. 32: *Evolution of the burrow of the little souslik,* Citellus pygmæus. 78

FIG. 33: *Summer burrow of an Asiatic jerboa.* 80

FIG. 34: *A subterranean rodent with almost hairless skin,* Heterocephalus glaber. 81

FIG. 35: *Reconstruction in perspective of the nest of a European mole.* 82

FIG. 36: *Diagram showing ground plan of a new burrow of a plains pocket gopher.* 84

FIG. 37: *Diagram of the burrow of the tuco tuco,* Ctenomys brasiliensis. 85

FIG. 38: *Nest of the European harvest mouse.* 89

FIG. 39: *Vertical section and ground plan of a lodge of the American beaver.* 92

FIG. 40: *Section of a European beaver pond in the Voronezh region of Russia.* 94

FIG. 41: *Diagram of a European beaver pond in the Voronezh region of Russia.* 95

FIG. 42: *Diagrammatic representation of the accepted concepts of territory and home range.* 96

FIG. 43: *A male European bison at his "rubbing tree."* 104

FIG. 44: *Territory of a dominant male European wild rabbit.* 105

FIG. 45: *Map of vicuna territories, Huaylarco, Peru.* 106

FIG. 46: *Defense posture of the great red kangaroo.* 110

FIG. 47: *Three-toed anteater in a "tripod" attitude.* 111

FIG. 48: *Posture of defense of the armadillo,* Tolypeutes conurus. 113

FIG. 49: *The armadillo* Chlamyphorus truncatus. 113

FIG. 50: *A pangolin,* Manis tricuspis, *rolled into a ball.* 114

FIG. 51: *Attitude of defense of the African porcupine,* Hystrix africæ-australis. 115

FIG. 52: *Appearance of the tip of a quill of the American porcupine.* 116

FIG. 53: *Virginia opossum "playing dead."* 117

FIG. 54: *Position of the striped skunk before the ejection of the secretion of its anal glands.* 118

FIG. 55: *A skunk,* Spilogale gracilis, *"standing on its hands."* 119

FIG. 56: *The genital region of the South American marsupial,* Lutreolina crassicaudata. 141

FIG. 57: *Female gray kangaroo assisting the passage of the embryo.* 144

FIG. 58: *Young brush wallaby in the mother's pouch.* 145

FIG. 59: *Diagram showing the posture of the male wild rabbit while "tail flagging."* 154

FIG. 60: *Prenuptial pursuit in roe deer.* 155

FIG. 61: *A male reindeer sniffing at his female.* 156

FIG. 62: *The "mating march" of Thomson's gazelle* 157

FIG. 63: *Male bottlenosed dolphin posturing.*   157

FIG. 64: *Prenuptial play of Indian elephants.*   158

FIG. 65: *Position of the female long-eared bat just after the birth of her young.*   168

FIG. 66: *Newborn European hare.*   171

FIG. 67: *Newborn wild rabbit.*   171

FIG. 68: *Milk teeth of a young mouse-eared bat.*   174

FIG. 69: *Transportation of the young in the European red squirrel.*   178

FIG. 70: *Female bear carrying her young.*   179

FIG. 71: *Transportation of its young by a female Sumatra pangolin.*   179

FIG. 72: *Female three-toed sloth transporting its young.*   180

FIG. 73: *Sea otter swimming on its back and carrying its young on the abdomen.*   181

FIG. 74: *A female common shrew and its "caravan" of young.*   182

FIG. 75: *Young foxes engaging in a mock fight.*   184

FIG. 76: *European badgers playing leapfrog.*   185

FIG. 77: *Otters sliding.*   186

FIG. 78: *Growth curves of a male Cairo spiny mouse and of a male Shaw's jird.*   192

FIG. 79: *Modifications in skulls of the chacma baboon due to growth of a morphological character.*   194

FIG. 80: *Dormouse in hibernation.*   197

FIG. 81: *The migration of Antarctic humpback whales in the Indian Ocean.*   209

FIG. 82: *Area of distribution and lines of migration of the harp seal.*   210

FIG. 83: *Some results obtained from markings used in studying the migrations of the harp seal.*   211

FIG. 84: *Migrations of two groups of large mouse-eared bats.*   213

FIG. 85: *Diagram showing the location of traps in Stickel's experiment.* 216

FIG. 86: *Pedal gland of the muntjac,* Cervulus muntjak. 226

FIG. 87: *Some types of cutaneous glands in the ungulates.* 227

FIG. 88: *Anal gland of the male civet,* Viverra zibethica. 228

FIG. 89: *Male* Antilope cervicapra *"marking" a twig.* 229

FIG. 90: *Some characteristic expressions of the wolf.* 231

FIG. 91: *The expressive function of tail movements in the wolf.* 232

FIG. 92: *Variations in the time at which daily activity begins for the European mole.* 262

FIG. 93: *Graphic method of estimating total population from the results of intensive trapping.* 286

FIG. 94: *Diagram showing the positions of the age rings on a chamois horn.* 290

FIG. 95: *The dry-weight, growth-rate curve of the lens of the eye, based on 92 cottontail rabbits of known age.* 292

FIG. 96: *Survival curves for males of five ungulate populations.* 298

FIG. 97: *Survival curves for females of five ungulate populations.* 298

FIG. 98: *Age variations in the reproduction of captive female European varying hares.* 304

FIG. 99: *Increasing litter mortality with increasing population size among house mice.* 312

FIG. 100: *Fluctuations in the abundance of the Canadian lynx.* 315

FIG. 101: *The relationship between "good" years in various species of Canadian mammals.* 317

FIG. 102: *The activity rhythm of a common shrew.* 332

THE *Natural History* OF *Mammals*

Locomotion

THE mammals have colonized all environments in the course of their evolution. They abound not only in the various terrestrial habitats but in addition some of them have become successfully adapted to aquatic and aerial life. We should not be surprised, therefore, to find among them a great variety of means of locomotion, which can be grouped under three principal heads: walking, swimming, and flying. But nature does not recognize rigid classifications, and it is possible, as we know, to walk, swim, and fly in many ways. In the following pages we shall examine some of the methods most commonly used.

Unhappily our knowledge of this chapter in mammalian biology is particularly meager. There exist a considerable number of works on the structural adaptation of recent and fossil species to different types of locomotion, and on their evolution in time. But we are much more poorly informed on the mechanics of movement in the living animal and on the physiological adaptations to running, diving, or flight. Much remains to be done on this subject, and close observation in the field, accompanied by well-directed experimentation, may well open new horizons for us.

TERRESTRIAL LOCOMOTION

THE method most frequently practiced by the great majority of land mammals is four-footed, or quadrupedal, locomotion. The mechanics of the normal quadrupedal *walk*, found in the majority of hoofed animals and members of the cat family and the dog family, may be schematized as follows:

In the slow *walk* (fig. 1), the animal's body is always supported by three legs, but when the speed increases it is supported by three or two lateral or diagonal legs. The sequence of the limbs' movements always shows a diagonal pattern, for instance: right forefoot, left hind foot, left forefoot, right hind foot, etc.

FIG. 1: *Typical "diagonal" gait of fox. Only one half of a stride is represented; the other is symmetrical.*

Certain species, such as the giraffe (fig. 2), normally use a different type of co-ordination of the members, called *ambling*. In the slow *amble*, the body is alternately supported by two or three diagonal or lateral legs, but the swifter the animal moves, the more the diagonal pattern is replaced by a lateral one, for instance: right forefoot, right hind foot, left forefoot, left hind foot, etc. The amble is the chief manner of rapid locomotion of the Camelidæ, Giraffidæ, Proboscidea, Hippopotamidæ, and big Ursidæ. If the speed of the animal still increases, the amble may change to the *rack,* in which for nearly half the time the animal floats in the air and for the other half is supported by one or two lateral legs.

The slow *trot* is nothing more than an accelerated walk, and is found in almost every species of mammals, with the exception of the amblers. It also follows the diagonal sequence of limb movements, and when the speed in-

FIG. 2: *A giraffe ambling. Drawn from photographs by the author.*

creases, the body alternately floats in the air and is supported by two diagonal legs.

FIG. 3: *Gallop of the hare, showing succession of positions of contact with the ground.*

The *gallop* is a succession of leaps during which the animal floats in the air or is supported alternately by its forelegs and hind legs (fig. 3). In the small- or medium-sized species the back of the animal is thus successively stretched and bent to a maximum degree, but in the horses and big Ruminantia there is practically no movement of the back (fig. 4).

FIG. 4: *Gallop of the deer. The back does not move as in the hare of fig. 3.*

The maximum speed attained by wild mammals at a gallop is considerable and can be maintained for rather long periods of time. Table 1 gives some examples furnished by reliable observers. In most cases these speeds have been determined by using an automobile, keeping the car abreast of the animal running on a course parallel with the road. The cheetah, or hunting leopard of India, appears to be the swiftest of all mammals. In full gallop an individual can reach 45 miles an hour two seconds after starting! At full speeds cheetahs are faster than the swiftest greyhounds, attaining rates of 60 to 70 miles an hour. Although we have to do here, of course, with extreme speeds that the animal cannot maintain for long, there is a record of a cheetah covering more than 700 yards in 20 seconds—a rate of slightly more than 71 miles an hour. It is obvious from all this that a trained cheetah is admirably suited to the hunt.

Table 1. *Maximum running speeds of some land mammals. (In part after Howell)*

SPECIES/SPEEDS IN MILES PER HOUR

Camel 9–10	*Roan antelope* 30–35
Sheep 11	*Caribou* 37
Kouprey 15–18	*European hare* 35–45
Crabeater seal 16	*Springbok* 35–60
Wild rabbit 20–25	*Mountain zebra* 40
African elephant 15–25	*Spotted hyena* 40
Black rhinoceros 28	*Coyote* 40
Wart hog 30	*Grant's gazelle* 40–50
Giraffe 28–35	*Horse* 44
Jackal 35	*Wildebeest* 50
Indian wild ass 30–32	*Lion* 50
Cape buffalo 35	*Cheetah* 70–75
Wolf 35–40	

LOCOMOTION OF PINNIPEDS ON LAND. The seals and related aquatic mammals returning to the land for only a short time each year exhibit all the intermediate stages between typical quadrupedal walking and an awkward creeping in which their rudimentary limbs no longer take any part.

The Falkland sea lion still uses its four limbs after the fashion of an ordinary mammal, but the soft tissues and tail extend so far toward the ankle joints that at each step the hindquarters as a whole are swung forward. Its gait can become rapid if the animal is excited, and on a pebbly beach an adult male can "run" as fast as a man (Hamilton). The enormous southern elephant seal of the subantarctic islands uses only its front legs in traveling on land. "The fore flippers are spread out at the side with the palms on the ground

7

and the fore part of the body is raised by them and hitched forward. At the same time that the fore part is being raised, the back is curved upwards, so that the hind flippers are drawn up slightly nearer, and as the front flippers hitch

FIG. 5: *Successive stages in the progress of an adult earless seal. Walking consists in a series of forward hitchings. In part after Harrison Matthews.*

forward, the back is straightened, and the body is pushed forward from the pelvic region" (Matthews). These massive creatures, however, can attain a maximum speed of 5 miles an hour and may stray up to 700 yards from the shore. Weddell's seal, a typically antarctic species wintering under the ice pack, has forelegs so small that they do not

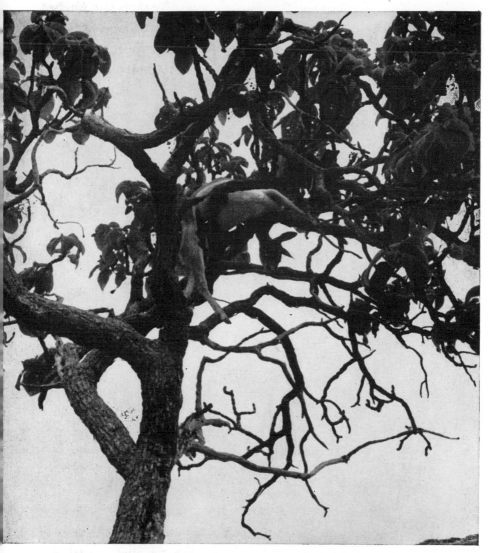

Storing of food. Here an oribi antelope has been killed and placed in a tree by a leopard, Panthera pardus. *Photograph by* G. F. de Witte, *taken at Lusinga, Belgian Congo, in January 1948. Courtesy of the* Institut des Parcs nationaux du Congo Belge.

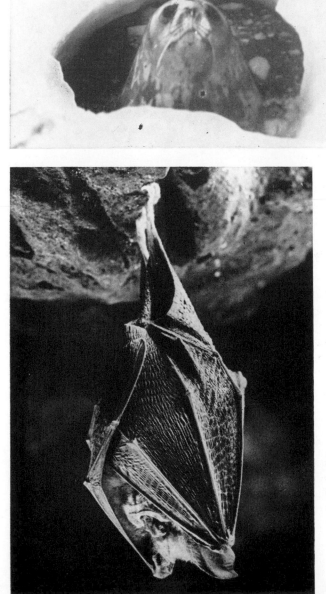

Breathing-hole of a Weddell's seal in the Antarctic ice pack, Adélie Land. Photograph by Harders. Courtesy of the Expeditions polaires françaises.

Resting and sleeping position of a lesser horseshoe bat. Photograph by Ernst Krause. Courtesy of Dr. M. Eisentraut.

even touch the ground when the animal is out of the water. Progression on land then becomes essentially a creeping motion in which the pelvic and pectoral regions are drawn alternately forward.

In the gray seal of the European seas these different types of locomotion are successively used as the individual grows. On the first day the young seal tries to walk on its four feet; it advances its forelegs one after the other and drags its body forward while its hind legs attempt to push. On the second day all systematic use of the hind legs is given up and little by little the front legs become synchronized in their movements; they are extended forward together to afford support to the animal so that it can draw its body forward. This method of locomotion persists until about the tenth day, at which point the young seal has become so fat that the front feet are no longer strong enough to accomplish propulsion by themselves. From now on the animal moves along on its belly (fig. 5) by alternately jerking forward the pectoral and pelvic regions (J. L. Davies).

BIPEDAL WALKING. Certain quadrupeds are able in special circumstances to maintain a bipedal attitude for a few steps. Some stags, for instance, fight in this position, and Waller's gazelle stands up on its hind legs to browse on foliage (fig. 6). But these are exceptional cases among the non-primates.[1]

The bipedal walk of the anthropoids (fig. 8) is altogether different, as witness this vivid description of it in the case of a lar gibbon: "Having mounted the large limb, the animal may stand semi-erect with its hands and arms held

---

[1] Certain armadillos (fig. 7) and pangolins can on occasion walk on the hind legs with the aid of the tail.

FIG. 6: *Erect bipedal posture of Waller's gazelle browsing on foliage. Based on photographs by Priemel.*

out from its sides and with the elbows and wrists flexed. The legs, too, will be only partially straightened and the trunk will be inclined slightly forward. As the gibbon progresses on the limb, its pelvis rotates markedly as one foot is placed directly before the other. . . ." (Carpenter). This manner of progression is not, however, the most frequent under

FIG. 7: *Bipedal walking in an armadillo,* Priodontes giganteus. *Drawn from a photograph from Grassé,* Traité de
zoologie, *Vol.* XVII.

natural conditions, and brachiation, or locomotion by means
of the arms, is the rule.

Chimpanzees and gorillas are also only partially bipedal.
They rarely stand quite upright, and when walking generally touch their knuckles to the ground with the digits extremely flexed (fig. 9). Man alone is completely bipedal, although the pelvis of the fossil Australopithecinæ of South
Africa gives us reason to suppose that these primates had as
erect a posture as our own.

LEAPING. Along with normal walking, quadrupedal or
bipedal, we find in certain mammals a very peculiar progression by leaps in which the tail plays an important part.

The clearest example of it is afforded by the Australian
kangaroos (family Macropodidæ). When they walk slowly,
the step may be analyzed as follows: The animal, being supported partly on its forelegs and partly on its tail, first raises

its hind legs together; then, in a second movement, it is supported on its hind feet, while its forefeet and its tail are raised. The kangaroos, then, really use five members in walking. When the animal accelerates its gait, it employs only the powerful extension of its hind legs, and, during the

FIG. 8: *Bipedal walk of the black gibbon,* Hylobates concolor. *Drawn from a photograph by Suschitzky.*

leap, the tail acts as a counterbalance and is held quite horizontal. So moving, the forester kangaroo can attain a speed of 25 miles an hour, the "peaks" approaching 29 or 30. At a slow pace the leaps may be from about 4 to 6 feet, but they rapidly lengthen with increased speed, and a large animal will cover 26 feet in one bound. Leaps up to nearly 40 feet have been reported. These extreme performances are probably attained only on an especially favorable terrain. It is worth noting that the tail of these large kangaroos has a very special structure: the hemal processes of the vertebræ are

FIG. 9: *Bipedal walk of the chimpanzee. Note how the animal uses the support of its front limbs.*

much flattened; the lower surface of the organ is well supplied with fatty tissue, and the intervertebral muscles are well developed.

Among the rodents a whole series of species normally move about by means of successive leaps or hops. Some, like the spring haas of South Africa, walk on four feet when they are not disturbed and leap by means of their hind legs only when they are frightened. It is the same with the North American jumping mouse. The jerboas of the Old World, on the other hand, generally use only their hind legs in locomotion, and their hind feet are the longest in comparison to the forefeet known among leaping mammals (fig. 10). The

FIG. 10: *Bipedal walk of the northern three-toed jerboa. After a photograph by Serebrennikov.*

tail, likewise, is proportionately very long. The lesser Egyptian jerboa when unhurried walks bipedally, with alternate movements of the hind limbs, the front feet being used to sift through the sand in search of food. When rapid, this animal's locomotion takes the form of a series of lengthy bipedal leaps during which the long tail serves as a balancing organ. The kangaroo rats of western North America, in addition to a bipedal walk used only when the animal is feeding or traveling a short distance, move mostly by long bipedal hops in the manner of the jerboas (fig. 11). When moving slowly, the Merriam kangaroo rat occasionally uses

FIG. 11: *Rapid bipedal locomotion of the Merriam kangaroo rat. Redrawn from Bartholomew and Caswell.*

quadrupedal hopping. Its hind legs supply the chief propulsive force, lifting the body forward and upward, but the forefeet support the body weight as the hind legs are drawn forward.

That very peculiar primate, the tarsier of the Malay Archipelago, often moves by leaps, although it is strictly a tree-dwelling form. As with the jerboas, it is the action of the hind legs that accomplishes locomotion, and in both species the tibia and fibula are united distally. One difference is, however, to be noted: in the tarsier it is the tarsal bones and not the metatarsals that are elongated, doubtless so as not to hinder the grasping action of the fingers. Photographs at five thousandths of a second, recently made at the National Zoological Park in Washington, have made it possible to analyze these movements. This little animal, weighing hardly 85 grams when adult, commonly makes leaps of about 6 feet during which it can rise to a height of 2 feet. Before it lands, the tail, held horizontally up to that point, is quickly raised over the back, while the paws are held out to absorb the shock (fig. 12).

ARBOREAL LOCOMOTION. A number of mammalian species spend their entire lives in trees, descending to the ground only rarely, or accidentally. This is true not only of certain monkeys and apes but also of many rodents and arboreal marsupials in tropical regions. Their methods of locomotion would be most interesting to study in detail and offer an almost unexplored field for research.

The techniques of arboreal locomotion would all seem to be more or less directly derived from the techniques of walking, but in some details they show interesting adaptations to a particular environment.

Mounting a tree trunk or a tropical vine by alternate grasping with the hand and foot of one or the other diagonal seems to be a method often used by some monkeys and even by certain species with powerful claws, the three-toed anteater, or tamandua, for example.

FIG. 12: *The leap of the tarsier at the outset. The animal has just left the ground and is rising, its tail extended. After a photograph at ⅕.₀₀₀ of a second by E. P. Walker.*

Some animals climb by alternate movement of the limbs of one side and then of the other, a method that is usually marked by slower progression. Others climb by successive holds, first by the front limbs and then by the hind ones. This method is common among squirrels when they climb a tree trunk, and it has been aptly remarked that in this case "the progress up a tree is essentially a gallop, the fore and hind feet being used alternately in pairs" (Hatt).

In nature, however, the technique of climbing can vary in the same species according to the character of the holds and the way the animal clings to its support. Species with prehensile fingers can grasp the support when it is not too big, as do most of the arboreal primates. Species with well-developed nails (squirrels, tamanduas, etc.) cling by means of their claws when this is at all possible. Other species (bears, sloths, koalas, etc.) literally embrace the support with their limbs and progress more slowly. Possession of a prehensile tail greatly facilitates arboreal locomotion, and certain New World monkeys, such as the spider monkeys, use at once the hands, arms, and tail to make contact with supports when they leap from one tree to another. The

FIG. 13: *Scales on the underside of the tail of a flying squirrel,* Anomalurus, *which serve as an "antiskid" device. From Grassé,* Traité de zoologie, *Vol. XVII.*

scales (fig. 13) beneath the tail of certain flying squirrels of Africa act as an "antiskid" device when the animals land on tree trunks. Among devices for clinging to the support should be mentioned also the adhesive disks of the tarsier's paws.

How animals descend tree trunks is a topic that deserves methodical study. It would appear that species with prehensile fingers, and also those which embrace the support with their limbs, generally descend with the head up. Squirrels, on the other hand, descend head downward (fig. 14), clinging by means of their claws and ordinarily using the four feet independently.

BRACHIATION. Certain monkeys of arboreal habit, such as gibbons and spider monkeys, have a special mode of progression that has been called brachiation. It corresponds in a way to the bipedal walk, but here it is the front limbs that are used in locomotion, not the hind ones. One and the same

FIG. 14: *A squirrel descending a tree trunk, head down. The animal clings to the bark by means of its claws.*

species, for instance the lar gibbon, can moreover use bipedal walking or bimanual brachiation according to whether it is progressing on the ground or in the trees. Carpenter believes that in their customary forest environment the gibbons he observed in Siam move about mostly by brachiation; walking on the ground is practiced only rather exceptionally—in 10 per cent of cases, he estimates.

The mechanism of this two-handed locomotion is simple. First one hand, say that of the right arm, grasps a branch and draws the body forward; then the body oscillates on the pivot made by the right hand, and the hand of the extended

FIG. 15: *Brachiation as performed by the lar gibbon. Drawn from a photograph.*

left arm lays hold on another branch (fig. 15). The gibbon advances rapidly in this way, being able to cover 10 feet in a single swing. If the animal goes from one branch to another that is a little farther away, a short glide occurs between holds.

Such a mode of locomotion is correlated with an extraordinary freedom of motion of the shoulder joint, far greater than that characteristic of man.

The red spider monkey of Panama normally moves about by walking on all fours on large branches, its long tail curved over its back. These monkeys use brachiation only in passing from one branch to another, and they show no hesitation in making impressive leaps, which may reach a length of 38 feet. During the leap the four legs and the prehensile tail are kept outspread to check the fall and to increase the chances of coming in contact with branches. Spider monkeys have been observed letting themselves fall vertically 20 to 25 feet from one branch to another of the same tree.

AQUATIC LOCOMOTION

SWIMMING BY LAND MAMMALS. Most strictly terrestrial mammals are capable of swimming, if need arises, or at least of keeping themselves at the surface of the water. Species as far from being aquatic as the hare or the European hedgehog sometimes take to the water voluntarily and, under greater compulsion, are able to cross a small stream when pursued. Most of the Muridæ—mice and their allies—do the same, and among the Mustelidæ the ermine, the polecat, and the mink are excellent swimmers. The hamster inflates its cheek pouches with air before taking to the water. The European mole can swim without apparent fatigue for several hundred yards, and the American star-nosed mole can do likewise. The latter has even been seen swimming beneath the ice in winter in small ponds and "sculling" with its tail.

Most ungulates, or hoofed animals, and carnivores can cross small stretches of water. An American black bear, for example, has been observed to swim for five miles! (Cahalane.) That wild boars can cross arms of the sea of considerable size is attested to by the fact that a number of them reached the French island of Oléron after having crossed at least a mile of salt water. The Texas armadillo is also a good swimmer, but if the stream is narrow it simply walks across on the bottom. On the other hand, the elephant seems unable to swim, and must walk on the bottom, the tip of its trunk out of the water (Verheyen).

Many monkeys have no fear at all of the water and swim with ease. Rhesus macaques normally swim across small streams, and in the experimental colony established on Santiago Island, Puerto Rico, it is not uncommon to see them bathing on the seashore. The lar gibbon, on the other hand, seems incapable of co-ordinated limb movements when placed in water; the fur very soon becomes wet, and experiment has shown that this animal can not even keep itself at the surface for one minute. Gorillas and chimpanzees appear equally incapable of swimming. In these land species it seems that swimming motions do not differ essentially from those of walking.

Even bats are able to keep themselves at the surface. In a recent work, Olof Ryberg cites a whole series of previous observations and adds some new ones that are very convincing. It now appears certain that species like Daubenton's bat, which customarily pursue insects close to the water, can take flight again after having remained some moments at the surface. The fish-eating bat of tropical America does the same.

SWIMMING IN AMPHIBIOUS AND AQUATIC MAMMALS. It is well known that beavers, otters, muskrats, and water rats normally take to the water. The American beaver, when swimming, keeps nine tenths of the body under water, and the front legs, folded back under the chest, are not used; only the hind legs (fig. 16), moving together, propel the animal. The beaver is capable, moreover, of "sculling" at a slow rate of speed, using its tail alone, but this behavior would seem much less frequent than in the muskrat.

FIG. 16: *Swimming position of the American beaver. After Grinnell, Dixon, and Linsdale.*

The sea otter of the north Pacific comes ashore only on very rare occasions and moves about on land very awkwardly. These otters rest and sleep while floating on their backs, preventing drift by occasional strokes of their tails. They swim on the belly, like fresh-water otters, only when in a hurry; otherwise they always move about on their backs, their four feet in the air, propelled by slow sideways movements of their tails.

Seals use co-ordinated movements of their rudimentary appendages for locomotion in water. But very great differences exist according to the species concerned and their adaptation, more or less nearly complete, to the marine environment. In the Falkland sea lion the front flippers alone are used at slow speeds, in a rowing manner. When the animal wishes to increase its speed it brings its hind limbs into play. The southern elephant seal, on the contrary, never uses its front limbs, which remain pressed against its body while the posterior limbs propel the animal. The same is true of Weddell's seal; the two hind feet are pressed one against the other by their palmar surfaces, with the fingers widely separated for maximum extension of the webs. This whole apparatus is set in motion by regular lateral undulations that enable the animal to maintain a cruising speed of 7 knots (Bertram).

With the cetaceans and sirenians—whales and sea cows —locomotion is accomplished by oscillations of the tail and the flippers in a vertical plane. But tail and flukes move out of phase, the flukes leading the tail by a quarter of a wavelength (Parry). The results obtained by this mode of propulsion are very remarkable: a maximum speed of 15 knots is common in the cetaceans, and blue whales have been observed to swim at speeds of 20 knots for 10 minutes and 14.5 knots for two hours.

SUBMERSION AND ITS MECHANISM. Naturally all the aquatic mammals are capable of distinctly longer submersion than the land species. While the dog has not been ob-

Table 2. *Maximum duration of submersion of some amphibious and aquatic mammals. (In part after Irving)*

SPECIES/MAXIMUM SUBMERSION OBSERVED, IN MINUTES

Muskrat 12		*Fin whale* 30	
Southern elephant seal 12		*Blue whale* 49	
American beaver 15		*Sperm whale* 75	
Common seal 15		*Greenland right whale* 80	
Florida manatee 16		*Bottlenose whale* 120	

served to remain under water more than 4 minutes and 25 seconds and the white rat more than 3 minutes and 6 seconds, it is quite otherwise with many amphibious and purely aquatic mammals. See Table 2.

Although it is possible that some of the extreme figures given in this table reflect inaccurate observations, it is none the less certain that sirenians, pinnipeds, and cetaceans can bear much longer immersion than land mammals.

Furthermore, these animals dive to considerable depths, as the observations of Scholander and of Laurie demonstrate. Young seals can go down to 240 feet, and the fin whale commonly plunges or "sounds" to depths varying from 275 to 1,150 feet. The sperm whale very probably reaches 3,000 feet!

By what mechanisms can they, as air-breathing vertebrates, endure such prolonged periods without oxygen and return from such great depths without the occurrence of gas bubbles in the bloodstream?

First, two negative statements: The performances of diving mammals are not due to larger lungs than those of land animals; nor does their blood pigment possess a better oxygen-carrying ability. Man, in fact, has a larger relative lung capacity than that of whales, and only seals possess a somewhat higher oxygen-binding ability than other mammals. But cetaceans can utilize much more oxygen from a given volume of air because the surface of their red blood corpuscles is larger and the proportion of their muscle haemoglobin is far greater than that of terrestrial mammals.

On the other hand, at each inhalation the diving mammals renew the air contained in their lungs more completely than do land forms: 90 per cent in the large whales, as compared with 15–20 per cent in man. Moreover, the respiratory center of diving mammals is remarkably insensitive to

increase in the amount of carbon dioxide in the blood; this
has been shown in the American beaver and muskrat as well
as in the Florida manatee, the seals, and the porpoises. These
first two adaptations thus serve, in one case, to increase
the amount of oxygen available at the beginning of the
dive and, in the other, to reduce the stimulating effect of
carbon dioxide on the respiratory center of the nervous
system.

Moreover, other physiological adaptations permit the
economical use of the oxygen stored up at the beginning and
restrict its employment to the most essential vital activities.
As soon as the dive is begun, the heart slows down considerably. In the gray seal the number of beats falls from
100 to 10 per minute, and this low pulse continues during
the 15 to 20 minutes of submersion. The occurrence of this
phenomenon in the bottlenose dolphin has been beautifully
demonstrated by Irving, Scholander, and Grinnell, who succeeded in taking electrocardiograms of animals diving in
semiliberty. At each dive there was a corresponding slow-
down in the heartbeat, of the order of 50 per cent. Thus the
available oxygen is economized during diving. It is the same
with the Florida manatee. In the common seal oxygen consumption during the first minutes of the dive falls to one
fifth of what it is when the animal is in repose! Moreover,
if the blood pressure remains normal in the large arteries (in
spite of the slow heartbeat), it falls rapidly in the small
arteries to the level of the pressure in the veins, with complete disappearance of the pulse. There is also a considerable
vasoconstriction in the mesenteric blood vessels, while the
circulation in the brain remains normal. Thus all the oxygen

available is at the disposal of the essential vital activities, the rest of the organism being in some way shut off from the circulation.

How do the diving whales avoid divers' paralysis—caisson disease or "the bends"? It is well known that one of the great dangers of diving, for men, is the frequent production, at the time of emergence, of gas bubbles in the blood which may lodge in the heart or brain and cause paralysis or even sudden death. What happens is this: During the descent, the pressure increases with depth, and the blood, passing through the lung capillaries, is charged with dissolved nitrogen, which increases in amount as the pressure rises; the blood will later yield this nitrogen to various tissues. If the return to the surface is too quick, the nitrogen can no longer remain dissolved and will separate out in the form of gaseous bubbles which will cause more or less serious disturbances. For a time it was thought that there existed in whale's blood a micro-organism capable of making use of this nitrogen dissolved in the plasma. Nothing of the kind exists in fact, and it would appear that things can be explained more simply. The cetacean does not live, like the human diver, in air constantly renewed. The animal carries in its lungs only a limited amount of nitrogen. Moreover, at the time of diving, the pressure of the water on the sides of the animal compresses the alveoli of the lungs and forces back into the bronchial tubes, the trachea, or the nasal cavities most of the gas not held by the blood corpuscles. In this way the dissolving of the nitrogen in the plasma is correspondingly reduced. Finally, the high rate of heartbeat that accompanies the return to the surface favors the elimination of the dissolved nitrogen. These safety devices, moreover, are by no means absolute, and Scholander has demonstrated the existence, at emergence, of gaseous embolisms in a seal submitted to an experimental dive of 150 fathoms. It is therefore likely that pinnipeds and cetaceans, when they dive to great depths, are also obliged to follow the rule of returning to the surface by slow stages.

AERIAL LOCOMOTION

WE find two different types of flight in mammals: the flapping flight peculiar to the bats, and the gliding practiced by the flying squirrels, the flying lemurs (Dermoptera), and the marsupials of the genera *Petaurus, Acrobates,* and *Schoïnobates.* These two types of flight are not of equal importance. For the mammals that practice gliding flight, this is hardly more than a secondary mode of locomotion, and is used principally, though not exclusively, as a means of escape. The bats, on the contrary, have become strictly aerial mammals and are entirely dependent on flying in their search for food and other activities.

GLIDING. The most classic examples of gliding are to be found among the squirrels. Even in the European red squirrel it is easy to observe (in spite of the absence in this animal of wing membranes—the patagium) a clear tendency to practice gliding. When a pursued squirrel reaches the top of a tree, it does not hesitate to launch itself into the void. Its outspread legs and extended tail serve to steady and balance the animal, and it usually arrives safely on the ground or on another tree trunk.

It is not surprising, then, that the North American flying squirrel, well equipped with parachute-like membranes spread between the limbs and the sides, proves to be an intrepid acrobat. Throwing itself from a treetop fifty feet or more above the ground, it glides easily, controlling its direction by varying the tension of its membranes and the slant of its tail. It can even turn at a right angle to avoid a branch. Before making contact with the tree trunk where it will end its course, it flips its tail upward. In response, the body turns up, the speed is checked, and the landing is made

FIG. 17: *Successive stages in gliding flight and landing in the North American flying squirrel.*

facing upward (fig. 17). The trunk may then be quickly climbed, with another gliding descent to follow.

In Asia the flying squirrels of the family Pteromyidæ are represented by many species that frequent the tropical zones as well as the mountain forests. The giants of this group belong to the genus *Petaurista*, some species of which can accomplish glides of 150 to 200 feet.

In Africa flying squirrels of the family Anomaluridæ glide in the same manner. Species belonging to the genus *Idiurus* would seem to be especially skillful gliders. Sanderson has observed in southern Nigeria two species of this genus lodging in groups in hollow trees. If they are disturbed in the daytime a veritable swarm of perhaps a hundred individuals emerges quickly, overruns trunk and branches, and takes "flight" among the trees. The little animals "take to the air in clouds," Sanderson writes, "floating away among the neighbouring trees like bits of soot from a

Fig. 18: *A gliding Australian marsupial*, Petaurus sciureus. *From Grassé*, Traité de zoologie, *Vol.* xvii.

chimney, steering themselves over and around obstacles with the facility of birds, and landing silently, hundreds of feet away, without any apparent loss of height."

In Australia the flying phalangers (fig. 18) behave in similar fashion. The sugar glider can glide for 50 yards and the greater glider-opossum for 120. An individual has even been observed to cover 590 yards in six successive "flights"!

The flying lemurs of the Malay Archipelago are almost as skillful. *Cynocephalus volans* easily covers 70 yards or more, and it is noteworthy that a mother in flight is able to carry her young one clinging to her lower surface.

FLAPPING FLIGHT. Among the mammals, this is found only in the Chiroptera, or bats, which have indeed become as aerial as the birds. The largest species, such as the Indo-Malayan *Pteropus vampyrus,* a fruit bat whose wingspread may be more than a yard, are capable of long, sustained flight. The Molossidæ, a family of tropical bats with relatively long and narrow wings, have a rapid flight which recalls that of the swifts. But most of the small bats have an irregular and capricious flight, broken by sudden changes in direction that may be horizontal as well as vertical. The flight of the little common bats called Pipistrelles even has some resemblance to the irregular flight of a large butterfly.

The only attempt so far made to analyze the flight of bats is the work of the German mammalogist Max Eisentraut. Using a motion-picture camera, he has succeeded in recording the wing movements of a number of small species. Without going into technical details, we may sum up his conclusions by saying that mechanically the normal flight of a bat is very much like that of a bird. The wing is lowered forward and downward, then is raised upward and backward (fig. 19). The body is kept almost horizontal and is raised slightly during the downbeat of the wings. The number of flaps per second varies with the species, from 12 in *Myotis* to 16 and 19 in the pipistrelle and the noctule.

Some species, such as the long-eared bat, can hover at a fixed point for some moments. In this case the body is almost vertical, but the wings keep up the same movements and the bat is in a sense flying vertically, the lift being just enough to counteract the force of gravity.

FIG. 19: *Path of wingtip during ordinary flight of a lesser horseshoe bat. After Eisentraut, 1937.*

Gliding flight is used by bats, but they do not seem able to use upward heat currents and to practice soaring, as do many birds.

The tail does not appear to play an important part in steering the flight. In some species the interfemoral membrane is curved forward before landing, probably acting as a brake.

The process of taking flight has been studied in a large mouse-eared bat, hanging from a branch by its hind feet. Instead of letting itself fall before beginning to fly, the animal begins by flapping its wings, with the result that the axis of the body is raised to a horizontal position before taking off.

"ECHO-SOUNDING" FLIGHT NAVIGATION IN BATS. Naturalists have long been deeply interested in the ease with which bats can fly in complete darkness and the fact that many of them feed on insects captured in flight at twilight or during the night. Their little eyes alone would seem to be quite unable to guide them in the labyrinths of the caves where many withdraw during the daytime, and still less to permit the bats to locate insects in flight or to avoid collision, in total darkness, with branches or other obstacles.

FIG. 20: *Upstroke of the wing of the little brown bat. Note the opening of the mouth (to permit the emission of super-sounds). After a photograph by H. E. Edgerton.*

As far back as the eighteenth century the great Italian naturalist Spallanzani demonstrated that blinded bats remained nevertheless perfectly able to fly about in a room without colliding with walls, furniture, or threads stretched across their way. Shortly after, the Swiss Louis Jurine showed that a bat with reduced hearing is, on the contrary, unable to avoid obstacles in flight. The later experiments of Rollinat and Trouessart in France and of Hahn in the United States confirmed these discoveries.

In 1920 the English physiologist Hartridge suggested that bats flying in darkness were able to sense the presence of obstacles by sending out ultrasonic vibrations whose echoes would be reflected back to their ears. It was only twenty years later, and after the development of radar, that two Americans, Griffin and Galambos, were able to demonstrate how well founded this hypothesis was. With the help of an apparatus that registered these inaudible vibrations, they established a whole series of curious facts.

To begin with, the species they studied—the big brown bat, the little brown bat, Keen's bat, and the eastern pipistrelle—gave out four different classes of sounds: (1) a shrill cry with a frequency of 7 kilocycles, or 7,000 cycles per second, perceptible to the human ear and continuing for about one quarter of a second; (2) a buzz, not audible unless the observer is quite close to the animal; (3) a very rapid and hardly perceptible click; and finally (4) the ultrasonic "cry," imperceptible to the human ear, of frequencies varying between 30 and 70 kilocycles. Those between 40 and 55 kilocycles are the most common. A bat in repose gives out, on the average, 5 to 10 of these "inaudible cries" each second; but when it takes flight they increase in frequency to 20 or 30 per second and even reach 60 in the vicinity of an obstacle. Buzzing and clicking always accompany the emission of the supersounds (fig. 20).

Further study by Griffin of the high-frequency sounds emitted by these bats has shown that the basic unit is an individual high-frequency sound of very short duration, which may contain from about 40 to 3,500 individual sound waves and which is repeated at varying rates depending upon the activity in which the bat is engaged. Such pulses are frequency-modulated, and the bat therefore has at its disposal a twofold range of wave lengths. This characteristic is very important, for the longer wave lengths, with superior carrying power, can inform the bat about distant and large objects whereas the shorter waves may be used to perceive small objects.

FIG. 21: *Diagrammatic record of the ultrasonic sounds emitted by a bat during 2½ seconds. For the first second the bat was cruising at 30 to 40 feet above the ground; but during the next second it made a sudden dive toward a pebble roughly one centimeter in diameter that had been tossed into the air. Note the great increase in pulse repetition rate and shortening of the pulse duration as the bat is engaged in active pursuit of this small target. After Griffin.*

The records obtained from bats flying under natural conditions, and especially from individuals pursuing flying insects, have shown, moreover, that the pulses emitted are different from those recorded in the laboratory. Instead of a pulse lasting 2 to 5 milliseconds and having an octave of frequency-drop from beginning to end, the big brown bat in cruising flight, for instance, emits pulses lasting 10 to 13 milliseconds and having a nearly constant frequency during most of this period. But when this bat dives toward a flying insect the long-duration pulses give way to a rapid series of the shorter-duration, frequency-modulated type (fig. 21). The bat is thus able to control not only the duration and repetition of the pulses, but also their frequency modulation. The duration is likewise varied in such a way that by the time the sound has gone out to an object of interest to the bat and returned, the original pulse has been completed. These records show furthermore that the echo-ranging system may also be used in the active pursuit of insect prey.

All the kinds of bats do not emit their ultrasonic sounds through the mouth, like the Vespertilionid bats first investigated. Horseshoe bats, or Rhinolophids, studied by Möhres in Germany, do so through their nostrils. The ultrasonic beam is thus oriented by the nose-leaf, whose contraction can even increase the range of the echo-ranging mechanism.

Among mammals, echo location is not restricted to bats. W. N. Kellog has demonstrated that porpoises can avoid invisible sheets of plate glass, find their way in turbid waters or in the dark, and detect fish by listening to the echoes of the clicks they produce in rapid successive series.

These noises contain a wide band of both sonic and ultrasonic frequencies ranging up to 170 kilocycles. Experiments performed on rats, by Rosenzweig and his co-workers, suggest that these animals can guide themselves in a maze by means of auditory cues, probably the echoes of sounds they produce. Moreover, Anderson has shown that rodents can hear sounds in the ultrasonic range and can produce ultrasonic cries.

The study of mammalian locomotion, as we have seen, poses at present a number of curious and unsuspected problems. The study of the diving of marine forms and of the ultrasonic "radar" of bats has brought us far indeed from the classical analysis of the horse's gaits. But there is nothing to be surprised at in this. Locomotion is in a way the fundamental activity of an animal, that which conditions most of its other activities, and in particular the search for food and for a mate. Parallel with the structural modifications of the skeleton and the muscles, therefore, one must expect to find physiological adaptations of the nervous system, the sense organs, and behavior, as illustrated by the few examples given in this chapter.

2

Food and Feeding Habits

THE classic distinction among herbivorous, carnivorous, and omnivorous forms is so firmly anchored in the minds of all that one might be tempted to suppose that the eating habits of the mammals are completely known to us. In point of fact we are still very far from being acquainted with the mere essentials of what we should know, even in the case of the commonest species. The problem is, indeed, not so simple as it may appear. The diet of a single species may vary greatly in time, as in space. Preferences and nutritional requirements are modified with age, and laboratory animals have already taught us a great deal in this connection. But there is more: unless a species is strictly confined to a specialized diet—and we shall cite some examples of this—the daily menu is strongly influenced by the availability of the various food substances suitable for consumption. It follows that for many animals the diet varies considerably from one season to another, and that in a given season the individuals inhabiting a certain part of the range of a species will not feed on the same things as others that inhabit a different region.

DIET

TO the difficulties inherent in the variability of most biological phenomena must be added the special technical difficulties met with in the study of the diet of wild species. The simplest approach to the problem, and that which was for long the only one employed, is direct observation of the feeding preferences of individuals living under natural conditions. A good field naturalist, watching the behavior of an elephant, an antelope, or a monkey, can make interesting observations on the fruits, herbaceous plants, or types of foliage sought or avoided by the animal. In similar fashion the bones or skulls brought by a carnivore into the vicinity of its lair often make it possible to identify the captured prey. But this direct method, applicable to species of some size, is of no help to us in ascertaining the diet of a small mammal, which, moreover, is usually nocturnal.

We must then resort to other evidence. The investigation of droppings, for example, enables us to recover numerous fragments of animal or plant origin, some of which are identifiable through careful study under the binocular or ordinary microscope. Hairs, teeth, small bones, seeds, fibers, and plant fragments sometimes permit generic or even specific identification. Dusi's recent work is an example of this. It must be noted, however, that only a part of the ingested material is detected by this examination of droppings; some foods leave no trace of their passage through the alimentary tract.

Investigation of the stomach contents also provides data of interest. If the animal is killed shortly after its last meal, ingested foods will be found in its stomach, and they will be quite easily identifiable. But if this meal has been eaten a longer time before capture, the less digestible foods have a better chance of being identified than the others, and the student will run the risk of gaining a false impression concerning the food preferences of the species. In any case this method, like the preceding, will show us what the animal consumes and not at all what it avoids.

The results of these analyses of the excrement or of the stomach contents will enable us to draw up a list of recognizable foods consumed by a given species, in a given locality, and at a given season. It can be completed by calculating what percentages of the various foods are found in the different samples examined. This prevents giving to such prey as has been identified in only 2 or 3 per cent of the stomachs the same importance as is given to what has been found in 75 or 90 per cent of the same stomachs. Sometimes it can be of a certain interest also to determine the relative volume of the foods ingested and recovered. This may be accomplished very easily by submerging the different foods successively in a graduated test tube previously filled with water to a given level.

VEGETARIAN DIETS. The artiodactyl ruminants—cud-chewing hoofed animals—are the most specialized of all the herbivores. In these mammals the entire digestive tube shows remarkable anatomical and physiological adaptations that help us to understand how their metabolic requirements are met by an exclusively vegetarian diet. Man needs, to be sure, a balanced food ration to keep himself in good health, that is, a ration containing, besides the vitamins and trace mineral elements, a minimum quantity of carbohydrates, fats, and proteins. Now, we know that the Bovidæ, or ox family, the Cervidæ, or deer family, and some other related families are nourished exclusively on herbaceous plants and foliage—foods composed largely of water, cellulose, and carbohydrates indigestible for man. Their organism ought, then, to be capable of finding in this vegetal raw material all the chemical elements needed for the metabolism of a mammal. And this is indeed the case.

It is well known that the stomach of the ruminants is provided with an enormous reservoir, the rumen or first stomach, where the food is stored after brief chewing. This rumen contains an extremely rich flora of anærobic bacteria that is absolutely essential to the good health of the adult animal. It is these bacteria, as Pasteur suspected as early as 1885, that hydrolyze the cellulose and other carbohydrates of plants, for the first stomach secretes no digestive enzyme at all. Further, in the rumen and the second stomach occur important fermentations that, acting on glucose, produce lactic acid, pyruvic acid, and fatty acids. Finally, the rumen bacteria synthesize both protein substances and certain vitamins (of group B).

In the non-ruminant herbivores it is the bacteria of the large intestine (in the horse family and in certain rodents[1]) or those of stomach diverticula (in the hippopotamus and in kangaroos) that have the same function. In both cases the length of the digestive tube, as compared with the total

---

[1] The daily amount of grass ingested by some Microtinæ (field mice and the like) is considerable, equal to or even greater than their own weight. Most of the herbivores must devote a large part of the day to eating, and they cannot fast for long without injurious effects. Schäfer (*Zool. Garten*, 10:29, 1938) points out that the giant panda spends 10 to 12 hours a day in eating. A manatee 15 feet long eats 80 to 100 pounds of plants a day.

Topography of the home range. A red-deer wallow. Courtesy of Professor Hediger, Basel.

Topography of the home range. A termite nest polished by the animals' rubbing in the home range of Burchell's zebra. Note the trampled ground around the nest. Buffalos also frequent these landmarks. Photograph by Hediger. Courtesy of the Institut des Parcs nationaux du Congo Belge.

Topography of the home range. Network of hippopotamus trails. Most of these trails are used for dozens of years in succession. Photograph by Hediger. Courtesy of the Institut des Parcs nationaux du Congo Belge.

Topography of the home range. Heap of dung deposited by the West African civet. Photograph by R. Verheyen, taken at Kenonga, Belgian Congo. Courtesy of the Institut des Parcs nationaux du Congo Belge.

length of the body, is much greater than in carnivores of similar size.[2]

Most of the herbivores so far mentioned eat a great variety of plants.[3] Young shoots, leaves, flowers, tender stems, and even the bark of many plants are commonly eaten by one and the same mammalian species. From one season to another the preferences of a given individual may change, and the relative abundance of certain plants may be a decisive factor in its choice.

There exist, however, a few well established instances in which the vegetarian diet of a species is narrowly specialized. The Australian koala eats only the leaves of the eucalyptus (about two and a half pounds a day, for an adult), to the exclusion of all other plants. And it should be added that the animal is to be found feeding on only a few species: *Eucalyptus punctata*, *E. microcorys*, *E. melliodora*, and *E. rostrata*. The three-toed sloth of the neotropical forests consumes only the leaves, buds, and young shoots of *Cecropia palmata* (a tree of the mulberry family) or, lacking that, of *Spondias lutea* (the hog plum tree). A little tree-

[2] The habit of "refection," or passing the food twice through the intestine instead of only once, seems to be a common phenomenon in the rabbits and hares. Domestic rabbits usually eat and swallow without chewing their night droppings, which form in the morning as much as half the total contents of the stomach. In the wild rabbit refection takes place twice daily, and the same habit is reported for the European hare (MOROT, C., *Rec. Méd. Vétér.* Paris, 59:635, 1881; MADSEN, H., *Nature*, 143:981, 1939; TAYLOR, E. L., *Nature*, 143:982, 1939). It is believed that this habit provides the animals with large amounts of B vitamins produced by bacteria in the food within the large intestine. The same habit has recently been reported in the common shrew (Crowcroft, P., *Nature*, 170:627, 1952).

[3] Poisonous plants raise some interesting questions. Hediger has observed, at the Berne Zoo, that exotic ruminants often poison themselves by eating *Solanum nigrum*, a poisonous plant that native chamois and ibex "instinctively" avoid. It would be of interest to analyze such behavior and to distinguish its innate and learned elements.

dwelling rodent, the red tree mouse of the humid forests of the northwestern United States, is closely associated with the Douglas fir; the needles and the bark of young shoots of this tree constitute its favorite food, and it cannot do without them, even in captivity. Young leaves are entirely consumed, but the sides and resin ducts of older leaves are discarded. Another curious instance of diet specialization is that of the giant panda, native to the mountainous regions of southeastern Asia. This rare but in some ways familiarly known animal lives almost exclusively on bamboo shoots, and certain bony modifications in the skeleton of its hand may be correlated with this special food habit. The point hardly needs to be emphasized that such narrowly specialized diets are probably a heavy handicap in the evolution of a species, for any change in the flora of its habitat may constitute a risk threatening to cause its extinction. On the other hand, a group of greater ecological plasticity will adapt itself more easily to modifications of the flora.

Fruits constitute a food sought by many mammals (fig. 22), especially in tropical regions. Among the bats, the family Pteropidæ of the Old World are almost exclusively frugivorous, and they therefore bear the vernacular name of fruit-eating bats. The preferred kinds of fruit often vary according to the season, but everywhere bananas, guavas, papayas, and other cultivated species are eaten quite as readily as the fruit of wild figs and of numerous native species. In tropical America the fruit bats of the genus *Artibeus* have similar habits; in the West Indies they attack, for instance, the fruits of palm trees of the genus *Acrocomia* and carry them into their sleeping-places, thus aiding in the dispersal of the palms. Many monkeys, such as the red spider monkey, are likewise great fruit lovers. In French Equatorial Africa, according to Malbrant and Maclatchy, the distribution of the mustached white-nosed monkey is "largely conditioned" by the existence of the palm *Elæis*.

Seeds constitute a vegetable food notable for its slight water content. This is of no account when the seeds are

FIG. 22: *Fat dormouse eating a grape. Note the attitude of the animal, sitting on its hind paws, and the use of its front members for manipulating the food.*

eaten along with fresh plant material or by species that drink regularly, but it may well be asked how certain desert rodents succeed in nourishing themselves almost exclusively on dry seeds all the year round without ever drinking.

As a matter of fact it has been possible to maintain in good health some rodents of the North African deserts, especially the Egyptian gerbil, and some kangaroo rats and pocket mice of the deserts of the southwestern United States, on a diet of barley and oat seeds in which the water content does not exceed 5 to 10 per cent. These rodents, which were given no drinking water, not only failed to lose

43

weight, but fattened normally. Under the same conditions an ordinary white rat rapidly loses 40 to 50 per cent of its weight and cannot long survive. Schmidt-Nielsen's recent studies have shown that the organism of the desert Heteromyidæ presents interesting physiological adaptations. There is no special reserve of water in the tissues, but, on the other hand, the urine is twice as concentrated as in other rodents. There is, therefore, a significant economy of metabolic water which is enough to cover most of the animal's needs. Not all the little desert mammals, moreover, are alike in this matter. The white-throated wood rat is quite unable to live on a diet made up exclusively of dried seeds, and in the deserts were it lives it has to find in succulent cacti the water it needs.

Bark is sought by many mammals, especially at certain seasons of the year. In Europe the bark eaters are chiefly represented by the deer, red squirrels, and voles. The damage these animals do to trees is often by no means negligible. The roe deer and the red deer pull off strips of bark from below upward, while the fallow deer gnaws the bark rather like a goat. The red squirrel injures young pine and larch; it denudes surfaces that may be as large as a hand and licks up the sap that exudes from the wound. Sometimes it leaves very characteristic spiral marks. The field vole and water vole gnaw into the wood, the former above, and the latter under, the ground. The hare also sometimes removes strips of bark.

In North America the porcupine feeds in winter almost exclusively on the inner bark of conifers and hardwoods, often denuding the trunks up to a great height. In springtime it attacks the sap-filled cambium of maples, particularly the sugar maple. The Canadian beaver is still more specialized. Its provisions for the winter consist entirely of branches and trunks of poplar, aspen, cottonwood, and willow, from which it gnaws the bark during the cold season. Bark of coniferous trees is not eaten. In spring and summer its menu is varied with aquatic plants and berries. Bradt calculated that in the Michigan colonies he studied each beaver cut down an average of six trees every ten days! The moose is also a great lover of bark, both in winter and in spring.

Mushrooms and lichens are not neglected as food by the mammals. In France the red squirrel frequently eats them, including even the poisonous amanitas. Hainard reports having twice seen a squirrel descend to the ground to get a mushroom before climbing up to eat it on a branch. Other observers have noted that this animal sometimes stores them up, impaled on broken branches. The roe deer also eats mushrooms at times, including *Russula emetica*, the subterranean truffle-like *Elaphomyces granulatus*, and *Cordyceps militaris*, which grows on insects. In America squirrels of the genus *Tamiasciurus* seem to eat fungi still more freely than their European cousins; they even dig for subterranean species. In the northern regions of Canada caribou consume a considerable quantity of mushrooms during July and August. Fungi can even constitute an effective emergency ration for species that normally eat few mushrooms. Tevis has recently reported that in 1950, after the failure of the seed crop of conifers and shrubs in the northern Sierra Nevada, chipmunks and ground squirrels turned to the sporophores of hypogeous fungi for food. As these were obtainable in large amounts, the rodent population did not appear to suffer from the failure of the seed crop.

Most unusual is the *nectarivorous diet* of some tropical mammals. Among the bats that feed on pollen and nectar should be mentioned the genera *Glossophaga, Choeronycteris,* and *Lonchophylla* (Glossophaginæ) and *Eonycteris* and *Megaloglossus* (Macroglossinæ). Allen calls attention to the lengthening of the tongue and the modifications in the dentition common to these various genera. It has since been shown that certain night-blooming tropical plants, such as the baobab and the saguaro, are regularly pollinated by the bats.

MEAT DIETS. These are extremely widespread among the mammals and are characteristic of whole orders. Mammals and birds are the favorite prey of typical carnivores such as the Canidæ, the Felidæ, or the Mustelidæ.[4] The large species—lions, tigers, leopards, hyenas, and the like—hunt the ungulates in particular, while the small species are satisfied with more modest prey. It is the diet of these last that so far has been most closely studied. The work of Scott on the food of the northern plains red fox in the Des Moines River valley (Iowa), may serve as a model of such research. It discloses in the first place a marked seasonal variability in the diet: in winter this fox is primarily carnivorous, while in the other seasons insects and plants constitute an important ele-

---

[4] There exist also some bats that are unquestionably carnivorous: *Phyllostomus hastatus* of tropical America accepts in captivity other bats, small rodents, and birds; *Megaderma lyra*, of the Far East, is normally predaceous on birds, rodents, and batrachians, a fact that has been verified in Ceylon. Among the Australian marsupials the carnivores are represented by the Dasyurinæ and the Tasmanian "wolf" *Thylacinus cynocephalus*. The habits of the little crest-tail marsupial-mouse of the Australian deserts are very curious; as soon as it sees its prey it gazes steadily at it, waves its tail as a lizard does, and pounces on it like a flash (Wood Jones, 1949).

ment in its daily menu. The relative abundance of the various foods naturally affects the precise composition of this menu, but food *preferences* are also definitely in evidence. Thus, the mammals most preferred are prairie meadow mice and, in less degree, lemming mice; the insectivores, to the contrary, seem to be systematically ignored. This is not a unique fact, since Southern and Watson have come to the same conclusion in their study of the European red fox in England. The animal is influenced also by its age in its choice of prey; young foxes seem at first to proceed on the basis of trial and error for the most part, and they tend to nibble at and then swallow whatever they find around the lair.

Some of the large carnivores prey especially on man. It is well known that certain tigers, lions, and panthers become "man-eaters," that is, they acquire a special taste for human flesh. Prater, in agreement with a number of good observers, holds that the success of a chance attack on man is what causes certain individuals to lose the innate fear of our species that is felt by most wild animals. Moreover, a period of famine may embolden a female suckling her young and thus favor the man-eating habit. This perhaps would account for the fact that most man-eaters are females. There are certain observations that favor this view: in India the great famine that occurred in Gujarat, from 1901 to 1903, was accompanied by a rise in man-eating among the tigers and panthers of the region. In Central Africa, on the Rwindi-Rutshuru plain that now forms the southern part of Albert National Park, "epidemics of anthropophagy" in lions broke out around 1860 and between 1904 and 1909, probably coinciding with notable reductions in the numbers of kobs and topis, antelopes native to the plain (Hubert).

Corpses and carrion can serve on occasion as food for the carnivores just mentioned, but this is exceptional. Some mammals, on the other hand, commonly seek out this type of food. Thus the spotted hyena is one of the chief scavengers of the African bush-veldt. Although it is quite capable of hunting living prey for itself, it is for the most part content to feed on the lion's leavings. Its stomach, in which digestion would seem to be very rapid, is filled with broken bones, hair, and sometimes feathers; Matthews seldom found undigested meat in it. Prater tells of a large male striped hyena, killed in the Hyderabad jungles, whose stomach was crammed with dried and unbroken bones, probably swallowed in that condition.

Reptiles: lizards sometimes constitute a portion of the diet of many small carnivores such as foxes, badgers, and the like. Turtle eggs are sought by others, such as skunks, which can dig up eggs of the snapping turtle from the sand. Some mammals have the more unusual taste for snakes, even including poisonous species. The common European hedgehog is perfectly capable of coping with a viper; Herter has seen one present its quills to the snake and then, at the right moment, seize the exhausted reptile and crush its head or spinal column. The hedgehog's resistance to the viper's poison, while not complete, is quite remarkable; it is perhaps 35 to 40 times greater than that of a guinea pig of the same weight. Curiously enough, it is equally resistant to the poison of bees and to cantharidin, the irritating substance in blister beetles. The mongooses (*Herpestes*), as is well known, are also fierce enemies of snakes. In India they attack highly poisonous species, including cobras. They attack in a variety of ways, but their extreme agility and the bristling of their fur constitute their best means of defense. Although the mongooses, like the hedgehog, are strongly resistant to poisons, a sufficient dose will kill them, for their immunity is not complete.

It is a remarkable fact that the resistance of a mammal to the poison of a snake can be observed in species that never come into contact with poisonous snakes. Vellard has recently shown, for instance, that the Andean skunk (*Conepatus inca*) of the Huaron region of Peru (altitude 13,300–14,000 feet), manifests an undeniable resistance to the poison of the Crotalidæ (rattlesnake family), although there are no snakes to be found at such altitudes. We have to do here with a natural primary resistance different from that of the skunks of lower and warmer regions; these latter commonly attack snakes and manifest a still stronger resistance, a true active immunity.

Fish forms the basic diet of some species. The European otter consumes a great variety: eels, trout, minnows, and others; but it does not spurn crayfish, frogs, snails, earthworms, and even rats and aquatic birds. Despite its name, the fishing cat of India is likewise not satisfied with fish and mollusks; it occasionally attacks not only birds but even dogs and cattle. More unexpected is the existence of fishing bats: *Noctilio leporinus* of tropical America (fig. 23), *Pizonyx vivesi* of the Gulf of California, and probably *Megaderma lyra* of India.

Arthropods make up the sole diet of the tropical American anteaters (*Myrmecophaga, Tamandua, Cyclopes,* etc.), of the Old World pangolins and aardvarks and the Australian banded anteaters. These animals present well-known morphological adaptations of claws and tongue which enable them to tear open and explore the galleries of the nests

FIG. 23: *The fish-eating bat with a fish just caught. After Gudger.*

FIG. 24: *The giant anteater, a strictly insectivorous mammal.*

of termites and ants (fig. 24). They consume considerable amounts of the eggs, cocoons, and adults of these insects. In the stomach of a young female of the relatively small three-toed anteater, Enders found more than a pound of ants! The aardvark of Africa, which may reach a total length of six feet, also feeds only on termites and ants that it captures by means of its long, protractile tongue.[5] The pangolins of Africa and Asia do likewise, and the African aardwolf is said to feed mainly on termites.

The small bats of the suborder Microchiroptera are in general insectivorous, and most of them, as already noted, catch the insects in flight, at twilight or during the night. It is likely that bats do not select the prey captured in this manner, but it is always possible for a distasteful insect to be rejected at once after capture. Poulton's careful study of the diet of English bats shows that the identifiable remains of insects, collected from the ground in the retreats where long-eared bats and greater horseshoe bats resort to devour their catch, are composed chiefly of the wings of noctuid (owlet) moths. Among 1,328 identifiable wings only 16 belonged to species without protective coloration, and 10 among these were wings of two species (*Spilosoma lubricipeda* and *S. menthrastri*) that are showy forms with warning coloration, often refused by insectivores in captivity. Is this small percentage due to choice on the part of the bats, or does it indicate only the relative rarity of species with warning coloration in the lepidopterous fauna of the regions under study? Further research is needed before an answer can be reached.

The diet of a majority of the insectivores is in reality much more varied than the name of the order would lead one to suppose. Let us take the European mole as an example. Hauchecorne's research in Germany has shown that of 200 stomachs investigated 178 contained earthworms;

[5] It is possible, however, to keep aardvarks alive in captivity on a different diet. The London Zoological Garden has maintained them for several years by giving them a thick gruel composed of milk, finely ground horsemeat, bran, and raw eggs.

130, the larvæ of beetles; 74, adult beetles; 70, flies; 35, moths or butterflies; 18, Hymenoptera—ants, wasps, and the like; 52, myriapods; 10, mollusks, such as snails; 3, parts of mice; 19, mole hairs; and 71, plant fragments. A single individual mole can eat in the course of a day the equivalent of its own weight in live food; this voracity is one of the reasons why moles are difficult to maintain in captivity. In like manner insects and spiders are consumed on occasion by omnivores such as rodents and even by some carnivores. Prater mentions the example of the Bengal fox, which at the time of termite swarming will come to catch the winged forms above the termite nests. Bears are fond of the brood and the honey of wild bees; in India the sloth bear attacks the nests of bees (*Apis dorsata* and *Apis indica*), and in North America the black bear robs the nests of wasps and bees and even artificial hives. In the mountains of California beehives are often placed high on platforms or surrounded with electrified barriers to protect them from greedy bears. In tropical Africa the ratel or honey-badger commonly robs bee nests. There exists, at least in Africa, a kind of commensalism between this mustelid and birds of the family Indicatoridæ, which indicate to it the presence of the wild bee nests.

Crustaceans constitute the basic food of only a few very specialized forms; namely, the whales of the suborder Mysticeti, in which the teeth are replaced by whalebone (fig. 25). In the South Atlantic, humpbacks, blue whales, and fin whales live almost exclusively on the plankton shrimp *Euphausia superba*. The astronomical quantities of shrimp which must be ingested daily to fill the needs of these marine monsters may well be imagined! The shrimp, however, live in enormous shoals near the surface during the antarctic summer, and it is then that the large whales migrate far south to fatten on this "krill." In winter these whales eat little and their blubber is much reduced in quantity. In the North Atlantic the euphausiid shrimp *Meganyctiphanes norvegica* is similarly consumed in summer.

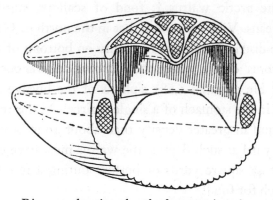

FIG. 25: *Diagram showing the plankton strainer formed by the whalebone of a* Balænoptera. *After Hentschel.*

Mollusks serve as the occasional prey of many terrestrial mammals and as the regular food of some marine forms. Thus the sea otter of the California coast appears to live chiefly on the red abalone. After having detached this shellfish from the bottom, the otter rises to the surface, turns on its back, breaks the shell, and eats the soft parts within. The shell is very hard, and so the animal sometimes makes use of one shell to open another, or, better, it places a small stone on its chest and pounds the shellfish on this improvised anvil. This extraordinary behavior—one of the few known instances of the use of a tool by a mammal other than man—was observed by Fisher and has since been seen by Murie, who even succeeded in filming it. Besides the abalones, the sea otter in California also eats sea urchins and crabs. In Alaska its diet is quite different. There the sea urchin *Strongylocentrotus drobachiensis* is its main food, and Murie has found remains of it in 188 droppings out of 198! This instance, among many others, shows how important geographical variations in diet may be.

The arctic walrus is fond of scallops, starfish, and crustaceans. Vibe has shown that in the north of Greenland (Thule district) walruses feed only on bottoms of less than 40 fathoms' depth, where the *Macoma calcaria* community occurs. He counted 1,881 siphons of the bivalve *Saxicava arctica* in the stomach of a single walrus! As this mollusk is not found in greater density than about 40 individuals per square yard at such depths, the walrus must have exploited at least 47 square yards of bottom during a few hours in its search for food!

The southern elephant seals of subantarctic islands eat cephalopods almost exclusively. A great many cuttlebones are found in their stomachs, together with stones and sand. When they are on land, during the reproductive period, they fast, and this period lasts for six weeks to two months each year. The Falkland sea lion also consumes cuttlefish whose "ink" colors the contents of its digestive tract a beautiful yellow, crustaceans (*Mundia* sp.) that color its excrement red, and also fish. It would seem that sperm whales feed almost exclusively on large cephalopods, and there are many stories told by old sailors recounting the titanic combats of these whales at grips with enormous devilfish.

Terrestrial oligochætes, such as earthworms, are sought by certain digging mammals. We have already seen that these worms form an important part of the mole's diet. Roonwal has recently noted that the manipur rat of Assam and Burma also seems fond of earthworms; four out of eight stomachs examined contained a large quantity of them; the rest contained insects. This is the only rat known to have such a diet, and it is noteworthy that the incisor teeth of this species are unusually weak. The rare Indo-Chinese civet (*Chrotogale owstoni*) also feeds by preference on earthworms.

To conclude this topic, something should be said about the mammals that feed on *blood*. The most famous of these are the vampires of tropical America. These bats belong to the genera *Desmodus*, *Diphylla*, and *Diæmus*, of which only the first is at all well known. Its dentition is admirably adapted to this particular diet; the incisors make a shallow wound, but one that bares many capillaries; [6] blood is then taken up by rapid movements of the tongue (Ditmars and Greenhall). Vampire bats normally attack horses, cattle, and barnyard fowls; occasionally man also becomes their victim. They are dangerous chiefly because they may transmit certain diseases, Chagas's disease in particular.

OMNIVOROUS MAMMALS. Examples of this dietary habit are to be found in many mammalian families, the rodents especially. The brown rat, invader of the cities and human establishments of almost the entire world, is able to eat almost anything: birds, other rodents, lizards, insects and spiders, garbage of all kinds, seeds, vegetables, fruits, and so on. There can be no doubt that its lack of dietary selec-

[6] Contrary to what has often been written, there is no anticoagulant in the saliva of the vampires (King and Saphir, *Zoologica*, 22: 281–287, 1937).

tivity has greatly favored its increase in numbers. The grizzly bear is another good example of the omnivores. Murie has carefully studied its diet in Alaska and gives a long list of the foods he has identified in droppings. Here again there are evident fluctuations in diet according to seasons. In spring the bear eats mostly roots, in June and July it feeds on reed grass (*Calamagrostis*) or on horsetail, and in August and September it turns its attention to berries. At any season it does not disdain ground squirrels or gophers (*Citellus*) and in June and July varies its diet with young caribou, baby Dall sheep, and hares. The badger is still another example of the complete omnivore. Neal has shown that in England it eats young mammals (especially rabbits), a great many insects, honey, mollusks, earthworms, grass, bark, tubers and rhizomes, and fruits and berries. To decide whether such an animal is beneficial or injurious would seem, then, to be primarily a matter of point of view.

MINERAL SALTS. It is well known that many herbivorous mammals, especially hoofed animals, have a special taste for salt and other mineral substances. In the eastern and southern African steppes many antelopes gather toward the end of the dry season at the so-called "bracks," where they greedily eat the "salty" soil or lick "salty" stones. African elephants sometimes dig ditches and holes of their own accord in certain places and return regularly to them. The camel is said to need halophytes (plants growing in salty soil) in its diet and to lose weight if they are lacking.

Such needs are usually supposed to indicate dietary deficiencies in sodium chloride, but the problem is probably more complex. One fact is certain: common salt may sometimes be lacking in the natural "salt licks" and "bracks," and in such cases phosphorus and other trace elements may be the chemicals sought. In their recent study of natural game licks in the Canadian Rockies, Cowan and Brink mention the frequent occurrence of manganese and copper in the soils they analyzed. Varlet similarly found that the soils of the elephants' "brush pharmacies" contained plenty of sulfates, magnesium, copper, nickel, some iron, and traces of chlorides.

The behavior involved should be compared with the pronounced taste of certain antelopes, like the bongo, for charred wood, and with that of the stag, when its horns are growing out, for the young grass that grows on areas recently burned over. Furthermore, stag and caribou often eat their own horns after shedding, and it has recently been shown that if calcium and other mineral salts lacking in the soil are then provided for the animals, no cast antlers are eaten.

THE SEARCH FOR FOOD

ALL the senses of the mammals are used in the search for food. Sight, smell, and touch are most often employed together, but their relative importance varies from group to group.

Pursuit by sight, practiced by most of the large carnivores, implies also an important participation by the sense of smell during that essential preliminary period in which the prey is discovered. Olfaction in wild species still remains to be investigated, but what we know about the sense of smell in dogs enables us to estimate its keenness. The experiments of many workers, especially those of Buytendijk and of Löhner, have shown in undeniable fashion that the dog is not only able to sense odors that escape us but also to analyze mixtures of odors and to pay exclusive attention to one of them. This fact is what explains the behavior of such police dogs as bloodhounds. The ability, developed by training, which they have of recognizing individual odors is truly astonishing. One of Löhner's experiments showed that a second's contact of a piece of wood with the hollow of the hand was enough for the wood to be recognized by the animal in the midst of a whole series of otherwise similar pieces! It is probable, however, that in nature the carnivores need but rarely to make use of such powers of discrimination.

With the scents disentangled and the prey singled out, the techniques of pursuit and capture vary according to the species. African wild dogs and wolves in Asia are noted for hunting in packs and family groups. In the case of the African hunting dog the leader precedes the pack by some hundreds of yards and presses the prey on the course while trying to outflank it so as to head it back toward the rest of the band. This technique is very successful, and this perhaps explains the fear which the wild dogs inspire in herbivores. Percival and many other observers have repeatedly noted that antelopes have little fear of lions and move away from them, when they see them, to a distance of only a hundred yards, whereas they flee for miles if a troop of wild dogs appears on the plain. Coyotes may chase their prey in relays: the pursuing animal is relieved after a time by another member of the pack. Lions and tigers also—and quite frequently—hunt in groups, but at night; probably the growls and other noises they make under these conditions serve to keep the group together and co-ordinated.

Lions have been observed to use the following technique: the male of a pair circles around a troop of antelopes at some distance and gets in front of it, with the wind at the lion's back; it then gives a prolonged roar and thus forces the prey to move toward a place where the female is in ambush. As soon as the victim is within easy reach, the lioness springs and bites the neck of its prey while clawing the skin of its head.

There are many species that in daylight prefer a stealthy approach to pursuit in full view. Foxes and numerous mustelids hunt in this manner. The ermine uses both sight and smell in its search; with wormlike suppleness it slips rapidly along close to the ground, hiding behind the smallest obstacles and rising from time to time on its hind legs. When the prey is overtaken, the ermine bleeds it at the throat immediately.

Other species hunt from cover, along a path or near a water hole. The wolverine hides behind a rock or on a branch of a tree, whence it drops onto its victim's back, often clinging there for a hundred yards or more. Another kind of lying in wait is practiced by certain species, such as the polar bear, which lurks in winter at holes in the ice.

When for various reasons sight cannot play an important part, the sense of smell alone or almost unaided enables the animal to carry on the search for food. The badger, for example, relies chiefly on scent in discovering the young rabbits that this species is clever in removing from the burrows. Probably the same method enables the arctic hare to survive in winter by seeking under several feet of snow the tufts of dwarf willow that form the basis of its diet at that season. Along with olfaction, touch also plays a considerable role. It has been shown, for example, that in the mole the tactile organs of the muzzle, the paws, the trunk, and the tail serve to notify the animal of the proximity of prey, perhaps by vibrations transmitted through the soil; olfaction comes into play only within a radius of less than three inches. Probably the vibrissæ or whiskers of many diving mammals are useful in much the same fashion. Seals often live in places where the water is quite turbid and the light dim. Fraser Darling once watched the activities of a blind seal whose eyes had probably been long since destroyed in fighting but whose condition was nevertheless good, indicating an excellent ability to obtain food without the aid of sight. European water shrews, when hunting under water, bristle their whiskers as they seek contact with prey. We have already discussed the methods by which bats hunt in flight; they show very well how complex some types of elementary behavior may actually be.

Certain methods of gathering food even among the herbivores are unusual and deserve closer study than they have received. We know that the African elephant gathers fruits by means of its trunk, but sometimes the whole tree is uprooted and toppled down; and in still other cases the elephant shakes the tree violently, holding the tree trunk between its tusks. The eland, to cite another instance, has the curious habit of using its horns to break small trees or branches; it wedges the tree trunk between its two horns and, with a twist of its head, breaks it cleanly off (Verheyen).

VENOMOUS MAMMALS. The existence of poisons to aid in the capture of prey was until recent years supposed to be confined to the lower vertebrates. The bite of shrews was reputed to be venomous, but serious students regarded this as mythical. Histologists were recently interested by the structure of certain cells in the salivary glands of the North American short-tailed shrew, and this led Pearson to make a study of the submaxillaries in this species. Having ground the glands with sand in a 0.9 per cent sodium chloride solution, he injected the liquid thus obtained into mice. A rapid effect was observed: less than one minute after the injection the animal trembled, its respiration became slower, and it lay on its side in a state of semi-torpor; with stronger dosage there ensued paralysis of the hind legs, convulsions, and death. Intravenous injection was considerably more effective than either intraperitoneal or subcutaneous injections; a dose as small as the extract of 0.3 milligram to each 20 grams of body weight was found to be lethal for mice in some instances. Pearson showed that the submaxillary glands of a single shrew contain more than 200 times this dose; in contrast, the parotid glands contain no poison at all. Extracts of other organs, prepared in like manner, caused no injury. It would be interesting to know what mammalian families possess or lack this very reptilian characteristic.

STORAGE OF FOOD

STORAGE of food has been frequently noted in certain mammals. This type of behavior has usually been interpreted as the expression of an adaptation to extreme climatic conditions; in other words, the animal "foresees" a winter or summer scarcity and stores up provisions for subsistence during the unfavorable season. The truth of the matter is probably quite different, and the classical interpretation has the disadvantage of assuming in the non-primate mammals the existence of psychological abilities that they almost certainly lack. It is therefore of the greatest interest, while attacking the problem experimentally, to collect observations made under natural conditions. The explanation of the phenomenon may appear through comparison of the various results obtained.

Among the carnivores temporary storage of food seems to be met with in all latitudes.[7] In the polar regions the prey of bears, foxes, and wolves is often only partially eaten, and the remainder is buried in the snow or left on the frozen ground. But intact prey may also be brought together in a cache. In the United States the northern plains red fox displays this behavior *throughout the year*. During the winter the cache is dug in the snow and in summer it is excavated in sand or a light soil; when it is stocked, the contents are carefully covered up. The fox later finds these "larders" with ease, whereas mock caches constructed by Scott along the animal's favorite trails were never dug into. It must be added that within a given area the number of "reserves" of food would seem to be in proportion to the abundance of game.

The storage of earthworms by the European mole has been the subject of much writing; several authors, indeed, have reported finding masses of earthworms, sometimes a

---

[7] When a leopard cannot consume its victim in a single meal, it drags the remainder up into a tree, thus preserving it from the greed of hyenas. Hoier observed a lump of flesh weighing more than 100 pounds, the remains of a young buffalo, that was hung up by a leopard, more than 12 feet above the ground, in the branches of an acacia.

thousand or more together, during the winter in mole nests or adjacent tunnels. But have we to do here with chance aggregations of the worms or with storage of food by the mole? Degerböl's experiment rather tends to tip the balance in favor of the second hypothesis. Having offered a captive mole more worms than it could consume at once, he repeatedly observed the animal storing them in a corner of its cage. To do this, it dug a hole, placed one to ten worms in it, and covered them with earth. Strange to say, the worms put in reserve were first bitten near the anterior end, which immobilized them without killing them. At one time Degerböl's mole buried 49 earthworms in the walls of its tunnel. "Storage" by the mole, then, would seem to occur when there is a superabundance of prey. The short-tailed shrew, referred to above, similarly forms reserves of mollusks, large scarabæid beetles, and even fragments of small mammals.

Among the rodents the establishment of food reserves is very common. Familiar in Europe are the provision chambers of the hamster, which may contain as much as 200 pounds of cereal seeds, peas, or potatoes. The common vole stores fresh plant material and seeds in summer and in the fall lays up the rhizomes, bulbs, tubers, or roots on which it lives in winter. These stores keep in a remarkably fresh condition, and Heim de Balsac has established the fact that in Lorraine the common vole disbuds the bulbs of *Ranunculus bulbosus* before storing them. The North American squirrels commonly store food. The American red squirrel is a great consumer of the seeds of conifers, as is the Fremont chickaree; both these species gather pine cones while still green and store them in moist, cool places. According to Shaw's observations, each animal may establish several temporary storehouses, each containing three to ten bushels of cones which are thus kept from drying out. These provisions are later distributed among a whole series of smaller caches under stones, leaves, or bark, and even in carefully concealed holes. The American red squirrel is very fond of mushrooms, and gathers them all summer and puts them to dry on branches (Hatt) or under bark. When they are dry it puts them away in its storehouses. Hardy has recently described one of these. It consisted of eight little cavities dug in an old, very dry stump of Douglas fir in a British Columbia forest. Six of the holes were filled with perfectly preserved mushrooms, all fully dried. Fifty-nine specimens belonging to 13 different species were counted, but the single species *Hymenogaster tener* was represented by 30 specimens. Except for a small bit of lichen, the storehouses contained nothing but mushrooms. The interesting point is that these very hygroscopic, or water-absorbent, materials were stored in a dry place, whereas the red squirrel ordinarily makes its stockpiles of green cones in damp earth. The amount of these stored foods actually used, however, is not very great: 10 per cent, according to Cahalane, in the case of the fox squirrel.

In more southern latitudes the same habit is to be met with in other species. The California ground squirrel, which estivates without previous accumulation of reserves, gathers together seeds and nuts in the fall, before its period of winter inactivity. The giant kangaroo rat studied by Shaw in Fresno County, California, on the contrary, collects seeds at the end of winter and the beginning of spring; it distributes them at first (to dry?) in a whole series of small cavities that are a little less than an inch in diameter and depth, carefully covered with soil and quite invisible. Around a burrow inhabited by a single individual, Shaw counted 875 of these caches in an area of about five square yards. From April on, these surface storehouses are emptied and the seeds transferred to subterranean storage places inside the burrow.[8] A related species, the large kangaroo rat of southern Arizona, gathers its reserve stores twice a year, in April and May and from September to November. It would be of great importance to study, in a single species, the variations in this behavior as affected by local meteorological conditions.

And, finally, the American beaver builds up its winter food reserves under water. The branches and tree trunks that will provide enough bark to last through the months of frost and snow are submerged near the animal's lodge, and deeply enough to avoid being "caught" in the ice.

[8] This fact was established as follows: Shaw opened some of the surface caches in March and colored the seeds with mercurochrome, also adding some rice grains. On May 4 the tinted seeds and the rice were found in the underground storage places.

CHAPTER 3

Home, Territory, and Home Range

MANY solitary terrestrial vertebrates resort faithfully to certain sites that serve as their lodging-places or shelters, seasonal or permanent. They return regularly to these homes for sleeping, hiding, or reproducing. In the vicinity of the shelter, the chief occupant of the home often shows itself decidedly intolerant of others of its kind, and forbids them access to it. This aggressiveness is the clearest manifestation of territorial behavior. At the same time, most animals prove to be more sedentary than is commonly supposed and restrict their movements to a particular area that they regularly frequent. This zone is called the home range, and it differs from the territory in that access to it is not denied others of the same species.

These facts have only recently been established, thanks to the intensive effort of many field workers. But we are still far from being able to decide in what degree they may apply to mammals in general. This chapter is therefore to be regarded as an attempt to classify the facts at present established, and the conclusions reached will serve as working hypotheses to point the way to new observations.

LODGING-PLACES AND SHELTERS

POSSESSION of lodging-places and shelters, temporary or permanent, though very frequent among the mammals, is by no means universal, and before beginning their study we may briefly survey those species whose constant nomadism prevents any sedentary life at all.

AQUATIC MAMMALS.   The pelagic habitat of the cetaceans—whales and their relatives—offers them no possibility of any shelter. They sleep in open water, in a fashion that seems quite peculiar to them. McBride and Hebb have made interesting observations on the sleep of the bottle-nosed dolphin at the Marine Studios in Florida. During the night the sleeping cetacean usually floats near the surface, but with the tail dangling somewhat. If there is no water current in the tank, the animal may remain almost motionless with the head about a foot below the surface. About every half minute a few slow strokes of the tail bring the head of the animal to the surface to breathe. If a current exists, the dolphin will attempt to maintain its position relative to the tank wall by slow beats of the tail either continuously or periodically. The eyes never remain closed for more than 15 to 30 seconds at a time.

The sea otter, although visiting the land at some points in its area of distribution, generally sleeps in open water. Fisher's observations, made off the coast of Monterey, California, are very suggestive in this connection. These animals appear to assume a resting position only when the sea is calm; then they turn on the back, the chin on the chest, the tail occasionally making a few lateral movements. For the night they ordinarily frequent a bed of algæ (*Macrocystis* or *Nereocystis*), always the same one during their stay in a given region, and one in which the herd gathers. They have the curious habit of clinging to the algæ or rolling themselves up in the plants to avoid drifting while asleep (figs. 26 and 27).

FIG. 26: *Sea otter sleeping "moored" to a float of* Nereocystis. *After a sketch by Fisher, 1939.*

FIG. 27: *Sea otter sleeping "wrapped up" in an alga to prevent drifting during the night. After a sketch by Fisher, 1939.*

Among the seals there are species that sleep in the water only at certain times of the year. At the time of reproduction they rest on land, and it is likely that on certain undisturbed coasts species like the monk seal of Mauritania sleep ashore the year round. Weddell's seal, indeed, poses a quite special problem. This Antarctic species does not migrate in winter and remains *under* the ice floe, resorting regularly for air to "breathing holes," which it prevents from freezing over by breaking the ice with its teeth. How, then, does it manage to take any rest? The problem remains unsolved, but possibly at times it takes advantage of air pockets existing under the ice. The walrus sometimes sleeps in a vertical position in the water, with its neck strongly inflated. Vibe considers this position correlated with the dilation of the pharyngeal pouches.

TEMPORARY SHELTERS. There are many mammals that have no permanent shelter and wander more or less throughout the year on their home range.

Most ungulates, or hoofed animals, belong in this category; but in some cases the females seek isolation and shelter toward the end of gestation. The female chamois, for instance, separates from the herd about a month before giving birth and at that time seeks out an isolated and sheltered place—a thicket, a winding passage in the rocks, a narrow grassy ledge, or the like. Females of the roebuck, of the white-tailed deer, of many antelopes, of the giraffe, and of the African elephant exhibit similar behavior. In all cases the chosen site undergoes no preparation, and the mother returns to it no more, once the offspring is capable of following her about.[1]

Among the smaller mammals many have rudimentary shelters scattered over their home range, where they repair

[1] It may well be that some ungulates of desert regions manifest a great partiality in summer for certain shelters under rocks or even for certain leafy trees. The fact has been pointed out for the Barbary sheep and the addax of the Sahara. In northeastern Mexico bighorn sheep take shelter during the warm hours in summer in small caves where the animals' excrement accumulates, as do the bones of dead individuals. It would seem that in all these cases it is the need for shade that causes the animals' constant resort to these temporary lodging-places.

to sleep, hide, and bring forth their young. The European hare is a good example: nocturnal in its activities, it spends the day in small excavations dug in the ground, under a bush, in high grass, even in the open; in winter it sometimes takes shelter under the snow, which it has allowed to cover it. It often abandons its form, or home, and does not return regularly to the same one, being much more faithful to its trails. Most of the rabbits, hares, and their relatives have similar habits, and many tropical mammals must behave in the same fashion. Thus the little opossum of Central America, the Isthmian marmosa, bears its young in rolled-up and half-dried leaves of the banana tree. It sleeps hidden in dead leaves or abandoned birds'-nests, but it almost never returns two days in succession to the same place. Bats pass the daytime sleeping in various lodging-places; the little insectivorous species retire by day into hollow trees, woodpecker holes, garrets, belfries, abandoned quarries, and the like. It is not rare for certain individuals to keep to the same dormitory during a single summer. Some solitary tropical bats hide during the day in odd places: in India *Hipposideros fulvus* uses porcupine burrows; in South Africa *Kerivoula nidicola* and *K. lanosa* have been found in old nests of Ploceidæ and Nectariniidæ; the Indo-Malayan *Tylonycteris pachypus*, whose paws bear remarkable suckers, sleeps inside bamboo stems; *Pipistrellus nanus* of East Africa hides in dried banana leaves, and *Rhynchiscus naso* of tropical America simply clings with all four feet and in small groups on the underside of a tree trunk overhanging water. All these lodging-places and shelters are clearly temporary, their very nature preventing any prolonged use. It is only certain large fruit-eating bats, which sleep hanging on tree branches, that show a definite attachment to their dormitories, some of which may be used for generations. Thus Eisentraut has observed a roost of *Eidolon helvum* in the Cameroons where about 10,000 individuals gathered.

There are also many primates that have no fixed lodging-place in their home range. The golden potto merely sleeps suspended by its four limbs from a horizontal branch;

FIG. 28: *Sleeping position of a potto.*

another species of potto (fig. 28) sleeps rolled in a ball, with its head between its hind feet. The tropical American howling monkeys wander constantly through their clan territory and spend the night in the trees, wherever they happen to be. The lar gibbons do no more than choose for sleeping particular trees that have heavy leafy tops of sufficient density.

The fact that certain species make some attempt to prepare even a temporary shelter introduces interesting complications. The den of the European wild boar, for example, is generally no more than an elongated hollow in smooth soil, sometimes screened by drooping fir boughs, where the animal retires in the morning to spend the day. The African wart hog may use the burrows of the aardvark for hiding, but more often frequents lairs of its own. Guiraud describes them in Senegal as sites kept meticulously neat, with numerous small, shallow dens dug out, and protected by extensive thickets of bushes that retain their leaves and are not thorny.

Certain tropical American bats prepare the leaves that they use as shelters to hide in. Thus *Artibeus watsoni* uses its teeth to cut two oblique lines converging like a V toward the median vein in the leaves of the palm *Geonoma*. This done, the terminal portion of the leaf falls into a vertical position, so that it forms with the rest of the leaf a kind of verdant tent into which the bat retires (fig. 29). Another species, *Uroderma bilobatum*, makes use of a similar technique that it has adapted to a palm of the genus *Pritchardia* introduced into Panama.

That odd lemuroid, the aye-aye of Madagascar, also builds temporary nests of globular form in leafy boughs, into which it withdraws to sleep in the daytime. The same nest is seldom used for more than one week.

Some anthropoids also crudely furnish the place where they spend the night. The chimpanzee constructs small platforms of branches and abandons them the next day. The gorilla sometimes makes temporary shelters of branches which probably serve also as lodgings for the night.

BURROWS. The burrow is the most widely used type of seasonal or permanent shelter among terrestrial mammals.

A gorilla "nest" at the foot of a tree. The male usually spends the night in such a shelter, while his female rests in a nest built in the tree. Note the animal's excrement at the entrance of the nest. Photograph by J. P. Harroy, taken in Albert National Park. Courtesy of the Institut des Parcs nationaux du Congo Belge.

Nest and eggs of the duckbilled platypus, Ornithorhyncus anatinus.
Courtesy of the New York Zoological Society.

Most of the orders, indeed, include species that construct or make use of burrows. The platypus, numerous insectivores, edentates, marsupials, and rodents dig them. Many carnivores provide themselves with holes during at least a part of the year.

FIG. 29: *Shelter of the bat* Artibeus watsoni, *made in a leaf of the palm* Geonoma decurrens. *Above, the leaf viewed from above, with the two lateral cuts; below, the leaf viewed from the side. After a photograph by F. M. Chapman.*

It would be most desirable to have extensive documentation and many diagrams of typical construction in the matter of animal burrows.[2] But unfortunately these are diffi-

[2] A point on which we are even less informed is the technique used by the animal in digging its burrow. Moles (*Talpa, Scalopus*) use their front paws alternately in loosening the soil; at regular intervals the excavated earth is kicked back with the hindfeet. The Texas armadillo loosens the earth with its nose and front paws, the soil collected under its abdomen being moved back periodically as follows: the animal

cult to obtain. The excavation of a burrow, indeed, is often a long and laborious undertaking. Moreover, no species follows a rigid plan, and all adapt their constructions to local conditions. To make the problem even more difficult, a burrow is constantly worked over by its occupant, and the older it gets the more complex it becomes.

In studying some examples of burrows, we shall observe a wide variation of type. Some, we shall find, are merely temporary subterranean shelters, while others are permanent constructions in which a single animal spends a whole year, or even its whole life. Still others are intended for occupancy by one male or female alone, or for housing a family group, sometimes for several successive generations.

The burrows of carnivores are usually of very simple architecture.[3] Many of them, moreover, make use of holes dug by other animals and merely adapt them to their own

---

supports itself on its front limbs and its tail, bends its back upward, and then uses its two posterior paws to throw the dug out soil behind it.

The rate of advance may be very great. Arlon has seen an eastern mole advance five feet or more in 26 minutes, a rate of about 12 feet an hour. Taber saw an armadillo bury itself completely in two minutes, and this in a soil so hard that one needed a pickaxe to dig a hole. Armadillos, furthermore, have remarkable physiological adaptations for digging galleries, adaptations that recall in some ways those of diving mammals. (See, for example, Scholander, Irving, and Grinnell, *Jour. Cell. Comp. Physiol.*, 21:53–63.)

Another curious problem is presented by the remarkable sense of direction shown by the blind fossorial mammals. Krizat and Godet have clearly shown that the European mole is able to orient itself in the absence of olfactory or tactile landmarks, and to manifest a knowledge of the relations existing between its burrow and its hunting territory. Eloff (*British Jour. Exper. Psychol.*, 42: 134–45, 1951) has likewise emphasized the sense of direction of the blind South African *Cryptomys bigalkei* and the Cape golden mole (*Bathyergus maritimus*).

[3] The polar bear may dig a real burrow in the snow at the time of giving birth to young. An example is provided by Pedersen (fig. 30), who observed one of these dens excavated at the foot of an iceberg. This of course was a temporary habitation, the family deserting it by the month of March.

requirements. Thus the North American coyotes use the burrows of badgers, skunks, or foxes; they limit themselves to enlarging, cleaning, and sometimes furnishing them with an air hole. Even the European red fox may very well take over old burrows of badgers and rabbits, although it is quite capable of digging its own.

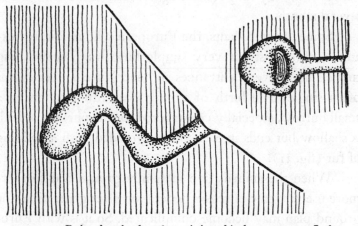

FIG. 30: *Polar bear's den for giving birth to young. Left and below, vertical section; right and above, horizontal section. The whole dug in snow and ice. After Pedersen.*

Its relative, the American red fox, normally constructs burrows of two kinds: a rearing den with a fairly large chamber at the end of a tunnel of varying depth, and temporary burrows that are still more rudimentary. Sheldon's observations, made on marked animals in the region around Lake Cayuga, in New York, indicate that the burrow for reproduction is occupied by the female and her young, which abandon it only when the milk teeth are lost. Kolosov's data tend to show that in Russia the European red fox and the corsak fox have similar habits.

Armadillos also appear to dig only simple burrows. Those of the Texas armadillo vary in depth from two to more than twelve feet and are very seldom branched (Taber). There is a single entrance as a rule, and the nest is located in the enlarged terminal portion of the tunnel. Each individual has and uses four to eight burrows, and each sex has its own, the young remaining in the mother's burrow for several months.

Some of the rodents, the European wild rabbit, for example, also construct very simple burrows. The winding tunnels have several entrances and end in a chamber that is often single. The birth of young most often occurs in a small burrow, especially constructed for the purpose, which is shallow but ends in a chamber provided with a bedding of fur (fig. 31).

When the animals live in family groups and furthermore use the same burrows generation after generation, the ground plan may become complicated. So it is with European badgers. It would seem that a new, or "young" burrow consists only of an entrance and an enlarged terminal chamber, the nest. But since badgers are gregarious and since a single network of burrows is inhabited by successive generations, it is understandable that their dwellings soon become extraordinarily labyrinthine. A burrow ten to twenty years old commonly has three to five entrances; three to six feet within is a rather large chamber, with its dirt floor hardened and tramped down by generations of occupants, that may represent the birth chamber of the original burrow. Other tunnels extend away from this antechamber, terminating in other chambers that serve as dormitories or nests. These last are often located under a large rock or among the roots of a tree and are furnished with bedding that is changed in spring and autumn. There are air holes in some cases, smaller in diameter than the entrance holes. With the passage of time these burrows, as we have noted, become veritable labyrinths, of which certain parts may be

FIG. 31: *The two types of wild rabbit burrows, seen in vertical section: 1, burrow for residence; 2 and 3, burrow for reproduction, open and closed. After Lincke.*

used by other species, such as foxes, rabbits, or rats. Neal refers to an instance in which the tunnels extended over a hundred yards from the entrance. The diagram in figure 32 clearly shows the mode of formation of these labyrinths for the little souslik of the Eurasian steppes.

Many burrowing mammals remain inside during the

FIG. 32: *Evolution of the burrow of the little souslik,*
Citellus pygmæus. *First year, I–III: I, primitive and tem-*
porary summer burrow; II, hibernation burrow, autumn;
III, the same with the entrance gallery blocked for the
winter and with a vertical exit gallery begun. Second
year: IV, the same in spring; V–VII, progressive modi-
fication and complication of the system of burrows during
succeeding years, with increase in size of the mound. The
parts temporarily blocked are indicated in black. After
Ognev. *From* Grassé, Traité de zoologie, *Vol.* XVII.

unfavorable season of the year or hibernate there. Their
dwellings, of course, permit the storage of supplies that are

often of great importance to the animals. The common vole of Europe digs burrows comprising a nest, so-called resting-chambers, storerooms, escape tunnels leading directly from the nest to the exterior, communicating galleries, and finally exit galleries leading to sources of food and continued in runways outside. In some cases there are also nests above ground in tufts of grass. For hibernating species there is no need at all for stores of food, but in that case the owner of the burrow often is immured in a special chamber.

Some mammals have burrows of two types: one for summer and one for winter. The hamster of Central Europe is an example. Its summer burrow is short and shallow, with a single storage place for food. The winter burrow, on the contrary, is dug to a depth of one or two yards and comprises an entrance gallery, one or two chambers, and several storage places.[4] The northern three-toed jerboa of the Kazakstan deserts also has different domiciles according to the seasons. The permanent summer burrow (one for each sex, the female's being more complicated than the male's) includes the remains of the initial gallery, abandoned and consequently filled up, a permanent exit closed during the daytime with a plug of sand, emergency exits ending four to six inches from the surface of the ground, a chamber furnished with bedding of plant material, and finally a deep, narrow passage to which the animal retires during the warmer hours of the day (fig. 33). Beside this permanent estivating burrow are found also temporary summer burrows in the form of simple unbranched tunnels. The essen-

[4] At least this is the arrangement reported by Eisentraut and Krumbiegel; but two nests investigated in Alsace by Didier and Matthias had a different plan: a spacious central chamber with lateral cavities and diverging entrance galleries.

tial characteristic of the winter burrow is that it is deeper and has a chamber always located at the end. While constructing its winter dwelling, the jerboa goes on living in its summer burrow.

FIG. 33: *Summer burrow of an Asiatic jerboa*, Stylodipus telum, *in sectional diagram:* a, *primary burrow;* b, *blind emergency exit. After Ognev. From Grassé,* Traité de zoologie, *Vol.* XVII.

THE BURROWS OF SUBTERRANEAN MAMMALS. All the burrows thus far described are constructed by mammals that use them for sleeping, hiding, and reproducing. There is another type of burrow, made by subterranean species; that is, species that spend their whole lives under ground and come to the surface only accidentally. Burrowing mammals are to be found in several orders: marsupials (*Notoryctes*), insectivores (*Talpa, Scalopus, Condylura*), and rodents (Geomyidæ, *Spalax, Ellobius*, etc.). All these have certain morphological characteristics in common: fossorial front feet, eyes small or even lacking, loss or reduction of the external ears, and so on. The burrows of only a few of them are satisfactorily known (and there is certainly much to be learned about the biology of such strange forms as *Heterocephalus glaber* [fig. 34] of Africa!), but they all would seem to consist of two parts: the home burrow containing the nest and stores, and the galleries used only for hunting food.

FIG. 34: *A subterranean rodent with almost hairless skin,* Heterocephalus glaber *of Kenya. Drawn from a photograph by Lt. Col. Stockley. From Grassé,* Traité de zoologie, *Vol.* XVII.

The earthworks of the European mole are among the best known. The *nest* is located under a good-sized mound or "fortress," often hidden under a bramble or placed near a tree stump. This large molehill is built over an oval chamber where the animal puts bedding composed of dead leaves surrounded with dry grass. The earthen vault above the nest commonly contains more or less circular galleries (fig. 35). From the central chamber usually extend a variable number of *permanent galleries* used by the animal in going to its hunting-grounds. The walls of these galleries are smooth and well compacted. Commonly enough a permanent gallery extends vertically below the floor of the central chamber itself; this is an escape gallery that also serves to drain the nest. Beyond these permanent galleries is an extensive network of *hunting-galleries*, dug out and altered daily by the animal, which at regular intervals throws the excavated dirt out on the surface of the ground, thus forming the familiar small molehills. The breeding-nest of the female is generally placed in a "fortress" smaller than that containing the winter nest.

FIG. 35: *Reconstruction in perspective of the nest of a European mole,* Talpa europæa, *surrounded by its concentric galleries. The "dome" of the nest was about 12 inches below the surface in silica-clayey soil; the "well" of the lower part of the nest was at a depth of about 27 inches. After Godet.*

The earthworks of the lesser mole rat are a little more complicated. Dr. Bodnar Béla describes them as comprising a nest, a "pairing-chamber," storage places, sanitary rooms, main galleries and, finally, temporary galleries. The nest is an oval or pear-shaped chamber, furnished with grass, and the smooth, hard walls are thickly plastered with clay. The pairing-chamber is constructed in spring under a molehill sixteen inches high that the animal begins to build the preceding autumn; it is a round chamber eight inches across, the walls covered with clay. After mating has taken place, the owner stops up the room and the gallery leading to it with earth. The storage places are sometimes no more than enlargements of a permanent gallery, but they may also be special chambers; in them may be found potatoes, onions, carrots, and roots. The sanitary rooms open on the main galleries, and when filled with droppings they are walled up by the mole rat. The main galleries, which are the deepest ones, connect the various parts of the dwelling just mentioned; they are lined with a thick layer of clay that makes them very durable and almost waterproof. As for the temporary galleries, they are used only in seeking food; these are winding, near the surface, and of variable diameter. Their walls are not plastered with clay, and, when they are no longer in use by the animal, it often happens that their connections with the main galleries are closed.

The North American Geomyidæ, or pocket gophers, also manifest extraordinary fossorial activity. The burrow of the plains pocket gopher investigated by Smith (fig. 36) belonged to a young female and had been constructed in a year. The total length of the central gallery was about 65 yards; the nest was at a depth of two feet. Of the two storerooms, one was at the end of a lateral gallery, the other in the wall of the central gallery. Secondary galleries on each side of this last probably represented old hunting-galleries; some of these ended in a molehill, while others did not. Most of them had been later filled with dirt, and some served as sanitary rooms. The reserve food was made up entirely of tubers of the Jerusalem artichoke (*Helianthus tuberosus*), from which the roots were removed (perhaps to make them keep?). With the northern pocket gopher, also, the differentiation between main and temporary galleries is quite clear: the nest is always located in the former. The pocket gophers remain active in wintertime and have the odd habit of making tunnels under the snow, at the surface of the ground. In these tunnels they accumulate the debris that

FIG. 36: *Diagram showing ground plan of a new burrow of a plains pocket gopher*, Geomys bursarius. *After Smith, 1948.*

they go on collecting from below, and when the snow thaws long serpentine ridges of earth are left in sight. In Europe the snow vole and the common vole display rather similar behavior. The tuco tucos of South America (fig. 37) would appear to be related in their biology.

FIG. 37: *Diagram of the burrow of the tuco tuco,* Ctenomys brasiliensis. *The figures indicate depths in centimeters; the small triangles indicate mounds at the surface. After Eisentraut. From Grassé,* Traité de zoologie, *Vol.* XVII.

SOME SECURITY DEVICES OF BURROWS. Certain architectural peculiarities of burrows can be interpreted as security devices against flooding and the intrusion of predators,[5] as well as means for maintaining constant the microclimate inside.

The black-tailed prairie dogs of the western United States build around the entrance of the burrow a kind of

[5] It has been maintained that white-throated wood rats "prevent" the access of predators to their nests by means of the spines of the jumping cholla (*Opuntia fulgida*). It is quite true that these rodents can move with ease among the spines of this justly feared cactus, but a recent observation of Reed and Carr shows that as protection the spines have only relative value. A hooded skunk they were pursuing took refuge in one of the wood rat nests, entering through an orifice so well "protected" that a child's hand could not have been thrust into it without danger.

crater that may be two feet high and three feet in diameter. This constitutes a real barrier against floods. Carefully kept in condition by the owner, it prevents heavy rain from running into the entrance tunnel that opens in the center of the crater and descends almost vertically to a depth varying from three to sixteen feet. Some distance from the entrance to this well there is almost always a lateral recess, a kind of listening post, where the prairie dog can stop before going deeper. At the bottom of the vertical tunnel the gallery turns sharply and takes a horizontal or slightly ascending direction before branching and coming to an end at the nest. If the rain is heavy enough for the sheet of water to submerge the entrance crater, the animal takes refuge in the pockets of air which remain in the ascending galleries and thus escapes drowning, for although the rains are sometimes excessive they usually last for only a few hours.

Many mammals temporarily stop up the mouths of their burrows. We have already noted that in summer the northern three-toed jerboa uses sand for this purpose in the daytime, and here we probably have to do with a reaction to the increased heat outside, since in autumn or in early spring the same animal leaves its burrow open during the daytime. In this way the constancy of the microclimate of the nest is favored, a condition necessary to the survival of these small mammals in regions marked by extremes of temperature. Burrowing species as large as the aardvark display comparable behavior.

Other species immure themselves inside their burrows only during estivation or hibernation; such is the case with the Alpine marmot and the little souslik in Europe, the woodchuck and the meadow jumping mouse in northern

America. In Madagascar the tenrec walls up with earth the entrance to its hibernation chamber during the dry season. Similar examples could be found in most regions of the world.

In other cases the blocking of the burrow at its mouth is a defense reaction against predators, alpine marmots often reacting in this way when an attempt is made to dig them out.

THE MICROCLIMATE OF BURROWS. One of the most important characteristics of burrows is the constancy of their microclimate. We shall see in a later chapter that most desert mammals cannot survive when removed from their dwellings at full midday, and if some have been successful in colonizing these parts of the world, it is certainly because of their habit of nocturnal activity and the microenvironment of the burrows into which they withdraw in the daytime. Unfortunately we still lack an exhaustive study of this problem, but some observations are very suggestive. Vorhies, for example, states that the desert Heteromyidæ (pocket rats and mice) of the southwestern United States die when the temperature is above 35° Centigrade but that, on the other hand, and even at the hottest periods, the temperature of the air inside the burrows never rises above 33°; in summer it remains at about 28°. Kachkarov and Korovine, in the Kara-Koum desert, showed that in April there could be a difference of 31 degrees between the temperature of the surface of the ground and that of the air in a gerbil burrow four inches from the entrance (59° and 28° respectively); inversely, during the night, the temperature of the ground may be 16 degrees lower than that of the burrow (May 7, at 4:30 a.m., 3° and 19° respectively). Heim de Balsac found that in the Sahara it was enough for an animal to bury itself four inches deep in order to escape the extraordinary temperatures of full noon. Moreover, the constancy of the temperature within the burrows is accompanied by a relative humidity higher than that at the surface because of the lower rate of evaporation. Thus, the animals escape underground both from high temperatures and from dehydration.

"NESTS," HUTS, AND EDIFICES ABOVE GROUND. Some rodents build "nests" above ground to shelter their young after birth; others construct more durable huts in which they live the year around. In both cases they show architectural abilities that are rather rare among vertebrates, apart from the birds.

The nest of the European harvest mouse (fig. 38) is a kind of ball made of interlaced gramineous leaves that generally belong to the same plants that support the edifice. These leaves, often split into strings, thus remain alive as long as the nest is occupied. There is no regular doorway; the female pushes her way in and out anywhere near the top. The nest is often suspended 20 inches above the ground. Outside the reproductive period the mice live in holes and they are frequently found in winter in straw stacks. It is probable that a single female builds several nests in succession in the course of the summer.

Squirrels in all latitudes also construct globular "nests," some of which are used as true nests and others as temporary lodgings only. Those of the European red squirrel are composed of a layer of twigs, often leafy, with another layer in-

FIG. 38: *Nest of the European harvest mouse.*

side of moss or bark fragments. They are placed in trees, frequently at the base of a large branch. A single individual has several of these nests, and often makes use also of holes in trees or even abandoned crow's nests. In North America

89

the fox squirrel builds summer "nests," light and fragile, and winter "nests" whose more solid construction may last for years. The American red squirrel uses at the same time aerial "nests," old woodpecker-holes, and burrows that connect chambers, six to eight inches in diameter, where the animal stores its reserves of food. The building of ball-shaped aerial nests is not peculiar to the squirrels of cold countries. In tropical Asia the Indian giant squirrel also builds them, a single animal using several located in different trees within its home range.

Very different from these temporary aerial "nests" are the durable structures of other species of rodents. The houses built by the dusky-footed wood rat of the southwestern United States represent the most simple type. Vestal has made an excellent study of these in Contra Costa County, California. They are conical in shape, often built around a tree trunk, and may exceed the average height of a man. Thus the average height of 301 of these nests was four feet, with extremes of 14 inches and 6 feet 9 inches! The average diameter at the base was more than 3 feet. These structures are built wholly of small branches, leaves, and plant debris. They are constantly kept in good condition and shelter only a single individual. Inside are one or more chambers connected by passageways, a nest, and a sanitary chamber. The nest is generally located about halfway up, in the driest part of the structure, and on the north side in those studied by Vestal. The owner of this edifice ranges hardly more than 100 feet from it to collect food. Some wood rats place their houses on branches.

Muskrat and beaver houses have often been described, sometimes in fantastic terms. The muskrat builds houses that are well known not only in North America but also in Europe, where this fur-bearing rodent has been introduced. This lodge, in which the female raises her young, is dome-shaped and ordinarily contains only one chamber. The animal enters the lodge through one of several tunnels opening below water level. The house is altered and worked over from year to year by its owner, and in some cases may reach a height of three feet and a diameter of nine at the base. In addition to this lodge, the muskrat builds light feeding-shelters, as well as platforms of plant material, and uncovered "rafts." Interesting regional variations have been noted in this animal's architecture. For example, in some parts of the United States they build no houses and live in burrows, whereas in Maryland they do build houses but always with flat tops. The causes of these geographical variations are not well understood.

The structures made by beavers have been known for several centuries, but the imagination of travelers often ascribes to them a degree of perfection that tends to falsify their descriptions. The American beaver generally builds houses that serve as a permanent habitation for the couple and its two last litters (Bradt, Warren). These houses rest on a foundation of boughs and mud over a peat-moss base, or even on a small natural islet. They are generally surrounded with water, and it is not uncommon for a willow bush to serve as the center around which a house is constructed (fig. 39). The walls of the house are composed of piled-up branches, cemented with earth or mud, and the whole may be two feet thick at the base. The dome itself is composed of boughs that always remain permeable to air, providing the chamber below with proper ventilation even

FIG. 39: *Vertical section and ground plan of a lodge of the American beaver, built around a bushy willow (h). The entrance (a) opens into a vestibule (b) communicating with the chamber (c). There are two accessory entrances (e and f). At (d) is a blind corridor. A wood rat has established its own nest at (j). After Grinnell, Dixon, and Linsdale.*

in the depth of winter. The interior of the house consists usually of only a single chamber, the floor of which is always a little above the water level; sometimes lateral alcoves are provided in the walls. The exits always open under water.

Beavers build dams across the watercourse, upstream and downstream from the house. These dams are constructed of tree branches, stones, and earth, and may be straight or crooked. Their length varies from a few to a hundred yards, and in height they range from one to twelve feet, according to circumstances. It would seem that the purpose of these dams is to hold constant the water level of the pool on which the house is built; thus freezing weather never prevents the animals from having free access to their sunken stores of wood and bark. Great admiration has been expressed for the marvelous "instinct" that leads the beavers to choose the best possible location for the dams, and to adjust their height properly. Modern observers have shown, however, that this praise is exaggerated, for in many cases the dams are not in fact built where they would be most efficient. Furthermore, the constant labor of reconstruction of the dams carried on by the members of the colony seems to correspond to a deep physiological need. Tevis has observed in New York a beaver family inhabiting a small lake produced by the construction of an artificial barrier of stones and cementing material. Now, although this barrier was in perfect condition, the beavers worked all summer "repairing" it with mud and branches just as if it were one of their ordinary dams. What is more, it seems that there is an inner need to obstruct all flowing water. Although the level of the artificial pond was to all appearances quite satisfactory, Tevis's beavers set about building a dam across the stream feeding the pond behind the barrier. The only observable result was to flood the surrounding area and to kill a growth of alder—an outcome of no apparent advantage to the colony.

The canals dug by beavers are also of great interest. Their function seems to be to facilitate the transportation by water of the tree trunks and branches cut in the woods worked by the colony. Very infrequently met with in the eastern United States, these canals are more common in the West, and one of them has been described that was 745 feet long.

Even in North America not all beavers live in houses. At least temporarily, many inhabit burrows that they dig in the banks of streams and that open under water. This is especially frequent in localities where the beavers are disturbed by man. The European beaver builds houses like those of its North American relative only in certain remote parts of its range, particularly in Scandinavia and Russia (figs. 40 and 41). The beavers of the Rhone valley appear to have lost this habit since the Middle Ages. It is probable that complete protection would cause it to reappear, since rudimentary houses have been built by some individuals in semicaptivity.

TERRITORY

IT is well known that during the breeding season most birds show themselves very intolerant of other members of

FIG. 40: *Section of a European beaver pond in the Voronezh region of Russia. Note the subterranean canals, with numerous openings, intermediate between the burrows of most European beavers and the canals of American beavers. After Klebovitch, in Ognev.*

FIG. 41: *Diagram of a European beaver pond in the Voronezh region of Russia: a, dams; b, subterranean canals with openings; c, house. After Ognev.*

FIG. 42: *Diagrammatic representation of the accepted concepts of territory and home range. Theoretical square with six occupants of the same species and sex. Redrawn from Burt.*

 Home range boundary
- - - - - - - Territorial boundary
▨▨▨▨▨ Neutral zone
● Nesting site (home)
○ Refuge site

the same species entering a definite zone around the nest. This zone, called the *territory*, thus becomes the exclusive "property" of the nesting couple for the time required for egg-laying, brooding, and raising the young. The size of the territory varies greatly according to the species. For most European passerine birds it may vary from 1,200 or 2,400 square yards to a little more than two and a half acres; but for many species, such as the English sparrow, the European black swift, and most birds that nest in colonies, it is reduced to the immediate vicinity of the nests. On the other hand the territory may be of considerable extent for certain birds of prey which are strong fliers. The time during which the territory is maintained is also very variable. With many passerines this time is limited to the reproductive period. In some species the reappearance of territorial behavior in autumn may be observed, while others establish a territory in their winter quarters. The same variability is encountered when we attempt to determine the role of the territory. In some cases it serves mating and feeding needs, in others it concerns mating only, in still others (winter territories) it is for feeding only. Thus the one and only characteristic common to all these types of territory is clearly *the intolerance of their "owners" toward other individuals of the same species,* and most ornithologists today agree in defining the territory as *"an area defended by its occupant against competing members of the same species."*

Territories so defined unquestionably exist with numerous species of fish (sticklebacks, Centrarchidæ of North America, some Cyprinidæ and Characidæ), and also with many lizards. Has something of the kind been observed among mammals?

The answer would seem to be yes in certain instances. Each band of vicuna inhabits, the year round, an area of from 20 to more than 100 acres in the Peruvian puna (fig. 45). Here the group feeds, rests, and rears its young. The boundaries of this area are defended by the adult male which acts as the leader of the band against any other adult

97

male trespassing on them, even when all the females of the band have left. Although the females of a band are hostile toward alien females, they do not take part in defending territorial boundaries. The male rarely takes action to prevent a female from leaving his territory. Yet the females remain, presumably because of their familiarity with the home range and because of the hostility shown toward them by members of surrounding bands. Once established, a territorial boundary is recognized by males on each side of it, even though one of them may be temporarily absent. When driven from its territory by men, a group returns to it within a period of several hours, although the members of the band may have been widely separated during the interim.

Among fur seals and elephant seals, it is only during the breeding season that the "harem bulls" defend a definite territory. Here again, it is the territory itself which is defended, not a particular area around a moving individual. When established bulls were driven from their territories by K. W. Kenyon, they returned in all observed instances to the exact site which they had left.

The 10,000 Uganda kobs of the Semliki game reserve have only thirteen traditional mating grounds, situated on ridges, knolls, and slightly raised areas characterized by short grass, good visibility, and proximity to a permanent stream. Each of these contains an average of twelve to fifteen more or less circular sites, varying from 20 to 60 yards in diameter, where adult males may be found at any time of the year, waiting for the females. The marking of fifty of these males by H. K. Buechner has shown that some remained at the same circular site for less than a day, others for several days or a few weeks; the longest period was two and a half months. Defense of boundaries between occupied territories was accomplished mostly by ritualized display rather than intensive fighting. But whenever a male invaded a given territory serious fighting between the occupant and the challenger took place. Such behavior reminds one strongly of the arena displays of some birds.

There are nevertheless many negative facts to place beside these few positive data. No trace of territorial ownership has ever been found for species as diverse as the mountain gorilla (Schaller), the East African baboon (de Vore), the bighorn sheep (Buechner), the California ground squirrel (Fitch), or the common vole (Reichstein). Among carnivores, several families may live together peacefully in the same burrow while their young are reared. In the Mount McKinley National Park in Alaska, Murie saw two she-wolves raising their litters at the same time in the same den. Sheldon reports that this is frequent with the American red fox, and Hainard has observed two females of the European red fox combining their litters and taking turns in nursing the whole group of young. In his study of the prairie spotted skunk in Iowa, Crabbe has shown that the several dens are not "owned" by single individuals or by single families, but are used in common by the whole local population, like the network of paths connecting them. Scott, finally, has been unable to discern that any true territory is maintained by the northern plains red fox; and, in his opinion, the "scent signals" that the male places by urinating on stones and other objects have rather a sexual significance, indicative of the rutting period.

Even in strongly territorial species the ownership of the territory is not always so personal and exclusive as previously thought. Carrick has shown, for instance, that in the large harems of southern elephant seals of Macquarie and Heard islands, the "beachmaster" usually shares his control with one or more assistants—each of them having his own sphere of influence among the cows. Among European wild rabbits "secondary" bucks are also allowed to maintain a territory within that of the dominant male of the warren (fig. 44).

THE HOME RANGE

AS already stated, the home range is the area over which the individual or the family group normally travels in search of food. A fundamental negative characteristic differentiating it from the territory is that the home range is not the exclusive "property" of the individual that frequents it. Thus, it is not defended by its occupant against other members of the same species, and several home ranges may overlap without giving rise to conflict.

We are better informed on the extent and variations of the home range of the mammals than on their territorial behavior; indeed, thanks to the technique of setting traps in grids, it is possible to gain an approximate idea of the area regularly frequented by a previously marked individual. It surely would not be wise to rely too confidently on the figures thus obtained, and Hayne has given us a timely reminder of the limitations of the method. Comparisons can still be made, however, and numerous authors, especially in

North America, have persistently studied the characteristics of the home ranges of the small mammals.

The brown rat, for instance, is much more sedentary than is generally supposed. Davis, Emlen, and Stokes have applied themselves to the study of its movements from place to place in the city of Baltimore and in the country. In doing this they first caught a number of individuals which they marked and released. Later a large proportion of these marked individuals were recaptured, and thus it was easy to ascertain the size of their home range. Of 362 rats marked and released, 119 were recaptured in the city after a week or more. Among the recaptured, 71 per cent of the adult males and 77 per cent of the adult females were taken within forty feet of the place where they had been captured the first time. On a Maryland farm the same experiment was carried on for a year with analogous results: 75.3 per cent of the adult males and 84 per cent of the adult females were recaptured within less than forty feet from where they were first caught; only 10 per cent of the females went from one to another of the farm buildings.

Extensive information on the home ranges of North American small mammals is to be found in the numerous papers of Blair, Burt, and Mohr. On the whole, the published figures indicate great variation among the species and, in the same species, between the sexes for different habitats and in different years. Generally the area of the home range varies from a fraction of an acre to a few acres; that of the males is often, but not always, greater than that of the females.[6] With desert mammals the area is as a rule larger than

[6] Sheldon has shown that in the American red fox only the female

with species of similar size living in temperate regions. The greater or lesser possibilities for food and cover furnished by the habitat would seem, then, in some way to determine the average extent of the home range. The density of the population, on the other hand, has some influence, and any overpopulation tends to reduce the home range of the individuals composing the population. But this "compressibility" is not unlimited; if we artificially overpopulate a habitat, the population of which is already in equilibrium and near the "carrying capacity," we can show that only a small proportion of the enforced immigrants are able to gain a foothold; most of them are obliged to emigrate. Blair's experiments with deer mice in George Reserve, Michigan, give ample proof of this, as do those of Calhoun on the brown rats of Baltimore. This mechanism is certainly what compels many young to emigrate away from their birthplace. Only a part remain to fill the places made vacant by the death of adults; the rest disperse to seek a less populated region at a distance. We shall return to these matters in the chapter devoted to the physiology of wild populations.[7]

The home range is not a prerogative of species inhabiting temperate or subtropical regions; even in the equatorial forest the small mammals are remarkably sedentary. Davis provides us with some Brazilian examples. Most of the

---

has a rather fixed home range, the male being much more given to wandering. One of these males traveled 23 miles in 11 days, and another, marked in late September, was retaken in early December at a distance of 40 miles!

[7] D. H. Salman has recently published a very pertinent study of the various factors, ecological and ethological, which govern the territorial behavior of the eastern cottontail rabbit; the conclusions reached in this work are certainly of very general application.

species he studied by marking failed to go more than three hundred feet or so from the place where they were first trapped. The same is true of arboreal forms; the woolly opossum remains in a single tree for several months!

Just as the home range of small species appears restricted, so that of the large mammals is sometimes extended. The brown bear in Russia frequents a zone of about 10 to 13 square miles. As for the Alaskan grizzly bear, Murie's observations indicate that the diameter of its home range does not exceed 9 miles. The family home range of wolves, studied by the same naturalist in the Mount McKinley National Park, may have as great a diameter as 50 miles! We shall return later to the home ranges of ungulate herds (ch. viii), and for the present shall only state, with Fraser Darling, that the area of a deer range varies with the abundance of food.

TOPOGRAPHY OF THE HOME RANGE. The mammals, particularly the large species, often lay out very exact landmarks within the home range. Apart from the main domicile, several secondary quarters exist, and even temporary refuges, as a rule. A single European hare always has several forms, just as a single Texas armadillo uses from 4 to 8 burrows concurrently. In addition to living-quarters, the home range may include wallowing-places for mud baths (deer), playgrounds and sunning-grounds (badger), and dung pits (badger). With the large mammals certain trees, rocks, or termite nests serve as landmarks or as "rubbing-posts" for the animals which visit them regularly (fig. 43). There is almost always a network of paths or trails connecting these different points, more or less noticeable to the casual observer but well known to beasts of prey and to poachers.[8] With the large ungulates, in regions where man does not disturb them too much, these paths are often used generation after generation, and they may become real trails. This is the case with the migration "routes" of caribou in the great Canadian North, as well with the elephant "roads" that were formerly common in eastern Africa;

FIG. 43: *A male European bison "at his rubbing tree."*

Percival describes these "roads" as perfectly smooth and free from vegetation, as much as 3 or 4 yards in width, and following the line of easiest slope in mountainous country. Our ravaging "civilization" hardly allows such manifestations of the might of great animals to exist any longer in the modern world. It is along these paths or trails that one generally finds "signposts"—secretions of the skin glands, urine, heaps of dung, barked trees, and the like (ch. viii).

[8] Even the arboreal primates exhibit behavior of this type. Malbrant and Maclatchy refer, for example, to "trails laid out in the foliage, veritable aerial routes" existing in the "food-gathering territory" of bands of tree-dwelling guenons (*Cercopithecus cephus*).

Beaver dam in Oregon. It is about two feet high. Note use of rock as base. Photograph by V. Scheffer. U.S. Fish and Wildlife Service.

An American beaver house, Fort Peck, Montana. Photograph by A. Van S. Pulling. U.S. Fish and Wildlife

Canal dug by beavers in state of Washington. Photograph by T. H. Scheffer, U.S. Fish and Wildlife Service.

They undoubtedly play an important part in the daily life of the mammals.

Both male and female European red foxes, for instance, "mark" their ranges by urine sprinkling; the vixen starts to do so earlier in the season than the male, according to Tembrock. This behavior apparently serves at least two different purposes. First, these scent marks stake out the home range of the pair, and thus notify any prospective

FIG. 44: *Territory of a dominant male European wild rabbit (M24). Within this area, two sedentary males (M32 and M20) maintain their own territories. The does are sedentary and always graze near home. After Lockley.*

competitor that the area is presently occupied. Second, the female's marks apparently play a role in the synchronization of male and female mating behavior; the male obviously gains information about the vixen's sexual condition by smelling her urine marks and, later, sniffing her anal region.

FIG. 45: *Map of the vicuna territories of the eastern part of the area studied by Koford (1957) at Huaylarco, Peru. The area lay along both sides of a shallow stream and dirt road. The letters and numbers designate the territories, which are also marked by heavy broken lines. The dotted line indicates the territorial change between February and April 1952.*

For Arctic foxes, golden jackals (*Canis aureus*), and raccoon dogs (*Nyctereutes procyonides*), the strongest stimulus to urine sprinkling is always the scent of a congener's fresh urine marker. But once dried, urine becomes completely ineffective. The smell of urine also induces rubbing and rolling among Arctic foxes and jackals. Heimburger has shown that trimethylamine has a similar effect and that synthetic urea plays the same role as the scent mark of a strange female.

The dung heaps so frequently found along the trails of

hippopotami or of the great one-horned rhinoceros of India (*Rhinoceros unicornis*) apparently also stimulate any conspecific animal passing by to defecate on them. There is nevertheless no evidence that these dung heaps "belong" to definite animals or that they mark individual "territories" (Grzimek, Gee).

One of the main advantages of the home range is probably that it assures to the individual frequenting it not only its daily food but also increased protection against predators. Davis very justly remarks that an animal taken by surprise on its home range finds with minimum delay a hiding-place in which to take refuge or a pathway along which to make its escape under the best possible conditions. On the other hand, a small rodent set at liberty outside its familiar range always takes much longer in finding shelter. This intimate knowledge of the surroundings made possible by an established home range probably explains also the ease with which many mammals accomplish their return to nest or lair—their homing; the keenness of their sense of smell provides them with guideposts unknown to human perceptions.

The sedentary nature of many small mammals, further, has consequences that would have hardly been suspected before the intensive studies of the last few years. Howard, having marked 675 young deer mice before they left the nest, found that 70 per cent of the young males and 85 per cent of the young females settled down no more than 500 feet from their birthplace. A high degree of inbreeding results from this; 4 to 10 per cent of the 186 litters observed were produced either by parent-offspring matings or by matings between sibs.

CHAPTER 4

Defense and Protection

IT is always a difficult matter, even for an objective observer, to estimate the value of the methods of defense and protection used by animals under natural conditions. Such and such behavior, attitude, or morphological character may seem to us to have a certain protective value even though it may actually be of no great use against the natural predator of the animal under observation. The scientific study of the behavior of wild mammals is only in its early stages, and it is likely that with further study the problem of their means of defense and protection will reveal itself to be much more complex than it now appears.

DEFENSIVE ATTITUDES

FLIGHT is the habitual reaction of the great majority of mammals before what they take to be an enemy. There is no need to mention examples of this behavior, common to both large and small species in all environments. It is not to be supposed, however, that flight in the presence of danger is resorted to invariably. Instead of fleeing, the animal often assumes an absolute immobility that enables it to escape detection. Some species frequently behave in this manner and others very rarely. As to the reasons why flight is preferred to complete immobility—or vice versa—we can only suggest hypotheses.

With most mammals flight before an enemy takes place only when the predator (or man) comes within a "critical distance" of the animal. Once this distance is attained, the animal makes off. If the animal is pursued and the distance between it and its enemy is dangerously diminished, the pursued may suddenly change its behavior and, abandoning flight, puts itself on the defensive (figs. 46, 47). If it is hard pressed, the defense reaction is released—a highly variable response according to the species concerned and employing all the weapons available to the animal (horns, hooves, tusks, teeth, etc.[1]). The "critical distances," of course, vary with the species and, in the same species, with sex, age, and local conditions. It is a curious fact that the critical distance is less for some animals when approached by, say, an automobile than when approached afoot.

Among the social species the group often displays remarkable organization for the detection of approaching danger. Although it would seem that the Alpine marmots have no true "lookouts," each animal is very much on the watch; when it perceives danger, it whistles, and this whistle puts the rest of the colony on the alert. A similar warning-system exists in some rodents other than the marmots, such as the mountain viscacha of Peru. Darling reports that, in the Scottish Highlands, when a herd of red deer is resting, one or more individuals keep watch in every direction. If,

[1] The Panama howling monkeys may break off branches to throw at intruders; red spider monkeys do the same (Carpenter), but the use of pebbles as projectiles by baboons has never been verified.

FIG. 46. *Defense posture of the great red kangaroo. Drawn from a photograph furnished by the New York Zoological Society.*

on the other hand, one deer is reposing by itself, it lies with its back toward the wind, keeping watch by sight over the zone in front and by scent over that to the rear. Musk oxen tend to arrange themselves in a circle when threatened; the

FIG. 47: *Three-toed anteater in a "tripod" attitude, head down, on the vertical trunk of a tree. After a sketch made by the author on Barro Colorado Island, Canal Zone, September 1951.*

young are grouped in the middle and the adults surround them, their powerful heads facing outward in all directions. Such behavior was perhaps very efficient against beasts of prey, but it has rather favored the destruction of the species by Eskimos and Indians, once these were armed with guns.

All the mammals that are covered over with a more or less tough armor (armadillos, pangolins), and those with hairs modified into sharp quills (hedgehogs, porcupines, etc.), assume special attitudes of defense appropriate to these structural characteristics. In the armadillos there even seems to exist a close relation between the structure of the scapular shield and the usual posture of defense. Thus armadillos of the genus *Tolypeutes*,[2] which have the scapular shield shaped in sections like a horseshoe, roll themselves into a ball when threatened, their head and tail ends fitting together in a remarkable manner (fig. 48). The species of *Euphractus*, on the other hand, which have the shield much more flattened on a low arc, cannot do the same but press themselves against the ground if they are taken by surprise and caught running about. The very curious animal *Chlamyphorus* (fig. 49) uses its posterior shield to close the burrow in which it takes refuge. As for the Old World pangolins, whose armor is made up of broad, horny scales regularly arranged to overlap like shingles on a roof, they are all able to roll themselves into a ball, like *Tolypeutes* (fig. 50). The female of the Indian pangolin even protects its young in case of danger by placing it on her belly and then curling her long protective tail around herself.

It is a common sight to see the European hedgehog roll itself into a ball and erect its quills. Although there is no

[2] This genus does not even dig burrows.

FIG. 48: *Posture of defense of the armadillo,* Tolypeutes conurus. *After a photograph by Eisentraut.*

FIG. 49: *The armadillo* Chlamyphorus truncatus.

doubt that this attitude is protective, it is questionable whether it affords perfect defense against all predators, for the hedgehog does form part of the menu of several carnivores, various Mustelidæ, the vultures, and the great horned owl, for example. Still, the German naturalist

Uttendorfer, who minutely analyzed the contents of 102,-
000 pellets of Central European birds of prey, found the remains of hedgehogs only 134 times!

The quills of the porcupines inhabiting the tropical and
subtropical regions of the Old World form an even more

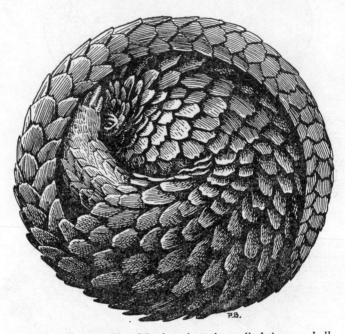

FIG. 50: *A pangolin,* Manis tricuspis, *rolled into a ball.
Drawn from a photograph by H. Lang.*

efficient means of defense. When an African porcupine
is irritated, it erects its quills (fig. 51), grunts and puffs
loudly, and produces a curious rustling sound by clashing its
quills together. But this is not the limit of its defense. If the
aggressor approaches, the porcupine, moving backwards,
throws itself quickly upon it, and the contact of the sharp
quills may inflict serious wounds on the enemy. Prater cites

two especially convincing observations: in one case a panther was mortally wounded, and in another case an almost adult tiger, its liver and lungs perforated in many places, was found dead a few yards from its victim. The American porcupine is less dangerous but is no more limited to a pas-

FIG. 51: *Attitude of defense, with quills erected, of the African porcupine,* Hystrix africæ-australis.

sive defense. If a dog approaches one too closely, it erects its quills, elevates its back, raises its tail slightly, and bends its nose down under its body. Keeping its back always toward its assailant, it strikes out repeatedly with its tail, always leaving some quills in the flesh of the aggressor. The structure of the tips of the quills enables them, moreover, to advance by themselves in the body of the victim, because of the contractions of the muscles in contact with the barbs of the imbedded quills (fig. 52). Shadle and Po-Chedley cite an instance in which a fragment three quarters of an inch long progressed almost two inches in thirty hours, and another only a quarter of an inch long advanced almost an inch and three quarters in less than two days.

Another very special type of defensive attitude, as we have mentioned, is complete immobilization, or "freezing behavior," in common parlance often called "playing pos-

FIG. 52: *Appearance of the tip of a quill, magnified about 45 times, of the American porcupine. After Shadle and Po-Chedley.*

sum." Fawns of the deer family provide us with a good example. For the first few days after birth the mother leaves them alone where they were born, and, at the slightest alarm, they "freeze" on the spot in perfect immobility. In many cases their spotted fur helps to make them hardly visible in the midst of the dappling of light and shade on the ground beneath the underbrush. This behavior has often been compared to that of the Virginia opossum. It is well known that in case of danger this marsupial can "play dead"; it lies on its side (fig. 53), limp, its tongue sometimes hanging out of its half-opened mouth, its eyes closed, and its heartbeat slow. This state may last for several minutes, during which the animal passively lets itself be handled; when the danger passes, the opossum resumes its normal behavior. It must always be noted that we have to do here with a relatively rare reaction, and it is possible that the performance is to be compared rather with the analogous states to be observed sometimes in certain birds, the protective function of which is not always clear.[3]

A last very special type of defensive attitude is the discharge of fetid secretions. Examples are found in several

FIG. 53: *Virginia opossum "playing dead." After a photograph by Viola McColm.*

families: among the civets (Viverridæ), the species of the genera *Viverra* and *Viverricula* use the perineal gland for this purpose; in the Herpestidæ the large species, like the striped-necked mongoose and the crab-eating mongoose, empty their stink glands when danger threatens. It is among the skunks (Mustelidæ), however, that this mode of defense reaches its greatest development; their anal glands are very large indeed, and the substance they secrete can be shot out with astonishing precision to a distance of up to about

[3] Very similar behavior has been reported for the jackal, the honey badger, and the striped hyena (Prater).

twelve feet (fig. 54). Before discharging this malodorous secretion, skunks first assume "threatening attitudes" that vary widely according to the species. Some stamp on the ground with their hind feet while others, such as the spotted

FIG. 54: *Position of the striped skunk*, Mephitis mephitis, *before the ejection of the secretion of its anal glands.*

skunk, walk for perhaps five seconds at a time on their front feet with the hindquarters elevated. It is a curious fact that the skunks, like the civets and the mongooses that use stink glands, have a special pattern of coat coloration. Its black

FIG. 55: *A skunk,* Spilogale gracilis, *"standing on its hands."*
In part after a drawing by M. M. Colbert.

and white contrast sharply, and the association of this conspicuous coat with the use of malodorous secretions has
been often emphasized (fig. 55).

Musk glands discharged in fright are found in a wide
variety of species. The peccary, for instance, has one on its

back, eight inches in front of the tail. When the animal is excited, the hairs of the back and neck bristle and the dorsal gland emits a musky secretion whose odor can be perceived by man at a distance of several hundred feet. Here it is not easy to see the defensive utility of this behavior, and it would seem rather that many intermediary stages exist between the emotional secretion of certain cutaneous glands induced by a state of fear and their intentional utilization for defense against an aggressor.

AUTOTOMY OF THE TAIL IN MAMMALS

THE extreme fragility of the tail in lizards is well known. Many species when seized by the caudal appendage free themselves by leaving it in the hunter's grasp. This experiment can be readily carried out with the European green lizard, and its tail may even break off during fights between males. Later a usually incomplete but quite clear regeneration occurs.

Caudal autotomy, or self-amputation of the tail, for escape also exists among mammals, but the manner in which it is accomplished has been studied only rather superficially. Cuénot was one of the first to call attention to this curious phenomenon, but he has been followed, since 1907, by only a very few naturalists.[4]

If we seize a long-tailed field mouse by the tail, we al-

[4] Mohr (1941) reports tail autotomy in 20 species of the genera *Perognathus, Glis, Dryomys, Eliomys, Muscardinus, Apodemus, Mus, Epimys, Graphiurus,* and *Claviglis.* This autotomy is often followed by a beginning of regeneration. Von Haffner (*Zool. Anzeiger,* 135:66, 1941) has studied this phenomenon in the forest, garden, and common dormice. His histological researches have shown that when part of a vertebra remains it will regenerate a vertebra similar to the original one but having also some resemblance to the last tail vertebra. When the tail is broken off at the level of an intervertebral disk, the latter regenerates a cartilaginous structure.

most always see that the cutaneous sheath of the tail separates at some point and remains in the hand, while the animal escapes. The wound scarcely bleeds at all, and the denuded portion of the tail dries up and falls off in two or three days. In this type of autotomy there is no voluntary or reflex action on the part of the animal. The caudal sheath breaks at the edge of one of the corneous rings with which the tail is provided, and does not adhere to the vertebræ with their accompanying muscles and blood vessels. It is possible, moreover, to observe autotomy quite as well in a field mouse recently dead as in a living individual. Gögl has made a careful histological study of this phenomenon and concludes that the autotomy always occurs at the level of a zone of least resistance. In the garden dormouse and the common dormouse there are only four to six possible points of breakage.

Has this peculiarity some protective value for the species that manifest it? Does this security device often act as such under natural conditions? These are questions which are very difficult to answer objectively in view of the meager information now at our disposal. One thing only is certain: in wild populations of species in which escape autotomy has been reported, a considerable proportion of individuals with amputated tails has been observed. Cuénot reports that he has seen more field mice with incomplete than with intact tails, and Hainard confirms the frequent occurrence of this mutilation. It would be of interest to have exact percentages for different localities. Enders notes that 20 to 25 per cent of the spiny rats taken by him on Barro Colorado Island, in the Panama Canal Zone, had incomplete tails.

THE PROBLEM OF CONCEALING COLORATION

THE temporary or permanent resemblance of the coat in certain mammals to the dominant ground color of their favored habitat long ago captured the attention of naturalists. According as rodents or carnivores were concerned, it has been interpreted as a means of protection against predators or as a form of camouflage facilitating the approach to prey. In both cases natural selection would favor species with "protective" coloration and would therefore account for the origin of this adaptation.

In reality the problem is not so simple as it would at first appear to be, and it seems appropriate to take up in succession the seasonal color change of arctic and alpine mammals and the permanent concealing coloration of desert species.

SEASONAL COLOR CHANGE OF ARCTIC MAMMALS. It is undeniable that among the species inhabiting the polar regions of the northern hemisphere many assume in summer a dark coat and in winter a white one. Further, it would seem that the duration of the winter coat is in direct relation to that of the period of snow. The different forms of the arctic hare of the great American North offer a good example. For example, the subspecies *grœnlandicus* of Ellesmere Island, at 80° north latitude, remains white the year round, while the subspecies *canus* of Hudson Bay assumes a dark coat from late June to late August. The molting date of the snowshoe hare is also influenced not only by latitude but also by altitude. Thus Smith has noted, in the Green Mountain massif (Vermont), that at mid-June the hares were in summer pelage at 2,800 feet, in lighter pelage already at 3,200 feet, and in pelage still spotted with white at 4,000 feet, at which altitude the snow lasts into May. The European varying hare gives evidence of a similar adaptation to local conditions. In the north of Scandinavia it becomes white in winter, as also in the Scottish Highlands (subspecies *scoticus*). On the other hand, in southern Sweden, in Ireland (subspecies *hibernicus*), and in the Faroe Islands (subspecies *seclusus*) it retains a dark livery the year round. The arctic fox, in its typical form, becomes white in winter, but in Iceland, where the climate is less severe, it generally retains its dark coat throughout the year. Among the Mustelidæ, also, we find good examples of seasonal color change. The ermine assumes for the winter a pelage that is all white except for the black tail-tip; the change in coloration appears to take place earlier in the autumn on mountains than in flat country. Thus Hainard observed a perfectly white ermine in October at Anzeindaz in Switzerland (2,500 feet), and one that was entirely brown at Bernex (500 feet). In mountains the summer pelage seems likewise to appear later than in flat country. In mild climates, as in Ireland or central and southern England, it is not uncommon for ermines to remain brown all winter, while in Scotland they are white during the cold season. The weasel also turns white in Scandinavia during the winter, at least in places where the snow lasts more than a hundred days. In England it generally remains brown in winter, whereas it turns white in the Alps, but not invariably (Hainard mentions several observations of brown weasels in December and January, at 2,000 feet in the Alpes Vaudoises).

There are exceptions, however, to this seasonal adaptation of coat color to that of the surroundings. In the first place there are species which remain brown while living most of the year amid the snows; this is true of the musk ox, reindeer, caribou,[5] and wolverine. Among the lemmings, the Hudson Bay and Greenland collared lemmings turn white in winter, while the brown lemming and Norway lemming remain in somber livery all year. Still, it is not rare to meet with collared and brown lemmings in the same habitat. Hamilton says that he has even caught them in the same burrows, under the snow. Other mammals, on the contrary, remain white even in summer. This is true of the polar bear and of Peary's caribou. In regard to these animals it may be said, however, that they are precisely species that live on backgrounds of snow or ice almost all the time, summer included.

More perplexing is the problem of the blue fox. It is well known that the arctic fox has two distinct forms: the "normal" form, brown in summer and white in winter, and the "blue" form, which retains all year a dark bluish-gray coat color. These two phases are genetically distinct, the "blue" apparently dominant and the "normal" recessive. What is more remarkable is the different frequency of these two phases in different parts of the distributional area of the species. Through the work of Braestrup and of Elton we are in fact certain that the "blue" foxes (at a disadvantage in winter because of natural selection) make up no more than 1 to 5 per cent of the total population of arctic foxes in Baffin Land and the Canadian arctic, whereas they represent 50 per cent of the population in western Greenland. The

[5] With the exception always of the Ellesmere Islands form (*Rangifer pearyi*)—smaller than typical *arcticus*—which retains an almost wholly white coat throughout the year.

difference in coat color, further, would seem to be associated with other characters; the fecundity of the two phases appears to be different (higher in the "normals"), and above all their diet is not the same, "normal" foxes living on lemmings for the most part and the "blues" on birds, fish, and arctic hares. Let us keep in mind for the time being this first *correlation between a pigmentary character and other characteristics of physiological and psychological nature;* we shall come upon others later on, and they are probably of very great theoretical importance.

What do we know, at the present time, regarding the cause of this seasonal color change? Is this characteristic genetically determined, or are we concerned with a simple phenotypic variation, sensitive to the least changes in environmental conditions? Raising the species just mentioned outside their natural habitats should solve this problem. No systematic experimentation on a large scale seems to have been carried out, but what we learn from the few planned experiments or chance observations that have been made tends rather to suggest that the two mechanisms may work together to produce the same result.

Degerböl and Möhl-Hansen, having received in the autumn of 1936 seven living specimens of the Greenland collared lemming caught in northeastern Greenland, undertook to breed them in the neighborhood of Copenhagen. These animals acquired their winter pelage only in January–February of 1937, whereas in their native region they become white late in September or early in October. Later on, from 1937 to 1942 and in spite of the fact that the winters were very hard (the temperature having gone down to −30° C), their offspring retained their summer coat in the wintertime. Only a few of them temporarily displayed blue-gray or light-gray fur.[6] In this case the disappearance of the winter coat was probably determined by the modification of an environmental factor, since it happened at the start and in all individuals. The responsible factor may be the daily period of light. We shall see in a later chapter that Bissonette and Bailey have been able, in the laboratory, to induce out of season the appearance of the white winter coat in two species of weasels, by progressively reducing the daily period of light to which the animals were exposed. In addition, two Russian zoologists, Novikov and Blagodat-skaia, have arrived at similar results, working on the varying hare of Siberia. On November 25 they took 10 white hares that had finished their fall molting. Four of these served as controls and four were submitted to artificial lighting that was progressively lengthened by a quarter of an hour each day to reach 15 hours on February 1; two males, finally, were kept in darkness from November 25 to June 1; in all three cases the diet and temperature were identical. When the spring molt of the controls began in late March to early April, it did not occur in the two males that remained in total darkness, and they were still white on June 1. In the second series, on the contrary, the progressive increase in daily period of light stimulated the appearance of rut at the beginning of December and of the spring molt in January. All these observations and experiments tend, then, to show that a disturbance of the annual rhythm of variation in the length of the days can affect the succession of molts. But

[6] In this species the first litter of the year, born in March and therefore under the snow, has the winter coat from the first (with the claws enlarged on the third and fourth fingers), whereas the young of later litters are born with the summer coat.

this is not enough to solve the whole problem of winter color change in arctic mammals.

The fact is that other species transplanted from their country of origin continue to whiten in winter, and this in spite of the fact that the annual rhythm of photoperiods is changed. Cott reports, for example, that the arctic foxes living in the London Zoo continue to become white in winter, despite the very mild climate of southern England. In this case, therefore, the characteristic is genetically determined and unaffected by environmental variations, contrary to the case of the Greenland collared lemming.

As reconstructed by Degerböl, the history of the subspecies of the varying hare that now inhabits the Faroe Islands is also very suggestive. The fauna of these islands included no land mammals before the eighth or ninth centuries. At about that epoch domestic mice were introduced by the first inhabitants, and today four distinct subspecies exist there. Toward 1768 it was the brown rat's turn. Finally, from Norway in 1854-5 a pair of varying hares was imported, whose descendants have multiplied ever since and given origin to the new subspecies *seclusus*, which has thus become differentiated in less than a century. Now, in the years immediately following their introduction all the hares of the Faroes turned white in winter, like their Norwegian ancestors. Twenty years later half of the total only became white in winter, and thirty years later at most one quarter! Toward 1890 only a very small percentage of the population whitened in the cold season, and today all the hares keep their dark coats throughout the year. During this same time the size has become smaller, the length of the molars is less than in the ancestral form, and some other characters bring this new subspecies *seclusus* closer to the subspecies *scoticus* of Scotland.[7] In such a case the disappearance of the white winter coat cannot be attributed to a mere phenotypic change due to one or several environmental factors. Here *the modification has been progressive and has required almost forty years to become universal.* This suggests a hereditary change or mutation spreading little by little throughout the population.

Let us suppose, for example, a mutation "winter fur dark" recessive to the form "winter fur white" and occurring from time to time among the typical varying hares of Norway. On the one hand this mutation would have little chance of appearing in the homozygous form because of the large number of individuals composing the total population and crossing freely among themselves. On the other hand the rare homozygotes that did appear (much more visible in winter than normal individuals with white fur) would be more seriously threatened than these by predators. This same mutation, quite to the contrary, if it occurred in the Faroes among a smaller population (in which recessive mutations have therefore a better chance of appearing in homozygous form), will have the advantage in winter over the individuals that whiten, because of the rarity of snow. Natural selection will therefore act in its favor, and the number of homozygotes will tend to become greater and greater. This may possibly be the explanation of the phenomena observed in the Faroe Islands; but it remains necessary to make crosses between *seclusus* and the Scandinavian *timidus* before asserting its truth.

[7] Which, to be sure, whitens in winter.

THE PERMANENT CONCEALING COLORATION OF DESERT MAMMALS. Most of the mammals permanently inhabiting the desert regions of both the Old and the New Worlds wear a very typical coat. The prevailing colors are the pale buff and tawny hues of the soil, and the general coloration of the animal thus corresponds very faithfully to that of the background, especially in a sandy desert. This appearance is due chemically to a partial depigmentation and to a predominance of the phæomelanins.

We have to do here with a fact of very wide application. In the Sahara, for example, Heim de Balsac's studies have shown that of 50 species, 39, or more than three quarters, are of a "desert" shade. Among the exceptions are two hedgehogs, a wild boar, the dama gazelle, the jackal, the hunting dog, the Libyan striped weasel, the honey badger, the Barbary ground squirrel, and the garden dormouse. Still it should be noted that the wild boar has a rufous band running from neck to tail that is lacking in other races, and that the dormouse is clearly depigmented in comparison with the races of Barbary and Europe. Moreover, all these "exceptions" inhabit the northern or southern borders of the Sahara rather than the desert proper. In central Asia and Asia Minor the same fur coloration is to be seen in desert rodents (*Dipus, Eremodipus, Ctenodactylus, Pygerethmus*, etc.), the corsak fox, and the Pallas cat. It is to be observed also in the desert rodents in the southwestern United States (kangaroo rats, some deer mice, antelope jackrabbits, etc.) and in the Australian desert marsupials (*Dasycercus cristicauda, Dasyuroides byrnei*).

It is a very significant fact that typical desert coloration is not confined to terrestrial mammals. It is to be found again among the bats that, however, fly only at night and spend the daytime in rocky clefts or in caves where vertebrate predators are hardly a menace. In the Sahara, for instance, the eight species of Chiroptera all have a paler tint than have related forms living in nondesert country; *Otonycteris hemprichii*, belonging to the Afro-Asiatic desert zone, has a pale yellowish fur, quite the color of sand (on which this species probably never settles down!). *Eptesicus isabellinus* has fur that is much lighter than that of the European *Eptesicus serotinus*. The case of *Pipistrellus kuhlii* is most curious from our present point of view: The distribution of this species includes, in fact, the Mediterranean and desert regions; in southern Europe its coat is dark brown, almost black; in the Algerian Tell (a hilly, maritime region) it becomes verdigris green with the membranes much diluted in color; in the northern Sahara, finally, this bat is yellowish or whitish gray with the membranes cream-colored or grayish. Nor do the subterranean rodents escape the general rule, although they pass almost the whole of their lives away from the light. Kachkarov and Korovine mention an *Ellobius* of central Asia that has fur of the same general tint as that of the other rodents.[8]

The "desert" coloration of the fur is certainly genetically determined and is quite different from a mere phenotypic variation. It does in fact persist, even if the animal's environment is changed. Sumner was able to show its continuance, in captivity, through four to twelve generations

---

[8] These same authors point out, however, that the underground rodents are much sought after by predators on the Asiatic steppes; thus *Myospalax* make up more than 75 per cent of the hoarded food of *Buteo hemilasius* in eastern Transbaikalia.

of deer mice, and the same can be said of the North African jirds and gerbils reproducing in captivity in Paris.

The widespread concealing coloration of the fur in desert mammals that scarcely emerge from their burrows except at night, and its presence in species for which it almost certainly has no protective value (bats), would lead us to believe that *this pigmentary character is perhaps merely the correlative* of other morphological or physiological peculiarities having still greater utility in the desert environment and also giving scope to natural selection. It is known, for example, that the light-colored Jersey cattle become more readily adapted to tropical regions than do dark-colored breeds. Now, the skin of these animals would seem to contain more sweat glands, which would improve their resistance to heat. It is also known that certain pigmentary characters of the brown rat are correlated with modifications of behavior as well as with variations in the weight of certain endocrine glands and in basal metabolism.[9] The problem of desert coloration should be re-examined from this angle, for the more our knowledge of mammalian genetics advances, the more evident it becomes that the effects of certain genes on pigmentation are only secondary to physiological modifications of much greater importance.

SOME OTHER CASES OF ADAPTIVE COLORATION. The dark-colored lava flows found at several places in the deserts of the southwestern United States support a fauna of small mammals among which are some whose color is remarkably close to the general shade of the rock. Benson has published

[9] See, for example, Keeler, *Jour. Heredity*, 33:371, 1942, and Schopbach, Keeler, and Breenberg, *Growth*, 7:83, 1943.

a beautiful study of the rodents of the Tularosa Basin in New Mexico. This is an extensive valley bordered on the west, north, and east by mountains and on the south by a sandy desert. In this basin one finds both dunes of white gypsum and quartz sand and black lava flows. The latter are practically *isolated* in the middle of the valley and have an area of a little more than 145 square miles. Now, if we compare the small mammals *confined* to these two habitats (excluding, of course, forms common to both), we note very considerable differences. In the genus *Perognathus* the subspecies *P. apache gypsi*, living among the dunes of gypsum sand, is almost white, whereas *P. intermedius ater*, of the lava flows, is quite black.

It is not to be supposed that in all cases the coat color of small mammals living on recent lava flows will match so closely the color of the rock. Hooper, for example, studying the rodents of the lava fields in Valencia County, New Mexico, did not find such close adaptation in coat color. Of the eight forms belonging to this biotope and hardly ever leaving it, only three (*Peromyscus nasutus, Neotoma albigula,* and *Neotoma mexicana*) showed some tendency toward darkening, certain individuals of these three species being more pigmented than the average of those living elsewhere than on the lava. The most probable explanation of this difference lies in all likelihood in the different degree of isolation of the lava flows in the Tularosa Basin and in Valencia County. In the first case the flows are isolated along 29/30 of their circumference; in the second, on the contrary, one tenth to three fifths, approximately, of the periphery of the flows is contiguous to other rock formations, which favors mixing of the rodent populations. At

Tularosa selection can work upon a practically isolated population, whereas at Valencia its effects are in part counterbalanced by a constant movement of emigration and immigration.

Like phenomena are to be found in certain mice (*Peromyscus*) of sandy regions: *P. polionotus leucocephalus*, which lives on geographically isolated sandy islands, is much paler than *P. polionotus albifrons*, which inhabits beaches not sufficiently isolated to prevent the immigration of some *P. polionotus polionotus*, a subspecies that ordinarily lives on the darker terrains of the interior.

DOES CONCEALING COLORATION REALLY PLAY A PROTECTIVE ROLE? In the course of this chapter we have repeatedly mentioned the action of natural selection as a factor in the origin of adaptive colorations. We have also noted that pigmentary characters are very often correlated with other important characters of a physiological and morphological nature that can themselves afford scope for such selection. What, then, is the real utility of concealing coloration? Are we to think that it has only a distinctly secondary protective value against vertebrate predators, and that this advantage in itself is too slight to be of any use to the species in the course of its evolution? Experimentation should enable us to solve this problem.

The main argument so far advanced against the value of concealing coloration in mammals rests in fact upon the nocturnal habits of most of the species concerned. "It is clear," says Heim de Balsac, "that a protection of this kind can be effective only with regard to predators that hunt by sight and in the daytime. It seems to us impossible to admit that concealing coloration, however perfect it may be in daylight, can work to any effect in the darkness of night."

The recent experiments of Dice reveal that the truth is in all probability nothing of the kind. This author has carried out fully convincing experiments showing that concealing coloration can work perfectly with respect to nocturnal birds of prey and can have a truly protective effect.

Let us examine this remarkable work in some detail. The predators employed were the barn owl and the long-eared owl. The prey consisted of different varieties of deer mice: the recessive form "ivory" and the form "discardgray." Only adults of similar size and activity were used.

Since previous experiments had shown that on the floor of a room free from obstructions owls are able to catch their prey in total darkness, presumably by means of the sense of hearing, Dice made use of the following apparatus: the floor of an experimental room was divided into two equal parts, each of which was about 9 by 10 feet in size. The floor of the two halves of the room was covered with an artificial soil whose color either matched closely or contrasted with the pelage colors of the mice used in the tests. Wooden sticks, painted to match the color of the soil, were planted in a checkerboard in the artificial soil and these vertical posts were connected by horizontal pieces of rough, split lath. The space above the floor of the experimental room was thus broken up by this "artificial jungle" into little cells, so that the mice had partial cover. The experimental room was lighted by lamps whose intensity could be varied at will, and it was ascertained, as a preliminary, that the nocturnal birds of prey employed could still use their sight at extraordinarily weak lightings (from a distance of 6 feet or more, under an illumination as low as 0.00000073 of a foot candle!)

Each form of the deer mouse was put in the presence of the owl for 15 minutes, first on a ground of the same color, then on one of a different color from that of its pelage. Further, in each half of the experimental room there were always, at the same time, four concealingly colored and four conspicuous mice.

Thus was realized experimentally a population composed of the *same* number of concealingly colored individuals (A) and conspicuous individuals (B) hunted by the same predator. If concealing coloration plays no role, the number of concealingly colored mice taken (a) and that of conspicuous mice taken (b) should be the same. But if one form is captured in preference to the other, it must be admitted that selection intervenes. In this case the relative selection in favor of or against type A will be measured by the difference between the observed value of (a) and its theoretical value, that is to say one half of (a + b), this difference being itself divided by one half of (a + b). Thus:

$$\textit{Index of selection} = \frac{a - \frac{1}{2}\,(a + b)}{\frac{1}{2}\,(a + b)} = \frac{a - b}{a + b}$$

Dice's index of selection will evidently vary between 1.0 and −1.0, zero corresponding to complete absence of selective effect.

A large number of trials were of course necessary to get statistically significant results (as shown by the chi-square test), and Table 3 gives an idea of the extent of these experiments. The conclusion derived from them is quite clear, and, under Dice's conditions, concealing coloration

Table 3. Experiment showing the protective role of the concealing coloration of the forms "ivory" and "discard-gray" of Peromyscus maniculatus against the barn owl (Dice)

ILLUMINATION (IN FOOT-CANDLES)	ON SILICA SAND		ON GULLY SOIL		CONSPICUOUS MICE TAKEN	CONCEALINGLY COLORED MICE TAKEN
	"IVORY"	"DISCARD-GRAY"	"IVORY"	"DISCARD-GRAY"		
0.24	1	4	3	1	7	2
0.017	4	2	3	1	5	5
0.004,8	1	4	4	1	8	2
0.001,4	2	11	9	7	20	9
0.000,10	7	7	11	3	18	10
0.000,026	4	6	6	4	12	8
0.000,013	3	7	7	6	14	9
0.000,003,5	0	4	7	1	11	1
0.000,002,0	2	5	4	5	9	7
0.000,000,53	1	2	2	2	3	2
0.000,000,31	4	3	2	2	6	6
0.000,000,08	3	3	8	4	11	7
Darkness	1	0	1	2	3	3
Totals	33	58	67	38	125	71
Totals excepting animals captured in darkness	32	58	66	36	124	68

The index of selection here is 0.292 and the chi-square of the deviation from a 1 : 1 ratio is 16.333, a highly significant amount.

Defensive attitude of the southern elephant seal, Macquarie Island. Photograph by Dr. Sapin-Jaloustre. Expeditions polaires françaises.

Llama giving birth. Note position of mother and newborn. Photograph by Hediger. Zoological Garden, Basel.

American bison giving birth. The mother is eating the afterbirth. Photograph by Hediger, Zoological Garden, Basel.

has consequently some protective value, even at degrees of illumination quite unusable by the human eye.

It would, further, be wholly unsound to hold that for a pigmentary character to have a selective value it must assure absolute protection. The absolute does not exist in biology, and one of the great merits of population genetics is to have demonstrated that "surprisingly slight selective advantages may control the direction of evolution and may have strong effects in accelerating its rate." [1]

It would certainly seem, then, that concealing coloration has some value in itself, even if this character is merely correlated with other characters that can otherwise give opportunity for the working of natural selection.

[1] Simpson, G. G. (1944). *Tempo and Mode in Evolution*, pp. 81-3, and see Allee, Emerson, Park, Park, and Schmidt. *Principles of Animal Ecology*, 1949, pp. 648-56.

CHAPTER 5

Sexual Life and Reproduction

THE sexual life of the mammals is infinitely more reserved and circumspect, in general, than that of other vertebrates. Among them we scarcely find any equivalent of those courtship activities in which birds display the most brilliantly colored portions of their plumage. The sounds they emit during the rutting period are for the most part far from seductive to the human ear, and the mediocre keenness of our sense of smell prevents us from entering the strange world of odors that appears to play a great part in the sexual and social life of the mammals. If it be added to all this that most wild species are nocturnal, or extremely shy in their relations with man, the reason for the poverty of our knowledge will be easily understood. It would be most important, however—if only to comprehend better the biology of our own species—to know the sexual behavior of a great many species belonging to a large variety of orders. Our present information, in fact, is unfortunately limited to very few forms, and it is probable that future observations will rather considerably modify the provisional conclusions we arrive at today.

THE OVIPAROUS MAMMALS

THE monotremes, those strange primitive mammals [1] of Australia, have kept among other reptilian characters a mode of reproduction unique among mammals. The platypus and the echidna in fact lay true eggs provided with a thin and leathery shell, from which hatch young that are nourished on the mother's milk.

The reproductive habits of the platypus have been known in some detail only in recent years, thanks to the observations of Burrell and of Fleay. The sexes come together after a short period of hibernation, from mid-September to mid-October in Victoria. This meeting takes place in the water, and there is a slight nuptial performance, during which the male holds the female's tail in his beak and the two animals swim in circles. Coition also occurs in the water, after which the female retires into a breeding-burrow separate from the one ordinarily lived in. There she places bedding composed of water-soaked leaves, the humidity of which seems to be required by the egg. In some cases the burrow is closed with one or several earthen plugs. Incubation of the two eggs is short, eight to ten days in the instance observed by Fleay. The young are blind for the first eleven weeks and are weaned at the age of five months.

The echidnas of the genus *Tachyglossus* do not dig burrows, and it would seem that the egg is laid directly [2] in

[1] Apart from some Pleistocene remains found in Australia, we unfortunately know nothing of the fossil history of this group that shows, we should note, a curious mixture of primitive and highly specialized characters.

[2] As a matter of fact this direct transfer of the egg from the cloaca to the pouch has never yet been actually observed. What makes this seem quite likely is the presence of excrement in the pouch along with the egg.

a pouch that develops during the breeding period. From this egg hatches an offspring that remains constantly in the pouch until its spiny covering develops. Later the mother places her young in some dry and well-shaded nook to which she returns to nurse it until it can feed for itself.

REPRODUCTION IN THE MARSUPIALS

ALTHOUGH the existence of marsupials in Australia and in America has been known for several centuries, and though some of these creatures are among the favorite guests in zoological gardens, we have but little knowledge of their sexual and reproductive habits. What has been observed, however, is very strange and should stimulate new observations.

It is well known that in the placental mammals, that is, all the mammals now living except the monotremes and marsupials, the embryo gets all the nutritive materials necessary for its growth by way of the placenta, which assures a constant diffusion through its body of materials from the maternal blood. This device permits a long gestation period. Nothing of the kind exists in the marsupials (except for the Paramelidæ), where the placenta is lacking or rudimentary. The embryo thus has no more to depend on than its store of yolk material, which is soon exhausted. Thereupon it is born, and it will continue its development in the marsupial pouch where, clinging to the mother's nipples, it will have the benefit of an abundant nourishment with protection against variations in the outer temperature.

Most of the marsupials so far studied have a well-marked reproductive season. In the Virginia opossum the female is seasonally polyœstrous, which means that throughout a part of the year (January to October in Texas) it exhibits a succession of œstrus cycles, each lasting 28 days, during which, however, the female seems receptive to the male for only 24 to 48 hours. Coitus is dorsal, the male mounting his partner and holding her with teeth and paws; when in copulation the male and female lie on their sides.

FIG. 56: *The genital region of the South American marsupial,* Lutreolina crassicaudata, *at the right in the male (note the position of the scrotum), and at the left in the female (note the marsupial pouch). Redrawn after Krieg.*

Other species such as the Tasmanian rat kangaroo, are also polyœstrous. The following forms have only one œstrus period per year: the marsupial cat, the koala, and many Macropodidæ, such as the great gray kangaroo, the red kangaroo, and the dama pademelon (fig. 56).

Gestation in all these animals is very short: twelve days and a half in the Virginia opossum, 8 to 12 days in the marsupial cat, 16 days in the silver-gray opossum, and 38 to

40 days for even such a giant species as the great gray kangaroo.

At the end of gestation the offspring is still in a very immature state and small in size. That of the Virginia opossum weighs only two grams and is no larger than a bee; its hind limbs are only mere buds whereas its front legs are already well developed and armed with strong claws. The newborn young of the great gray kangaroo is only an inch long, its eyes are closed but its mouth is widely open. Only its front paws are functional; the hind ones remain bent and crossed, covered by the tail. It is a remarkable fact that in spite of this extreme immaturity the newborn animal is capable of making its own way, without help by its mother, from the cloacal orifice to the entrance of the marsupial pouch. Hartman, to mention one observer, has described the behavior of the newborn opossum in great detail: "After assuming the sitting posture, our specimen bent her body forward and licked the vulva; however, her position at this time was such that we could not see the embryos, which very likely passed into the pouch with the first licking of the genital opening. Hence we went to the outside where we could plainly hear her lap up the chorionic fluid; then suddenly a tiny bit of flesh appeared at the vulva and scampered up over the entanglement of hair into the pouch to join the other fetuses, which now could be seen to have made the trip without our having observed them. Unerringly the embryo traveled by its own efforts. Without any assistance on the mother's part, other than to free it of liquid on its first emergence into the world, this ten-day-old embryo, in appearance more like a worm than a mammal, is able, immediately upon release from its liquid medium, to crawl a full three inches over a difficult terrain. Indeed, it can do more: after it has arrived at the pouch it is able to find the nipple amid a forest of hair." Hartman then anesthetized the mother with ether and took some embryos out of the pouch; one of them, placed near the vulva, returned at once into the pouch; two or three others did the same but took a little longer; a fourth got lost at first and needed twenty minutes before it succeeded in finding a nipple. Only twelve days after conception these embryos not only have a digestive tube and a respiratory apparatus enabling them to feed and breathe normally, but they also possess a neuromuscular development advanced enough to enable them to move by themselves from the vulva to the pouch.

Somewhat similar behavior has been observed in the red kangaroo, the great gray kangaroo, and the short-tailed wallaby. Figure 57, borrowed from Matthews's work, shows well the position of the mother, whose intervention would seem to be limited to licking the fur between the vulva and the entrance to the pouch. The average duration of the embryo's journey is 15 minutes for the great gray kangaroo and from 5 to 30 minutes for the red kangaroo. If the offspring accidentally falls to the ground or fails to find the opening of the pouch, the mother makes no attempt whatever to help it. But Hediger has seen a great gray kangaroo mother at the Basel Zoo aid her offspring with her lips, and Schneider, at Leipzig, has seen another do the same with her paws.

The sojourn of the young in the marsupial pouch (fig. 58) is prolonged: 7 to 8 weeks for the marsupial cat, 90 to 100 days for the Virginia opossum, and 4 months in the case of Lesueur's rat kangaroo! During all this time the mother's role is not merely passive, and it seems to be established that the control of the sphincter that closes the entrance to the pouch is voluntary on her part. There is another curious phenomenon in the koala which has been described ap-

FIG. 57: *Female gray kangaroo assisting the passage of the embryo from the cloaca to the marsupial pouch. After Matthews.*

parently for the first time by Minchin. Toward the age of six months the young begins to be weaned from mother's milk and becomes gradually adapted to the vegetal diet of the species consisting exclusively, as we have already noted, of eucalyptus leaves. Now, at the time of the weaning, it would seem that the mother is able to provide her offspring with a kind of pap made of eucalyptus leaves which the young eats directly from the mother's anus. This vegetable "soup" contains no excrement and is produced during only one month, every two or three days, between three and four o'clock in the afternoon. At this period the growth of the young is greatly accelerated.

Not all females among the marsupials have a pouch. It

FIG. 58: *Young brush wallaby in the mother's pouch. Natural size. After J. Vosseler, 1930.*

is lacking, for example, in the crested-tailed pouch-mouse, the murine opossum, and the marsupial banded anteater. Here the young merely cling, though firmly, to the mother's nipples. Beach has studied in some detail the behavior of a female murine opossum weighing 51 grams that was carrying five young. When walking she had to keep her hindquarters elevated to prevent the young from being rubbed on the ground; the latter clung so firmly to the nipples that by laying hold of one with forceps it was possible to lift the whole family! After the first month, however, the young do not remain constantly suspended from their mother. Their eyes open at this point and they begin to share in the mother's food. When frightened they take refuge in their mother's fur or on her back, no longer always attaching themselves to her nipples, as before weaning. At this age the attitude of defense typical of this species also begins to appear: mouth open, position sitting up. The maternal behavior of the female seems to be much like that of the white rat: gathering strips of paper to build a kind of nest [3] and searching for and carrying back young accidentally scattered. It is to be emphasized that the murine opossum does not transport her young in her mouth but pushes them toward her abdomen so that they will of their own accord seize upon her nipples. Curiously enough, newborn rats could release or set off this reaction as well as could the opossum's own young.

THE PLACENTAL MAMMALS

SEXUAL PERIODICITY AND REPRODUCTIVE SEASONS. Female mammals (the higher primates excepted) are not sexually receptive at all times. Copulation takes place, on the contrary, only at a specific period in the sexual cycle, that of *œstrus* or "heat." Ovulation occurs at the same time,

---

[3] Such materials are carried either in the mouth or by means of the tail. Use of the tail for the transportation of nesting materials is known also in the Virginia opossum (Pray, *Jour. Mammal.*, 2:109, 1921), in the South American opossum (Hediger, *Zool. Garten*, 7:28, 1934), and in the dark rat kangaroo of Australia.

whether spontaneously or as a result of coitus as in many lagomorphs, certain Sciuridæ, Felidæ, and Mustelidæ, and in some Soricidæ. Œstrus is accompanied by a whole series of psycho-physiological phenomena to which we shall return later in this chapter; it is preceded by a phase marked by growth of the Graafian follicles, known as *prœstrus*, and followed by *metœstrus*, which itself precedes a period of sexual quiescence, called *diœstrus*. These stages together make up the œstrus cycle, the duration of which is variable: five days in the white rat, 19 to 22 days in the horse, 28 days in the rhesus monkey, 34 to 35 days in the chimpanzee, and so on.

The number of ovarian cycles per year varies widely according to the species. In this connection it is convenient to distinguish two main categories: the *monœstrous species* having only one œstrus per year, and the *polyœstrous species* in which several œstrus cycles occur successively in the course of a single year. The polyœstrous group can itself be subdivided into *permanent* polyœstrous species in which the cycles are repeated with a regular periodicity, and *seasonal* polyœstrous species in which there exists a prolonged phase of sexual inactivity (anœstrus) that may last for several months.

It is as yet impossible to formulate a truly precise statement on sexual periodicity in the various groups of mammals. It would seem, however, according to the recent review of the subject by Asdell, that the females of the Ursidæ, of most of the Canidæ, of the pinnipeds, and of some Cervinæ have only one œstrus per year, while many bats, most of the primates, the tropical Felidæ, some cetaceans, most of the Sciuridæ, Heteromyidæ, Cricetidæ, and

Muridæ, the elephants, the tropical Cervinæ, and the Bovinæ are permanently polyœstrous. Among the seasonal polyœstrous forms are to be found certain lower primates (Senegal bush baby), the Felidæ of temperate regions, many Sciuridæ, some Geomyidæ, the Caprinæ, and the Equidæ. In general it would seem that species inhabiting the temperate regions tend particularly to reproduce at a certain period of the year, but our knowledge of the biology of tropical forms is far too imperfect to permit us to be very positive in the matter. It would be a mistake, further, to believe that all mammals with seasonal reproduction carry on the reproductive process at the same season in a given country. The differences between various groups are very striking. Thus, in our latitudes, many rodents reproduce in early spring, whereas the Equidæ favor the end of spring and the beginning of summer, the Caprinæ the end of summer and early autumn, and the Cervidæ the beginning of winter. Abundance of food can also have an influence: some Muridæ that are permanently polyœstrous in the laboratory have in nature a more or less prolonged anœstrous phase in summer and in winter.

It is not rare, also, to encounter variations of sexual periodicity within a single species due to climatic or other ecological differences. The European field vole, for example, reproduces in England only from February to October (Baker and Ranson), whereas it does so the year round in the south of France (Département du Tarn, Raynaud).

During the period of sexual inactivity it is common to find important morphological changes in the genital tract. Matthews and Godet have shown that in the European mole an involution of the gonads and accessory glands takes place between June and November; in the female the vagina becomes closed and one finds in that region only a scar with pigmented borders; at that time it is even difficult to recognize the sexes, the clitoris having the same size as the penis.

The male gonads are often more active during a certain portion of the year than during others. This annual cycle in testicular activity has been thoroughly studied in some species. In the thirteen-lined ground squirrel, for example, spermatogenesis is most active just before the end of hibernation, in March; in April and May mating occurs, and in June the testicles decrease in size, leaving the scrotum and returning into the peritoneal cavity. In consequence the males of many wild mammals have a period of rut, corresponding to the female period of heat. Most of the males of domesticated species, however, as well as those of many tropical forms, seem capable of reproducing throughout the year.[4]

SEXUAL PROMISCUITY, POLYGAMY, MONOGAMY. Much has been written on the structure of the family group in wild mammals. Yet this subject remains one of the least known, and it is unwise to make any attempt at generalization. Most of the reports of older authors rest on impressions rather than observations, and only by the marking of wild individuals followed through several seasons will it be possible to get any idea of what happens in reality.

Many small mammals (rodents, insectivores, bats) seem

[4] But Groome (*Proc. Zool. Soc. London,* (A) 110:37, 1940) has shown that a true annual cycle of testicular activity exists in certain tropical bats of the family Pteropidæ.

to practice complete sexual promiscuity. The receptive female is mounted by the first male at hand, and, after the sexual act, no relation whatever exists any longer between the two partners. The young are raised by the mother, and at each period of heat it is a different male that couples with the same female as a result of chance encounters. The males may occasionally fight among themselves during the breeding season, and in the absence of females; but this would seem to be rather a manifestation of the aggressiveness of rutting animals than a real struggle to "take possession" of a partner.

Quite different is the behavior of the polygamous species, to be discussed at greater length in the chapter devoted to the social life of mammals. In these species the males, at the breeding season, gain possession of a true harem that in some cases they may jealously defend against the enterprises of other males. In this connection we shall describe the behavior of deer, sea lions, and sea elephants. It would be a mistake, however, to suppose that such spectacular performances are universal. In an excellent study of the wild rabbit, Southern gives proof that during the breeding season the adult males each take over a "sphere of influence" in the colony, with each female also clearly manifesting very definite territorial behavior. A single male is thus concerned with several females (one to seven), but marking experiments pursued from 1940 to 1942 do not seem to indicate the least constancy in conjugal bonds from one year to another. Furthermore, the "jealousy" of the males does not appear to be very great, since Southern noted on only two or three occasions any show of chasing away a strange male.

The monogamous family, in contrast, is very rare

among mammals. Yet it would seem to exist among certain Canidæ, in the American beaver, and in the lar gibbon. Murie has published an account of his precise observation of wolves in Mount McKinley National Park, Alaska. In one den an easily recognizable pair raised five young during the summer of 1940, living the while with two adult males and an adult female; toward the end of the summer two more males came to join the group. Throughout the autumn and winter of 1940–1 the seven adults and five young wolves hunted together. In the following spring the structure of the group underwent modification; the young individuals disappeared; the original pair returned to the den of the preceding year, where it raised four new offspring; the adult female, not mated in 1940, mated with one of the extra males and raised six young in a near-by den before returning in July with her family to live in the den of the other pair. Here we thus have proof of a conjugal bond between two individuals lasting through two years in succession. In most foxes the monogamous couple seems not to last beyond the reproductive season. In the lar gibbon, on the contrary, Carpenter has reported that the family group consists permanently of the two parents and a number of young. It would seem that the same is true of the American beaver, where the typical colony is made up of the two parents and the two last litters.

PRELIMINARIES TO MATING. Observers are for the most part very sparing of details on this phase of the reproductive cycle. There are many reasons for this: spectacular attitudinizing is rare and almost never takes on the appearance of true courtship, as with many birds. Furthermore, the meeting of the sexes very often takes place at twilight, or even at night, and much care and luck are needed in order to be a witness of the event without disturbing the animals. In many cases, therefore, our knowledge is based essentially on captive individuals.

The species are many in which the preliminaries to mating are quite simple and consist merely in the pursuit of females in heat by males. This is true of many rodents and in particular of the white rat, an albino mutation of the brown rat and a favored laboratory animal. The female white rat gets in heat late in the day, and œstrus lasts only thirteen hours on the average. It is indicated by a revival of activity, suddenness in movement, and a quivering of the ears or of the entire body. The male, which hitherto has paid no attention to her, now approaches the female and nuzzles or licks her. The female runs away, with her partner in pursuit, but the chase is usually a short one, and the male overtakes her and mounts her from the rear. The female then elevates her pelvis and hollows her back,[5] while the front paws of her mate hold her firmly. Copulation then takes place. A very similar type of behavior has been described for a great many Muridæ.[6] Sometimes the pursuit is more prolonged and is accompanied by various sounds. The male hedgehog circles for hours around his female, puffing and extending his snout toward her. Sometimes the two animals bite or scratch each other or seem to be fighting. With

---

[5] This receptive posture is typical of the rat in œstrus and can be evoked, in the absence of the male, by mere digital stimulation of the hindmost part of the back and around the base of the tail of the female.

[6] Among others, the deer mouse, white-footed mouse, rice rat, dusky-footed wood rat, golden hamster, boreal redback vole, and house mouse. (See Reed, 1946, for more details.) I have myself observed something very similar in the North African zebra mouse.

the North American short-tailed shrew the pursuit of the female by the male is accompanied by a series of unmusical clicks; if the female is not receptive, she repulses the male with loud squeaks and sometimes a long, shrill chatter. The initiative in the preliminaries to mating is not always the prerogative of the male. The female of the Ord kangaroo rat, for example, pursues the male and noses at his genitals. In the European red squirrel, carefully studied in semi-captivity by Raspopov and Issakov at the Moscow Zoo, the odor of female urine is decidedly exciting to the males, and if a male does not pursue a female, she will roll on the ground before him, rubbing her genitals on the snow. Analogous behavior is frequent in the carnivores. The cat in heat rolls herself on the ground and rubs herself against objects everywhere, while giving a characteristic low vocalization. The crouch is a most specific posture; the animal rests on chest and forearms, with pelvis and tail elevated, and tends to execute treading movements of the hind legs. The female sable in heat urinates frequently and touches her enlarged genitals to stones or other projecting objects, which are thus covered with an oily and odorous secretion.

It is not rare for the male to discharge urine upon the female during the preliminaries to mating. The rutting male of the European wild rabbit chases the females, elevates his haunches so that he walks "stiff-legged," lays his tail flat along his back,[7] displaying its white underside (fig. 59), and

---

[7] This exhibition surely plays an important part in bringing the sexes together. Southern has several times seen males walk stiffly away from a female for half a dozen yards, giving her a full view of the elevated tail, then approach her again, and repeat this kind of display three or four times in succession. The male sometimes circles around the female while pointing the white spot of his tail sideways toward her, or

sends toward his desired partner a jet of urine that seldom misses its mark. A male has even been seen to leap on a female and urinate on her in passing. The male American porcupine, closely studied by Shadle and his associates, first

FIG. 59: *Diagram showing the posture of the male wild rabbit while "tail flagging." After Southern.*

explores by smelling any trace of urine and all foreign objects near by, then the body and the genitals of the female. If he is sufficiently stimulated sexually, he sniffs at her, rubs noses with her, and then rears up on his hind legs and tail and walks upright toward the female, usually with the penis fully erect. When the two are face to face, the male emits some jets of urine on his partner. In the case of the moose the male paws the ground and urinates repeatedly on a small area where he awaits his cow.

The male giraffe knows that a female comes into heat in a very peculiar way—called "urine testing" by Innis— which can be observed all the year round in Transvaal. While a female is eating or chewing, a bull often walks up to her and licks her tail, or takes it between his lips, or merely lays his head on her flank. Without seeming to pay any attention, the female then urinates and the male collects some of the urine in his mouth or on his tongue. He

he may go back and forth in front of her with his tail twisted in the appropriate direction at each passage.

then raises his head, closes his mouth, and curls back his lips in a characteristic fashion, called *Das Flehmen* by German ethologists. On several occasions Innis has seen a male eject the urine from his mouth in a long thin stream. The same bull may collect as many as three separate lots of urine from the urinating female, and two or three different males may "test" the urine of the same female at one time. Backhaus has also observed and photographed this very curious behavior. Its most likely explanation is

FIG. 60: *Prenuptial pursuit in roe deer.*

that it enables the male to follow the œstrous cycle of the female and to know when she is coming into heat.

Some elaborate types of prenuptial play have been described in various groups of mammals. In the deer family the pursuit of a doe by a buck is usually a very simple affair. The roebuck tirelessly pursues his female day and night, emitting a characteristic panting sound (fig. 60). The male Barren Ground caribou in rut adopts a characteristic stiff-legged gait, lays back his antlers, raises his muzzle, curls up his nose, and sniffs at the female (Pruitt); similar behavior was observed long ago among European reindeer by Paleolithic mammalogists (fig. 61). Bovids

FIG. 61: *A male reindeer sniffing at his female. From an engraving from Laugerie-Basse.*

and giraffids have more complicated rituals (Walther). In all the species so far studied, the essential of the mating behavior is the chase, during which the buck, often in attitudes of display, follows the female. In duikers, antelopes, oryxes, roan antelopes, waterbuck, reedbuck, wild goats, wild sheep, giraffe, and okapi (but not in Bovine, Tragelaphine, and Alcelaphine bovids), this "mating march" is accompanied by the "stiff foreleg upthrust" (fig. 62), in which the male lifts one of his stretched-out front legs and touches one of the rear legs of the female. Some of these ungulates also perform what Walther calls the "mating whirl-around," in which both sexes step in a circle around each other. The male Tragelaphine bovids approach the female sideways, with neck outstretched, and lay head and neck on the female's back.

Even some aquatic mammals have distinctive displays. The manatee simply approaches a presumed female, nuzzles and "embraces" her, and presents his venter (Moore). Precopulatory behavior in bottlenosed dolphins consists of

FIG. 62: *The "mating march" of Thomson's gazelle. After Walther (1958).*

a prolonged companionship between male and female. Then follow such activities as posturing (fig. 63), stroking with flippers, rubbing, nuzzling, mounting, jaw clapping, and yelping on the part of the male (Tavolga and Essapian).

COPULATION. Following such preliminaries, the male mounts the female. In almost all cases, among small mam-

FIG. 63: *Male bottlenosed dolphin posturing. After Tavolga and Essapian.*

157

FIG. 64: *Prenuptial play of Indian elephants. Right, male. After a photograph by K. M. Schneider, 1930. The same behavior has been observed in juvenile male African elephants, leading to mutual erection.*

mals as among the largest, copulation is dorso-ventral, the male astride his partner.

The act may be very brief, but repeated. This is true of the rodents, where in a short time 65 to 75 repetitions (exceptionally as many as 175) have been observed in the golden hamster, and 224 within two hours in Shaw's jird! Frequently both animals lick their genitals thoroughly after each copulation. In the American porcupine, where the male does not hold the female with his front legs, the number of copulations is not so great but each one lasts longer, from one to five minutes. The male short-tailed shrew, the only insectivore studied in some detail from this point of view, mounts the female from behind and holds her not only by clasping her lumbar region with his front legs but also by grasping with his mouth the fur on the back of her neck or shoulders. Copulation in this species is of variable duration, from a few seconds to 25 minutes; it may be repeated six times in an hour and more than 20 times in a day.

Copulation in the carnivores is generally accompanied by characteristic calls and vocalizations. The male seizes his female with his teeth, at the base of the neck, while astride her. The copulation of the Mustelidæ is prolonged—a half hour in the sable, an hour in the ferret, from 5 to 20 minutes in the striped skunk, and is repeated up to a dozen times.

Copulation in bats has been studied in but a few species, and this only in recent years. The little brown bat and the small-footed myotis copulate in the fall, and occasionally in winter, on the vertical walls of caves, the animals hanging head down. The male takes the initiative; he mounts the female from behind and with his teeth grasps her hair at the base of the skull. He then pushes his hindquarters backward and downward, bringing his erect penis beneath her inter-femoral membrane and, with a forward movement, close to the vaginal orifice (Wimsatt).

Yet some cases of ventral copulation are known, in which the two sexes unite belly to belly. This would seem to be true of the hamster, according to Petzsch, and also of the two-toed sloth (Britton and Enders). Contrary to what was formerly thought, beavers practice dorso-ventral copulation, like most other mammals.

Some mammals copulate in the water. Beside the cetaceans, this is true of the muskrat, the European otter, the sea otter, the pigmy hippopotamus, certain tapirs, the harp seal, and the gray seal.[8]

MONKEYS AND APES. Because the sexual behavior of only a few species is well known, it is impossible at the

---

[8] At least in some colonies, like that of Ramsey Island. In others (Rona) coupling takes place on land (Davies).

moment to generalize. We must, therefore, limit ourselves to giving a few examples taken from the most thorough studies (Carpenter, Yerkes).

The female Panama howling monkey when in heat makes herself conspicuous by her provocative posturing and, above all, by rhythmical movements of the tongue, which is protruded and moved rapidly in and out and up and down. The male replies with the same lingual movements. Copulation is dorso-ventral and quick. The initiative may be taken by either sex, and, within a clan, a single female may be covered by several males successively.

In the rhesus monkey the female in heat is easily recognized by her sexual swelling and coloration, her hyperactivity, her enticing approaches and gestures, and an increase in grooming behavior. To copulate, the male places his hands on the hips or midspinal region of the female while supporting most of his weight on her hind legs, which he grasps with his feet in the popliteal region. Copulation consists in a series of quick insertions of the penis ending in ejaculation. After dismounting, the male characteristically eats the ejaculate that adheres to his penis. The female meanwhile usually grooms the male. During her œstrus period of nine days, one female has relations with an average of three males.

The sole peculiarity of the female lar gibbon while in œstrus is a slight eversion of the vaginal orifice with changes in the turgidity and color of the labia. When the two sexes meet, they engage in a momentary embrace. The male then explores the vaginal opening of the female, and she presents to him with her body bent forward the ischial callosities held high over sharply flexed legs. Intromission of the penis is accomplished from behind and below. The sexual act usually takes place on tree branches.

As with the several species just mentioned, coupling in chimpanzees occurs preferably while the female is in œstrus. In the lesser chimpanzee it takes place for the most part during the middle third of the cycle. Either sex may take the initiative in the sexual approach. Quite often copulation is preceded by a kind of play in which the male follows the female around, both slapping the ground with hands or feet. As this movement gains speed, the animals become excited. When the female is receptive, she crouches before the male and he mounts her from behind, resting with all his weight upon her or remaining half upright. It is a curious fact that the morphological or psychological traits of certain males make them clearly preferred by certain females.

ANOMALIES OF SEXUAL BEHAVIOR. The existence of autoerotic manifestations and homosexual behavior among mammals has been pointed out repeatedly. The anomalies were supposed to be caused by the abnormalities of life in captivity, until they were observed in wild species under natural conditions.

Autoeroticism would seem to be frequent in males. Pearson has noted it in a short-tailed shrew that was sleeping. The stag in rut gently rubs the tips of its antlers to and fro through the herbage and this stimulation promptly induces erection and ejaculation (Darling). Male bottlenosed dolphins masturbate by rubbing the penis on the bottom or against other males, even on other aquatic animals, such as turtles or sharks (McBride and Hebb) and the Indian elephant does it by means of his trunk (Schneider). In the rhesus monkey manual and buccal masturbation is extremely common among adult and immature males (Carpenter).

The manifestations of autoeroticism in the female sex are more difficult to demonstrate; but Carpenter has repeatedly observed manual or buccal stimulation of the nipples in the case of a rhesus female.

Homosexuality exists without question in the two sexes. Males attempting to mount other males have been observed in the house mouse, several of the small bats, adult and adolescent rhesus monkeys, and even the bottlenosed dolphin. In the last-mentioned species the "active" male swims on his back and goes under the "passive" male. Attempts made by females in heat to mount other females are still more common, and have been observed in the brown rat, the guinea pig (90 per cent of the females in certain breeds regularly show this behavior), the short-tailed shrew (Pearson), the rhesus monkey (Carpenter), and the chimpanzee (Young). The nymphomania of cows that even try to get astride of other individuals is also well known.[9]

GESTATION. Table 4 shows the length of the gestation period and the number of young per litter for a number of species representative of the various orders of mammals. It will be noted that the duration of gestation is roughly proportional to the size of the animal—from around three weeks for the small rodents to almost two years for the rhinoceros and elephant.

A closer look at the data, however, reveals some ex-

[9] For a physiological study of this deviation in behavior see Garm, O. (1949), *Acta Endocrinologica*, Suppl. 3, pp. 1-144, Copenhagen.

ceptions that merit our attention for a moment. Certain Mustelidæ (the badger, the martens, the long-tailed weasel), the bears, and the armadillos have gestation periods abnormally prolonged when compared with related forms of similar size. The reason for this lies in a *delayed implantation* of the fertilized egg, the development of which is thus interrupted during a more or less lengthy period. Thus, in the badger, copulation takes place in July or August in southern England, but implantation of the blastocyst is accomplished only in December or early January, after five months of quiescence. Growth of the embryo then becomes rapid, and the young are born eight weeks later, toward the end of February. In the Texas armadillo the process is similar. Here fertilization takes place in July or August and is followed by a period of about fourteen weeks during which implantation is delayed; this occurs in December and the embryo develops rapidly until the time of birth in February or March. In Argentina the embryo of another armadillo (*Dasypus hybridus*) also remains free for two months before becoming implanted in the uterine wall. A like phenomenon has been reported for the roe deer (copulation in July–August, implantation in late December or early January, birth in April–May), for the Alaska fur seal, and for certain bears.

In the bats of various countries rut and copulation often occur in the fall; [1] this is true of the pipistrelle, the serotine, the large mouse-eared bat, and the long-eared bat in Europe, of *Pipistrellus abramus* in Japan, and of the little brown bat, the gray myotis, the Indiana myotis, and the Keen bat in the

---

[1] The occurrence of a second copulation, in spring, after the awakening from hibernation, is not excluded in some cases.

Table 4. *Length of gestation and number of young per litter in some mammals. (After Asdell, Baumann, Mohr, etc.)*

SPECIES/LENGTH OF GESTATION (IN DAYS)/NUMBER OF YOUNG PER LITTER

INSECTIVORES
Erinaceus europæus 34–49
  4–6
Talpa europæa about 28–42
  1–7
Scalopus aquaticus about 42
  2–5
Blarina brevicauda 17–20
  3–8
Sorex araneus 19–21 1–10
BATS
Myotis myotis 50–70 1
Nyctalus noctula 70–73 1–2
Tadarida cynocephala 77–84
  1
PRIMATES
Urogale everetti less than 54
  1
Microcebus murinus 59–62
  1–3
Nycticebus tardigradus 174–
  180 1
Lemur macao about 146 1–2
Indri indri about 60 1
Hapale jacchus 140–150 1–3
Ateles ater about 140 1
Alouatta seniculus about 140
  1
Macaca mulatta 146–180
  1–2
Papio hamadryas about 183
  1–2
Hylobates lar 200–212 1
Pan satyrus 196–260 1–2
EDENTATES
Bradypus griseus 120–180 1
Myrmecophaga tridactyla
  about 190 1

Dasypus novemcinctus
  about 260 4–5
RODENTS AND LAGOMORPHS
Lepus europæus about 42
  1–4
Lepus americanus about 38
  1–7
Citellus columbianus 23–24
  2–7
Citellus tridecemlineatus about
  28 5–13
Cynomys leucurus 28–32
  2–10
Marmota marmota 35–42
  2–5
Tamias striatus about 31
  2–8
Sciurus vulgaris 32–40 3–5
Sciurus carolinensis about 44
  3–5
Glaucomys volans about 40
  2–6
Muscardinus avellanarius
  about 21–28 2–7
Castor canadensis about 128
  1–6
Cricetus cricetus about 20
  4–18
Peromyscus maniculatus 22–27
  4–6
Sigmodon hispidus about 27
  2–10
Clethrionomys gapperi 17–19
  3–8
Microtus pennsylvanicus
  about 21 1–9
Ondatra zibethica 22–30
  1–11

SPECIES/LENGTH OF GESTATION (IN DAYS)/NUMBER OF YOUNG PER LITTER

Gerbillus (Dipodillus) dasyurus
  simoni 20–21 1–7
Pachyuromys duprasi 19–22
  3–6
Mus musculus 18–20 4–7
Apodemus sylvaticus 23–26
  2–9
Micromys minutus about 21
  3–6
Erethizon dorsatum about 112
  1–2
Hystrix africæ-australis
  about 112 1–4
Myocastor coypus 135–150
  about 9
Hydrochærus isthmius
  104–111 1

CETACEANS
Tursiops truncatus 330–360
  1
Phocæna phocæna about 183
  1
Physeter catodon about 365
  1
Balænoptera physalus 305–365
  1

CARNIVORES
Ursus americanus 200–210
  1–3
Ursus arctos 210–250 1–3
Procyon lotor about 63 1–7
Nasua nasua about 77 4–5
Lutra lutra 61–63 2–4
Martes americana 220–265
  1–5
Martes martes 270–285 1–4
Martes pennanti 338–358
  1–5
Mephitis mephitis about 62
  4–7
Mustela frenata 229–236
  5–8

Mustela vison 39–76 3–10
Mustela furo about 42 5–13
Aonyx capensis about 63
  2–5
Canis latrans 60–65 5–10
Canis lupus about 63 3–12
Vulpes vulpes about 56 3–7
Vulpes fulva 49–55 1–8
Lycaon pictus 63–80 2–6
Thos adustus 57–60 3–7
Crocuta crocuta about 110
  1–2
Felis leo 105–113 2–6
Felis tigris 105–109 1–6
Felis pardus 92–95 1–4
Felis onca 93–110 2–4
Felis concolor 90–93 1–4
Felis sylvestris about 68 3–6
Felis lybica about 56 2–5
Lynx canadensis about 60
  1–4
Acinonyx jubatus about 95
  2–4

PINNIPEDS
Arctocephalus australis about
  330 1
Arctocephalus pusillus 330–
  365 1–2
Otaria flavescens about 330 1
Leptonychotes weddelli about
  310 1–2
Phoca vitulina about 280
  1–2

PROBOSCIDIANS
Elephas maximus 607–641
  1–2

SIRENIANS
Trichechus manatus about
  152 1

PERISSODACTYLS
Rhinoceros bicornis 530–550
  1

165

SPECIES/LENGTH OF GESTATION (IN DAYS)/NUMBER OF YOUNG PER LITTER

Equus zebra   about 365   1

Tapirus indicus   390–395   1

ARTIODACTYLS

Hippopotamus amphibius
233–234   1

Chœropsis liberiensis   201–210
1

Sus scrofa   112–115   3–12

Phacochœrus œthiopicus
170–175   3–4

Camelus bactrianus   370–440
1

Capreolus capreolus   about 280
2

Alces alces   240–250   2

Cervus canadensis   210–230
1–3

Cervus elaphus   about 234
1–2

Odocoileus virginianus
about 210   1–2

Giraffa camelopardalis
420–450   1–2

Bos gaurus   about 270   1–2

Ovis canadensis   about 180   1

Oryx beisa   260–300   1

Taurotragus oryx   255–270   1

Antilope cervicapra   about 180
1–2

Rupicapra rupicapra   153–210
1–2

United States. Sperm is then stored in the uterus of the female, where it remains alive all winter; in the spring ovulation occurs, and the egg is fertilized in the oviduct. An experiment by Herlant proves that it is really the stored sperm that fertilizes the eggs, for this physiologist, having stimulated premature ovulation in mid-December in the serotine and in the greater horseshoe bat by injecting pituitary and placental extracts, observed the fertilization of the egg and the beginning of embryonic development occurring two months in advance of the normal rhythm. Retarded fertilization does not exist, however, in all the European species. Courrier has shown that in the south European *Miniopterus schreibersi* ovulation and copulation both take place in the autumn; but during the hibernation of the mother the development of the fetus is slowed down and birth occurs only in the following spring. This slowing down of embryonic development in winter is probably correlated with the climatic conditions peculiar to the habitat of this species, since the other species of *Miniopterus*, all inhabitants of warm regions, appear to have a much shorter period of gestation (110 days, for example, in *Miniopterus australis* of the New Hebrides).

A few cases of *superfetation*—that is, the occurrence of a second fertilization before parturition, and the overlapping of two gestations—have been established with certainty. Hediger has shown, for example, that the female European hare is usually covered a second time one to five days before the birth of her young.

PARTURITION. The actual birth of young has been observed in very few species—most often in captivity—and the mother's behavior on this occasion is but poorly known to us. The most common position would seem to be lying down, but some species give birth while standing. The agouti gives birth while in a squatting position. In the bats the female ready to bring forth young suspends herself sometimes by all four feet, back downward, in such a way that the newborn is received in the "apron" formed by the interfemoral membrane (fig. 65). In other cases parturition takes place in the normal resting-position, with head down. In *Erophylla planifrons* the mother is supported by only one of her two hind feet, the other assisting in the emergence of the newborn and in the rupture of the embryonic membranes.

In the ungulates Hediger distinguishes two different types of behavior. The females of the Equidæ and the ruminants, having given birth while lying down, arise at once, break the membranes that enclose the newborn, eat the afterbirth, bite off the umbilical cord if necessary, and carefully lick the young, including its anal and genital regions. The second category includes species like the wild boar or the hippopotamus, and here the females do not busy themselves with their young immediately after birth by eating the afterbirth and licking the newborn.

FIG. 65: *Position of the female long-eared bat just after the birth of her young. After Eisentraut, 1936.*

The primates give birth quite often in an upright position. A female lar gibbon has been seen to bring forth while hanging from a branch, and Yerkes describes and figures parturition in the chimpanzee: the mother stands up or crouches on all fours, and she eats the afterbirth.

In cetaceans, the sea otter, and often the hippopotamus, parturition takes place in the water. It has been possible to observe the process precisely in the bottlenosed dolphin at the Marine Studios in Florida. Labor appears to be short (21 to 23 minutes in the two cases studied); the mother turns about immediately to bite through the umbilical cord, and the young goes to the surface to breathe within ten seconds of its birth. An hour and a quarter after it is born

Birth of young in the bottlenosed dolphin or porpoise, Tursiops truncatus: ABOVE, *early stage;* BELOW, *late stage. Photographs by Marine Studios, Marineland, Florida.*

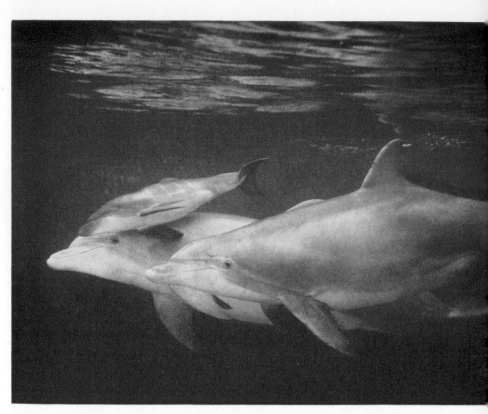

Mother bottlenosed dolphin and newborn young asleep, another female apparently standing guard. Photograph by Marine Studios, Marineland, Florida.

the offspring begins nursing. In the Florida manatee, finally, the mother carries the newborn on her back, completely out of the water, for 45 minutes; then she gradually immerses it during the following two hours.

Head presentation seems to be most frequent in a majority of the orders where the young are ordinarily born single. It has been observed in the elephant, the moose, the bison, the giraffe, the chamois, and in many primates (macaques, baboons, gibbons, gorillas, chimpanzees). In many ungulates the head appears resting on the front feet. Among the cetaceans head presentation would seem to be more frequent in the whalebone whales, and breech presentation in the toothed whales. In bats the legs and the tail often appear first. For rodents or carnivores with large litters and young of smaller size, head presentation is less frequent.

In the Muridæ and the Cricetidæ it is common for a period of heat to follow immediately after the female has given birth.

CHAPTER 6

Development and Longevity

IN this chapter we shall consider some aspects of the different phases in the life cycle of the individual, from birth to death. These successive stages—growth, maturity, and old age—certainly pose a whole series of most interesting problems.

DEVELOPMENT

THE NEWBORN. There is an evident correlation between the length of gestation and the condition of the newborn young: the longer the fetus remains in the maternal uterus, the more advanced will be its development at the time of birth. A few examples will illustrate this general law. The newborn white rat, after 21 days of gestation, is a little naked creature, blind and totally dependent upon its mother for what it needs to live. The guinea pig, on the contrary, after 67 to 68 days of development within the uterus, is born with its eyes open, covered with fur that protects it pretty well against cold, and capable very soon of feeding itself. The hare (fig. 66) and the rabbit (fig. 67), though closely related species, present the same contrast in the appearance of their newborn.

It is thus possible to distinguish two main categories of young: those which depend entirely on their mother during a more or less prolonged period of time, and those with development sufficiently advanced at birth to enable them to

FIG. 66: *Newborn European hare.*

FIG. 67: *Newborn wild rabbit.*

find their own food very soon. Most of the rodents belong to the first category; their imperfect thermo-regulation makes them true poikilotherms (cold-blooded animals), which gives them some advantages. Adolph and Fairfield have recently shown that newborn rats are endowed with remarkable resistance to cold and to lack of oxygen. At 3°

the respiratory exchange may fall to zero in the young (age o to 10 days) without fatal results, and these little rats can even survive for two hours, at 10°, in an atmosphere of nitrogen! Bears similarly have young that are but little developed at birth. Those of the brown bear are the size of a large rat, though the mother weighs more than 200 pounds, and those of the black bear have a weight of less than a pound. They are nourished for the first two months exclusively on the mother's milk, and, as they are born in the depth of winter, they are protected from the cold as much by her thick fur as by the hibernation shelter.

The young of many ungulates are very different. In the roe deer the first hour of life is spent in being licked and cleaned up, while the young individual is already attempting to get to its feet; after the second hour the fawn can leave its birthplace under its own power. The newborn chamois can get to its feet and even walk slowly a few moments after it comes into the world, when its hair is still wet with amniotic fluid. It does not follow its mother, however, until it is a week old, and it begins to eat grass at ten days, although nursing lasts for about two months. The young Mongolian wild ass can run at the end of an hour, but quickly grows tired. The behavior of a newborn giraffe has been witnessed by Davis at the Zoological Park in Washington; the young maintained its equilibrium on its feet only five minutes after being born and began to nurse three quarters of an hour later, even before the placenta was expelled. The agouti begins to nibble at plants within an hour of its birth, and the mountain vizcacha does likewise. The young American porcupine also comes into the world remarkably well developed. It weighs over one pound, whereas its mother hardly exceeds thirteen, and it is able to climb trees and eat leaves and tender shoots on its own account when two days old. It is curious to note that it displays from the start the defense reaction described in a preceding chapter. The young hare, on the other hand, has a special defensive attitude that it loses later on (Hediger). It leaps toad-fashion at the disturbing object, growling and trying to bite. Somewhat similar behavior has been described in the antelope jackrabbit and the blacktail jackrabbit, which when frightened rear up on their hind legs and endeavor to strike with their front ones.

LACTATION. We are especially ill informed concerning the length of the lactation period in wild mammals. This is difficult to determine precisely, moreover, because the young continue to suck for a long time after having begun to feed for themselves. The condition of the teeth is not, in itself, a sure means of gauging the ability of a young animal to obtain its food independently (fig. 68). In many Phocidæ the definitive dentition is present from birth, and yet Weddell's seal, for example, is not weaned before reaching the age of 45 to 50 days. Most small rodents nurse no more than 10 to 20 days, but the walrus continues to do so for almost two years.

Another point on which we have little documentation is the composition of the milk in the various groups. But there would seem to be very sharp differences according to the species, as Table 5 shows.

Thus, if we compare cow's milk with that of the harp seal, we see that the latter contains 12 times more fat and 3 to 4 times more proteins than the former. On the other hand, it shows no sugars, even though Sivertsen's analyses were made on fresh milk. What can be the reason for such a peculiarity? It is unknown at present. At most we can refer to the similarity of reindeer milk to that of seals and

FIG. 68: *Milk teeth of a young mouse-eared bat eight days old. After Eisentraut.*

whales. May we not have to do here with a character favoring the growth of the young in regions of cold climate, rather than with a special peculiarity of the pinnipeds and cetaceans? Future research will clear up this point, but at the moment it would seem that some relation exists between the protein content of a particular milk and the rapidity of growth. Table 6, borrowed from Sivertsen, gives some examples of that correlation. Here again we need studies on more species before drawing conclusions with certainty. Richness in calcium and phosphorus also appears to be related to peculiarities of growth. In the seals, where the

Table 5. *Chemical composition of the milk of various mammals (in grams per 100 grams of whole milk). For more data see D. M. Ben Schaub, International Zoo Yearbook, Vol. 4, 1963, pp. 333-42.*

	WATER	PROTEIN	FAT	SUGAR	ASH
Marsupials					
Kangaroo (wallaroo)	73.5	9.7	8.1	3.1	1.5
Primates					
Rhesus monkey	88.4	2.2	2.7	6.4	0.2
Orang-utan	88.5	1.4	3.5	6.0	0.2
Man	88.0	1.2	3.8	7.0	0.2
Edentates					
Giant anteater	63.0	11.0	20.0	0.3	0.8
Lagomorphs					
Rabbit	71.3	12.3	13.1	1.9	2.3
Rodents					
Guinea pig	81.9	7.4	7.2	2.7	0.8
Rat	72.9	9.2	12.6	3.3	1.4
Carnivores					
Cat	81.6	10.1	6.3	4.4	0.7
Dog	76.3	9.3	9.5	3.0	1.2
European red fox	81.6	6.6	5.9	4.9	0.9
Pinnipeds					
California sea lion	47.3	13.5	35	0	0.6
Harp seal	43.8	11.9	42.8	0	0.9
Hooded seal	49.9	6.7	40.4	0	0.9
Cetaceans					
Bottlenosed dolphin	44.9	10.6	34.9	0.9	0.5
Blue whale	47.2	12.8	38 1	?	1.4
Fin whale	54.1	13.1	30.6	?	1.4
Ungulates					
Indian elephant	70.7	3.6	17.6	5.6	0.6
Zebra	86.2	3.0	4.8	5.3	0.7
Black rhinoceros		1.5	0.3	6.5	0.3
Collared peccary		5.8	3.5	6.5	0.6
Hippopotamus	90.4	0.6	4.5	4.4	0.1
Camel	87.7	3.5	3.4	4.8	0.7
White-tailed deer	65.9	10.4	19.7	2.6	1.4
Reindeer	64.8	10.7	20.3	2.5	1.4
Giraffe	77.1	5.8	12.5	3.4	0.9
American bison	86.9	4.8	1.7	5.7	0.9
Cow	87.0	3.3	3.7	4.8	0.7

weight of the young increases much more rapidly than the size during lactation, the milk is very rich in fats and relatively poor in calcium. In the whales, on the contrary, where the young suckle for six to seven months, the considerable increase in size is accompanied by a high milk content in mineral elements essential for skeletal growth.[1]

Table 6. *Correlation between protein content of milk and rapidity of growth of young (After Sivertsen)*

	MAN	HORSE	COW	PIG	SHEEP	DOG	CAT	RABBIT	HARP SEAL
Number of days needed for doubling birth weight of young on the average	180	60	47	18	10	8	9	6	5
Protein content of milk, in grams per 1,000	12	26	33	37	51	93	101	123	119

The positions assumed by the mother during lactation vary with the species. Most of the ruminants give suck while standing, but there are exceptions like the roe deer. The rodents feed their young while lying down, save for some large species like the capybara. Pigs and hippopotami also give suck while lying down. The doe hare sits on its hindquarters while nursing its young, and the wild rabbit may lie on its back. The Florida manatee nurses its young under water, the mother browsing on aquatic plants while the baby takes its nourishment. The suckling of the bottlenosed dolphin is very brief, taking only a few seconds; the mother swims slowly and turns on her side, and the milk is squeezed out by a contraction of the muscles surrounding the mammary gland as soon as the young animal touches the nipple. This occurs generally among the cetaceans.

Regurgitation of food by parent animals, after wean-

[1] In the blue whale the length of the young increases by about 30 feet in seven months.

ing, has been observed in several wild Canidæ, particularly the wolf and the European red fox.

CARE OF THE YOUNG. Generally the mother alone attends to the rearing of the young, and the latter remain with her for a time varying from a few weeks in many small mammals to several months in the larger species.

The male parent, however, may sometimes share actively in raising the offspring. Murie has shown that the male wolf provides a large part of the family food, and Hainard saw a male fox repeatedly bringing food to the burrow. Burt has noted similar behavior on the part of the male long-tailed weasel. In other cases the male parent confines himself to defending the offspring from intruders; this has been reported in some ungulates (banteng, yak, European bison, roebuck) as well as in the African porcupine. Even among the rodents, finally, where the male usually has no concern with the female after mating, some interest in the young has been noted on the part of the males (in captivity, to be sure). Horner, for example, reports that several males of deer mice assisted in the maintenance of the nest or in the transportation of the offspring.

A more elaborate form of assistance has recently been observed by Dieterlen in the Cairo spiny mouse. In 66 per cent of the births that occurred in his laboratory, strange females helped the mother during the delivery. Moreover, the young may be taken care of, and even suckled, by "aunts"; if necessary they can even be permanently adopted. Lion cubs also may be nursed by foster mothers (Guggisberg).

Recent experiments on laboratory animals show that

"maternal care" may have far-reaching effects on the development of the individual. In rats, mice, and mouse lemurs at least, licking is essential for the establishment of the reflexes of elimination. Handling by the parents speeds up learning in rats and increases further resistance to stress in mice (Barnett). If deprived of the presence of a mother, and of age-mates, an infant monkey will behave atypically (Harlow).

FIG. 69: *Transportation of the young in the European red squirrel.*

TRANSPORTATION OF THE YOUNG. This is accomplished in very different ways according to the species concerned. When danger threatens, many rodents, Canidæ, and Felidæ carry their young away one by one, taking hold of them with the teeth by the skin of the back, the neck, or the abdomen (fig. 69). She-bears do likewise, taking the whole

FIG. 70: *Female bear carrying her young. After a Globe photograph.*

FIG. 71: *Transportation of its young by a female Sumatra pangolin,* Manis javanica. *After Haenel, 1931.*

head of the cub in the mouth (fig. 70). The giant anteater carries her single offspring astride on her back, and the pangolins carry theirs astride the base of the tail (fig. 71). Many young marsupials ride on their mother's back, after leaving the pouch. Finally certain rodents, such as the common redbacked vole and the common vole, merely cling desperately to their mother's nipples when in danger.

Among the tree-dwelling mammals also we find several different methods of transportation. The sloths (fig. 72) set their young on the abdomen, howling monkeys and guenons carry theirs on the belly, many platyrrhine mon-

FIG. 72: *Female three-toed sloth transporting its young. Barro Colorado. After a photograph by Gross.*

keys and several types of macaques and langurs carry their infants both dorsally and ventrally; the gibbons hold theirs low down over the pelvis, almost over one leg. Panama howling monkeys are also very careful of their young when the latter begin to move about by themselves in the trees. On several occasions Carpenter saw mothers helping young to make a difficult crossing by bending branches near together and by making a bridge of their own bodies.

Very young bats are carried by their mothers in flight, clinging to nipples or fur by means of their milk teeth (fig. 68). This feat becomes quite remarkable in the red bat, for a single female may have and carry as many as four off-spring! It is a curious fact that the "flying lemurs" or Dermoptera carry their young in the same way during their volplaning from tree to tree.

The sea otter commonly carries its young on the abdomen when it is swimming on its back (fig. 73), and it

FIG. 73: *Sea otter swimming on its back and carrying its young on the abdomen. After a sketch by Fisher, 1940.*

suckles and sleeps in the same position; but after it is two days old, the female lets her offspring float amongst the sea-weed that forms its "nursery" when she must dive in search of food. The young walrus continues for some time to ride astride the neck of its mother, and the little hippopotamus does not scorn the support of its mother's broad back.

The young of many ungulates seem at a certain stage of development to have an innate tendency to follow their mothers or, in their absence, other individuals of different species. Couturier emphasizes, for example, the propensity of chamois less than three months old to rush to meet any moving body, even a man. Heck also relates that after he had passed in a carriage near a young wild zebra, the animal began to follow the vehicle.

Should we connect with this type of behavior the formation of "caravans" of offspring reported in certain shrews, the hedgehog, and the weasel? Wahlström has closely studied the phenomenon in the bicolor white-

FIG. 74: *A female common shrew and its "caravan" of young. After Schröder and Schoenichen, 1938.*

toothed shrew: the mother is followed by her offspring, the first of which takes hold of the mother's skin with its teeth, near the base of the tail; the rest follow in line, each holding similarly to the one in front of it (fig. 74). The result is a file or "caravan" whose members are so firmly joined that one can sometimes raise the whole group by lifting the mother. The young display this type of behavior only during the first three weeks after birth, and the caravan breaks up when its members regain their nest.

PLAY. The most superficial observer cannot fail to notice the existence among young mammals of certain activities without evident object that seem to afford pleasure to those taking part in them. Such behavior we call play, by analogy with what we are familiar with in the human species. We are completely ignorant about the cause of these activities and their significance in animals, although there is no lack of speculation on the subject, as a glance through Beach's and Holzapfel's reviews will indicate.

Most of the playing is collective. Young fawns of the red deer, for example, very often play at racing. Darling tells us how they sometimes leave a given place more or less together and dash forward, but without there being any real finish line. Sometimes a member of the group chases the others until it has touched one of them and then the pursuer in turn becomes the pursued. At other times the race takes place around a hillock, which may become the goal that the winner is to attain, as in "king-o'-the-castle." Walking or running in single file, like "follow-the-leader," is also engaged in by many young ungulates and by numerous monkeys. The young of carnivores often chase inanimate objects, such as a rolling pebble or bone. These make-believe victims are often set in motion again by a stroke of the paw, when they are recaptured. A coyote has been seen playing with a crow that it allowed to escape before catching it again, and it is common for small rodents to serve in the same way for the amusement of the young before being eaten. McBride and Hebb saw young dolphins juggling ob-

183

jects floating on the surface or chasing small fish before letting them go and catching them again. Mock fights with wrestling and biting are common—among fox cubs, for instance (fig. 75). The game of leapfrog is played by several

R.H.
Bernex
22 mai 35

FIG. 75: *Young foxes engaging in a mock fight. Sketch furnished by Robert Hainard.*

species, such as the European badger, as is proved by the fine photograph in Neal's book (fig. 76). Sliding is a favorite game of the otters, in Europe as in North America, and many observers have described how they let themselves go on their bellies down a wet river bank or on a snowy slope (fig. 77). Minks do the same.

Among solitary types of play there has been included a whole series of behavior patterns, certain of which have

FIG. 76: *European badgers playing leapfrog. Drawn from a photograph by E. Neal.*

probably a different significance. It would seem that the simplest of them are only manifestations of superfluous energy. Such are apparently aimless running and jumping, even that odd "exercise dance" of the North American porcupine, described by Schadle, during which the animal, raised on its hindquarters and tail, rocks rhythmically from

185

side to side alternately raising and stamping the hind feet. The young individual in many carnivores (wolves, foxes, otters) sometimes chases its tail and thus gets into a frantic roundelay on one spot. The tendency of young mammals to bite and scratch apparently at random also belongs in this category, in all probability.

FIG. 77: *Otters sliding. Redrawn from Liers.*

Young chimpanzees have a curious propensity for decorating themselves with leafy branches, flowers, and pieces of cloth or paper. Yerkes tells us also that they may smear flat surfaces with their excreta, and Kohler has seen them wet white clay with saliva and use it in the same way. Meng, the young gorilla a year and a half old observed by Julian Huxley at the London Zoo, on three occasions traced the outline of his shadow with his forefinger upon the wall of his cage.

INNATE BEHAVIOR AND LEARNING PROCESSES IN YOUNG MAMMALS. Modifications in the behavior of the young animal during its period of growth make a most interesting study; they can indeed give us some insight into the relative importance of innate and learned factors in juvenile behavior, and it is to be regretted that up to now so few observations have been made on this engrossing problem.

What is known would seem to indicate in the first place that there is a definite sequence in the appearance of the various behavior patterns which is characteristic of each species. In the European red squirrel, for instance, Eibl-Eibesfeldt has recorded the following evolution in behavior: for five days after birth the young individual, hairless and blind, does no more than suckle, being quite unable to move its limbs in co-ordinated fashion. On the sixth day it utters its first cry of distress, and at this time some pigment appears in its skin. On the eighth day the fur begins to grow out, on the twenty-third the lower incisor teeth break through the gums, and on the thirty-second the eyes open. On the thirty-sixth day cleaning movements are seen, on the forty-second the young first leave the nest of their own accord, and on the forty-fifth they are able to eat ant pupæ for themselves. On the sixtieth day the first nut is opened, on the sixty-eighth the first rough nest is built, and on the seventy-fourth the mother leaves her young. The first attempt at copulation was observed at the age of 130 days, in a young male.

Chronological sequences of this kind certainly are not absolutely fixed, and retardation of the growth processes—through inadequate nutrition, for example—very probably cause delay in the maturation of behavior. But such schedules none the less enable us to make comparative studies of the relative times at which the various behavior patterns appear.

Rearing young animals in captivity can also give us information regarding the respective roles of heredity and learning in the modification of juvenile behavior. If we can separate young mammals from the mother at a very early age and raise them in isolation, any modifications observed are very likely to be due to maturation of the innate behavior patterns and to trial-and-error learning. Students of Konrad Lorenz have recently made such studies on some European species, and without surveying their conclusions in detail we may recall a few of their interesting results.

The first rough attempts at shelter construction characteristic of the species occur early in life and even in individuals isolated from their kind. Eibl-Eibesfeldt's badger, for example, made its first attempt to dig a burrow at 101 days and undertook its first olfactory marking of its territory on the 118th day, when its first wrestling play was observed. The common dormouse, raised in isolation by Zippelius and Goethe, built its first sketchy globular nest at the age of 55 days and quite without parental contact. These examples therefore tend to prove that the methods of shelter construction in mammals are in large part innate.

Quite to the contrary, it would seem that the defense reactions of young animals against normal enemies of their species are principally learned. Young African giant rats, born in captivity in Paris, were totally indifferent in the presence of a good-sized python and even approached calmly to sniff at its snout. Conversely the same snake was violently attacked by the parent rats, which had probably become acquainted with it in their native Africa. Yerkes's young chimpanzees also showed themselves relatively indifferent to a snake, although adult animals had shown fear of it. In this connection Yerkes even refers to the influence of "social tradition."

In any case the part played by the parents in the "education" of their young has long since been emphasized by many observers. Thus, Liers informs us that young otters do not enter the water of their own accord but are dragged in by their mother, who pulls them by the skin of the neck and catches small prey (crayfish, frogs, and little fish) to lure them on. Moreover their first attempts at swimming are awkward, the young learning little by little to swim properly. In the gray seal also the mother plays an active part in her offspring's first efforts to swim. Goddard[2] describes one of these "swimming lessons" as follows: "One of the young seals went into the sea and joined its mother. . . . At first the youngster appeared to be floating with its head under water, and every now and then it churned up the water with its hind limbs and made a big splash. The cow then swam underneath it and pushed it above the surface with her back. For a minute or two she carried it on her back, but the calf did not seem able to maintain that position for very long. As soon as the cow's back broke the surface, or even came near it, the calf slipped off, as it naturally had no means of holding on. Every now and then, when the calf appeared to be in distress, the cow put her head under its forequarters and pushed its head above water. After a time the calf was able to swim quite well with its head above the surface."

It goes without saying that such behavior should be re-

2 In G. Watt, *The Farne Islands*, London, pp. 186–7.

corded in moving pictures whenever possible, the camera lens being more impartial than the eye of the overenthusiastic observer.

SEXUAL MATURITY. Maturity of the gonads and the resulting ability to reproduce signalize an important stage in individual development. Although this does not mean that growth ceases, it none the less signifies psychologically the end of the period of juvenility and the beginning of maturity.

Not much is precisely known about the age at which various species of wild mammals reach maturity. In Asdell's work, cited in the preceding chapter, are to be found a number of facts that give us some idea of the great differences in this respect existing among the main orders.

Some of the small rodents become sexually mature at a very early age. The female meadow vole can reproduce at the age of 25 days and the male at 45. Sexual maturity in the hispid cotton rat is reached at about 40 to 50 days, that of the brush mouse at 50 days, that of the nutria at 8 months, that of the fox squirrel and of the woodchuck at 1 year, and that of the American beaver at 2 years. Many of the small European bats reproduce at 12 to 15 months, but the female of the Florida free-tailed bat can do so at 7. In the carnivores the age of sexual maturity varies widely: 10 months for the European red fox, a year for the American otter, the fisher, and the stoat, 2 years for the sable and the coyote, and 6 years for the brown bear. Maturity in the pinnipeds and cetaceans comes relatively early: 2 years in the common seal, the finback whale, and the fin whale; 3 years in the white whale, 4 years in the bottlenosed dolphin, 4 to 5 years in female walruses, and 5 to 6 in their males. Ungulate sexual development is also rapid, considering size: the roe deer is mature at 14 months and the red deer at 18, the bighorn sheep at 2 years and a half, and the chamois at 3 years. The rhinoceros can reproduce after age 4 to 5 and the Indian elephant after 15. Among the primates puberty is attained at 14 months in the female common marmoset, toward 3 years in the female toque monkey, around 8 to 10 years in the lar gibbon, and at 8 years and 11 months, on the average, in the female chimpanzee.

DURATION OF THE GROWTH PERIOD. We know still less about this subject than about the preceding, and the few observations that have been made concern only increase in weight, which, beyond a certain age, is not necessarily parallel with growth.[3]

We have no intention of undertaking here an analysis of the mechanisms responsible for growth. Such problems are of particular interest to biometricians and physiologists, and they have been fully discussed in some recent works.[4] We wish only to dwell on some special points that have important ecological bearings.

The accompanying graph (fig. 78) is typical for curves of weight increase in all mammals studied hitherto. It reflects observations of two rodents from Palestine kept by Bodenheimer under conditions as similar as possible to those in which they live in the wild state. We see that the period of rapid growth in the male Shaw's jird ends at the age of

[3] In old animals weight often tends to go on increasing slowly, due to the accumulation of fat, when the growth of the skeleton has long since come to an end.

[4] See especially J. Huxley, *Problems of Relative Growth*, London, 1932, and G. Teissier, *Les lois quantitatives de la croissance*, Paris, 1934.

about 150 days and that maximum weight is reached during the second year, after which the animal slowly loses weight. In the case of the Cairo spiny mouse the growth of the male is similarly almost complete at the end of about 150 days, but afterwards the weight tends to increase slightly up to

FIG. 78: *Growth curves of a male Cairo spiny mouse (A. d.) and of a male Shaw's jird (M. t.) from birth to death. After Bodenheimer.*

the third year. Shortly before death there is a slight emaciation with large fluctuations in weight. Female growth curves, less regular because of successive pregnancies, would show a slight retardation when compared with those of males. Growth curves of white rats and white mice of pure stock, raised in the laboratory under constant conditions of temperature and diet, show the same characteristics. In the case of the white rat, for example, we can distinguish, with reference to the total weight and that of the main organs, three successive stages in the life cycle: the growth period, extending from birth to the age of about 400 days; the period of maturity, from 400 to 600 days, and lastly the period of senility or loss in weight, beyond 600 days.

Unfortunately there is no comparable documentation for the large mammals. Regarding the higher primates, the studies of Grether and Yerkes have shown that young chimpanzees of both sexes increase in weight progressively and regularly from birth to their seventh year. At that time puberty intervenes, and beyond this stage the males become larger than the females. At the age of twelve both adult weight and psychological maturity are reached. Some authors believe that the slow growth of the primates [5] is correlated with the fact that their mental powers are more highly developed than are those of rodents or ungulates. It would seem wise to wait until the growth of more species has been studied before accepting this hypothesis as proved (fig. 79).

The statements just given on the growth rate of some mammals are valid, furthermore, only under well-defined conditions. It is common knowledge that the number of young in a litter, like the quality of nourishment, can affect the growth rate of offspring. The studies of McCay and his co-workers [6] on the white rat afford striking proof. They showed that it was possible to check the animals' growth rate markedly by reducing the amount of available food. Moreover, in slowing up the growth rate they clearly increased the longevity of the "retarded" rats as compared with controls of the same stock. And this increase in length

[5] Schultz estimates that generally speaking the growth period lasts 3 years in the lemurs, 7 years in the Old World monkeys, 9 years in the gibbons, and 11 years in the anthropoid apes (and 20 years in man).

[6] See especially *Journal of Nutrition*, Vol. 10, 1935, p. 63 and Vol. 18, 1939, p. 14. These results have been confirmed by several authors.

FIG. 79: *An example of modifications due to growth of a morphological character. Skulls of the chacma baboon,* Papio porcarius, *at different ages. From above downward: 1, newborn; 2, skull with milk teeth; 3, adult female; 4, adult male. Behavior changes due to growth are even more impressive.*

of life was not inconsiderable, since in one case it approached 100 per cent!

HIBERNATION

WHEN conditions become unfavorable, some species of mammals are able to pass into a lethargic state that may last for weeks or even for months. This phenomenon being especially noticeable in some of the familiar rodents and bats of our latitudes, it has been called "winter sleep" or hibernation. As a matter of fact, however, something quite analogous occurs in certain species in warm countries during the hot and dry summer season, and such *estivation* seems hardly to differ in attributes or mechanism from hibernation.

First of all, what groups are known to exhibit this phenomenon? The female platypus hibernates from mid-September to mid-October in Victoria, Australia, and the Australian spiny anteater does likewise when the temperature drops sufficiently.[7] In the United States the Virginia opossum, which has recently extended its area of distribution considerably toward the north, spends several months in a state of torpidity [8] during the winter cold; in Australia the pigmy opossum behaves in similar fashion in the state of Victoria. Among the insectivores the European hedgehog begins its sleep when the outside temperature goes below 15 °C.; its body temperature drops and in midwinter is about

[7] The ability to endure fasting shown by this species has been mentioned by several authors; in captivity it may go more than a month without eating.

[8] Without much reduction in its body temperature, it would seem; Davis points out, however, that in Brazil (near Teresopolis) the woolly opossum becomes lethargic when it is cold at night, and its body temperature goes down (this author found a rectal temperature of 16.5° C. when the temperature outside was 10° C.).

6° C. In Madagascar the tenrec hibernates during the dry season of the austral winter, that is, from May to October. Rand describes its winter burrow as consisting of a first part running parallel to the surface, followed by a second descending part stopped with earth, and ending in the hibernation chamber. This chamber is very clean, containing neither hairs nor excrement, and here the animal sleeps, in a rolled-up position. Among the bats of temperate regions the Vespertilionidæ retire for the winter into caves, attics, and hollow trees or other natural cavities. Some species of Rhinolophidæ and Molossidæ do likewise. All are true hibernators with very low body temperature and with slow and irregular breathing. Sound as their sleep may be, many observers have recorded temporary awakenings, with certain individuals changing places inside the same grotto. The rodents also present numerous examples typical of hibernating mammals. In Europe the best known are the fat dormouse, the common dormouse (fig. 80), the garden dormouse, the hamster, and the Alpine marmot. In North America the ground squirrels, the marmots, and the jumping mice hibernate, and in the Old World deserts the jerboas regularly estivate. Even such primitive primates as the mouse lemurs (*Chirogaleus* and *Microcebus*) of Madagascar hibernate, and I have recently demonstrated that their body temperature can then drop below 20° C. There is much more to be learned from a detailed study of the duration and other features of hibernation in a given species at different points of its range. In regard to the ground squirrels, for instance, not only does the duration of hibernation in the different species appear to be directly proportional to the severity of the climate, but Fitch's researches on the California ground squirrel of the San Joaquin region in California have revealed that not all individuals in the *same* population behave in the same manner. A large proportion of adult females hibernate from the beginning of summer to

FIG. 80: *Dormouse in hibernation. Note the position of the animal. Drawn at the end of March when animal was in a very emaciated condition.*

December or January,[9] whereas hibernation is much less frequent and shorter in the adult males and in the young of both sexes; moreover there are great variations within the same population from year to year. The carnivores also afford some instances of hibernation, but here the sleep is always less profound than in the preceding examples, and in particular the body temperature remains at a degree close to the normal for waking individuals. Bears may sleep in this

[9] Not far from the place where Fitch made his observations the dates of hibernation are quite different; about 20 miles away, but at a higher altitude (4,500 feet instead of 1,100), the California ground squirrels hibernate from November 1 to April 1!

way for several months in the winter, and without eating anything at all. The European badger hibernates in northern Russia and northern Scandinavia but remains active all winter in England and in France, as well as in the Caucasus.

The general term "hibernation" thus includes a whole series of states ranging from mere transitory torpor, without clear reduction in temperature, to the true winter sleep accompanied by a large and lasting drop in body temperature.

What do we know about the physiological mechanisms of true hibernation? Much has been written on the subject, and in Kayser's recent review of the facts we have a good resumé of the literature. Without going too much into detail, we may say that in true hibernators there appears in autumn a reduction in the heat production needed for keeping the temperature up, the lethargic state being preceded by a disturbance of the thermo-regulation, involving both the mechanisms of heat production and of heat loss. The imperfectly homoiothermous or warm-blooded animal then becomes poikilothermous or cold-blooded, and the body temperature falls to a point close to that of the environment (in bats rectal temperatures below zero Centigrade have been recorded!). At the same time there occurs a distinct involution of many endocrine glands: anterior pituitary, adrenal cortex, thyroid, parathyroids, and gonads. Even the islets of Langerhans become modified; in winter only insulin cells are to be found, although in summer there are two different kinds of cells. The great reduction in metabolic rate in the sleeping animal is accompanied by a slowing down of the heartbeat, respiratory movements are few and irregular (Cheyne-Stokes breathing), and the increased concentration of carbon dioxide no longer brings on increased ventilation. Yet regulation is not entirely absent during the winter sleep, and if the outer temperature drops too much the heartbeat becomes more rapid. While the period of lethargy lasts, stored fat is burned to supply the energy needed by the fasting animal.

Recent experimentation has thrown some light also on the question of what factors induce hibernation. Reduced temperature seems to play a necessary part for species in our latitudes, and Kayser reports that he has never observed torpidity in an individual of a hibernating species that is kept at a temperature above 13° C. In addition to temperature the second factor necessary to winter sleep is fasting.[1] By combining cold and fasting, it has been possible to hold fat dormice in winter sleep for a year. Further, the sleep can be brought on in the hamster or fat dormouse if removal of the pituitary and cold are combined with fasting, with the injection of insulin or of a hypothermia-producing drug, or with the removal of the adrenal medulla. But in all these cases the animals never survive for more than a few days, and the sleep thus induced is only an approximation to real winter torpor.

Whatever its precise physiological mechanism, hibernation does afford a definite advantage to the species that practice it. The large proportion of hibernators in the small mammal fauna of subarctic and desert regions goes to show that it has probably played a determining role in the populating of zones marked by climatic extremes that but for this physiological adaptation would be uninhabitable.

[1] This may be the main factor in species that inhabit warm and dry regions and estivate in summer.

LONGEVITY

THERE are many ways to approach the problem of life duration in wild species. In a later chapter we shall deal, for example, with the study of population structure according to age and with the life expectancy at the time of birth. In all these cases we shall see that a majority of individuals live much shorter lives than the possible maximum, because of the various mortality factors incident to natural conditions. Thus many small rodents that could live perfectly well for several years in the laboratory, where they are protected from predators and disease, do not live for more than several months in nature.

Since this chapter is devoted to the successive stages of the life cycle, we shall consider here only the data on the *potential length of life* of wild mammals; that is, the maximum ages that the various species can attain. It is of course true that potential longevity can be measured almost exclusively in captivity, for under natural conditions only an extremely small percentage of individuals become very old, and it is exceptional to encounter one that shows clear signs of senility. This is probably the reason why some authors have thought that growth could continue throughout life in several small mammals, the Microtinæ in particular. Recent research has shown that nothing of the kind occurs (fig. 78), and so far as we know at present, continuing growth is an attribute of reptiles and fishes only. Information provided by zoological gardens, however, is helpful only in connection with certain groups that are easy to feed and that reproduce readily in captivity. For many species that are difficult to feed properly the zoos furnish data of questionable interest.

We are indebted to Major S. S. Flower for an excellent compilation of observations made by the great zoological gardens on the longevity of many species. We have drawn upon this work for some data that have been gathered in Table 7, which contains in addition a number of records

Table 7. *Approximate potential longevity in some mammals (in years)*

MONOTREMES
  Platypus 10
  Echidna 40

MARSUPIALS
  Macropus major 11½
  Trichosurus vulpecula 12
  Vombatus ursinus 26

INSECTIVORES
  Blarina brevicauda 2½
  Crocidura russula 4
  Erinaceus algirus 5½

BATS
  Desmodus rufus 12½
  Pteropus giganteus 17
  Roussettus leachi 19½
  Myotis lucifugus 20½

PRIMATES
  Cheirogaleus major 8½
  Galago crassicaudatus 12
  Tarsius sp. 12
  Lemur fulvus 25½
  Cebus fatuellus 29
  Macaca mulatta 29
  Chimpanzee 40
  Papio porcarius 45

RODENTS
  Micromys minutus 2½
  Dipodomys meriammi 5½
  Jaculus jaculus 6½
  Glis glis 8
  Marmota marmota 13½
  Sciurus carolinensis 14½

Castor canadensis 19
Hystrix cristata 20

CARNIVORES
  Lutra canadensis 14
  Martes martes 15
  Canis lupus 16½
  Herpestes smithii 17½
  Potos flavus 22
  Crocuta crocuta 25
  Felis leo 30
  Ursus arctos 34

PINNIPEDS
  Arctocephalus pusillus 20
  Zalophus californianus 23

CETACEANS
  Balænoptera musculus 26
  Physeter catodon 32
  Balænoptera physalus 43

EDENTATES
  Cholœpus didactylus 11
  Myrmecophaga tridactyla 14
  Euphractus villosus 15½

UNGULATES
  Cephalophus maxwelli 9
  Sus scrofa 19½
  Cervus unicolor 26
  Equus burchelli 28
  Giraffa camelopardalis 28
  Anoa depressicornis 28
  Chœropsis liberiensis 39
  Rhinoceros unicornis 47
  Hippopotamus amphibius 49½
  Elephas maximus 69

201

published since 1931. Examination of these figures will show that man has the greatest potential longevity of all the mammals, inasmuch as he can—barely—exceed one hundred years. Next to man, the groups that have very long lives are the elephants, hippopotami, horses, rhinoceroses, monkeys, and certain carnivores. The figures given for bats indicate that they also have a remarkably high maximum longevity. The groups that have a notably brief potential lifetime are mainly the small insectivores and the small rodents.

CHAPTER 7

Migrations

TRUE migrations may be defined as seasonal and regular passages between an area where reproduction takes place and a zone in which the winter is spent; as everyone knows, many birds make such double journeys between the temperate or subpolar regions and the tropics of the Old World or the New. But the word *migration* is often used to designate other and very different phenomena that are quite unrelated to the true migratory journeys. Thus people speak of the "migrations" of lemmings, which, as will be shown in the last chapter, are nothing but mere emigrations without return that draw off the periodic overpopulation from certain regions. Paleontologists and zoogeographers also commonly refer to the "migrations" of certain groups or certain species from one continent into another. Nowadays reference is similarly made to the "migration" northward of the Texas armadillo, which, starting from the Mexican frontier and Texas, spread in 75 years over northeastern Oklahoma and Louisiana before crossing the Mississippi valley and advancing into southwestern Arkansas and eastern Oklahoma. In this case the word "migration" becomes synonymous with the extension of the range of a species, and the underlying causes of such a process certainly have nothing in common with those of true migrations.

THE MIGRATIONS OF WILD MAMMALS

WE know much less about the migrations of mammals than about those of birds. The phenomenon is a rare one among our terrestrial species, and such recent techniques as bat banding and the marking of whales and seals have not as yet afforded all that can be wished for in the way of results. The few instances to be given in this chapter will show, nevertheless, that migrations are not peculiar to birds and fishes and that there is still much to be done before we can describe them precisely or understand their mechanism.

Among terrestrial mammals the best examples of true migration—varying widely in extent, to be sure—are to be found among the large ungulates [1] that inhabit regions in great part undisturbed by man. The most spectacular are the migrations of caribou in the vast northern regions of America. Clarke, Hoare, and Murie have provided some exact information on these movements and have shown how variable they are according to the districts concerned. During the summer the herds occupy the barrens, which they begin to leave as early as July in order to move toward the timber line—that is, usually but not always, toward the south. A temporary return northward is usually witnessed in August and September. During the cold season the animals wander about in their winter zone, and their move-

[1] This is not to say that the ungulates have a monopoly in these seasonal movements, for instances are known in other orders, including the primates. Malbrant and Maclatchy lay stress, for example, on the regularity of the "seasonal migrations that bring the bands together on the same dates and in the same places" in the African Cercopithecidæ (Old World monkeys), especially a mangabey (*Cercocebus albigena*).

ments from place to place may show some regularity. Thus
the caribou studied by Clarke went back and forth from
east to west or vice versa, whereas the herds observed by
Hoare in the Reliance region moved counterclockwise in
circles. The caribou set out again between late February and
early May and return to the barrens for the summer. The
routes followed would seem to be much the same from year
to year, and the herds use trails that are quite visible on the
ground and from the air. When certain streams are crossed,
mass drownings can occur, as witness one mentioned by
Clarke that resulted in the death of 525 animals. Under some
circumstances males may move in compact bands of 100 to
1,000 head; but this segregation of the sexes is not invariable,
as appears from the fact that copulation takes place during
the autumn migration, the young being brought forth during the spring migration.

When the American bison was abundant, it carried out
impressive migrations, over a more or less circular route,
that might result in the herds spending the winter 200 or
even 400 miles south of the zone occupied in summer.

The migrations of other species, such as the elk, the
Dall sheep, or the mule deer, are much less extended. Russell
has carefully studied this last species in the Yellowstone and
Yosemite National Parks, where they are not interfered
with by human activities. In these two areas the species so-
journs successively in summer pasturage of higher altitude,
where it spends the season of mild weather, and in a wintering zone, at low altitude, where it arrives in autumn and
from which it sets out again in the spring. These summer
and winter habitats are not far apart, say from 10 to 60 miles
as the crow flies. The first snowfalls on the summer pas-

turages initiate the fall migration, regardless of the temperature. In spring, on the other hand, the return migration does not occur until several weeks after the snow melts, and the animals are en route only when the growth of vegetation is sufficiently advanced to assure their subsistence at higher altitudes. The period of rut coincides with the fall migration and the beginning of the sojourn in winter quarters; the young are brought forth in late June or early July shortly after the return to summer pasturage. It appears evident that the accessibility of food is a dominant factor in causing these migrations. In Yellowstone Park, for example, there is an especially interesting district, that of the geysers. Although it is situated at an altitude of 7,500 feet, snow does not remain on the ground in winter because of the abundance of hot springs. Now, the approximately 70 mule deer that inhabit this particular region never migrate, remaining there in sedentary fashion the year round. In Manitoba likewise the ample sufficiency of food, the good cover, and the comparatively thin layer of snow on the ground are correlated with a completely sedentary habit of the species.

The aquatic mammals afford several examples of migration on the grand scale, since some of them move periodically between subpolar latitudes and tropical waters. The seasonal abundance of certain whales in certain localities has long been well known to whalers. The gray whale, for instance, is found in numbers from the beginning of winter to the end of spring in the Pacific along the California coast, where it comes to give birth to its young in lagoons and estuaries; at the approach of summer this species returns northward along the coast and spends the summer in the

Arctic Ocean and the Sea of Okhotsk. A similar migration has been observed along the Asian coast, and whales of this species are hunted in winter off the coast of Korea.

No longer ago than 1932 the Discovery Committee succeeded in perfecting a practical method for marking whales. The invention consists of a stainless steel tube about 10 inches in length, engraved on the outside with a serial number, the address of the Colonial Office in London, and a promise of reward to the finder. This tube, contained in a special cartridge, can be fired as a projectile from a special cannon of sufficient power to hit a whale 70 or 80 yards from the boat. The tube buries itself in the animal's blubber without causing a serious wound, and it will be easily found later when the fat is removed on the deck of the factory-ship. From 1932 to 1938—in the course of five whaling-seasons in the Antarctic, that is—668 blue whales, 3,915 fin whales, and 548 humpbacks were marked, and of these 33 (4.94 per cent), 118 (3.01 per cent), and 36 (6.59 per cent), respectively, were recovered later, some of them 4 years after marking. Rayner has made a very careful analysis of these recoveries up to 1939, and this has enabled him to draw the following conclusions: the blue whales met with around South Georgia do not constitute a fixed population, nor do those hunted at the same time off Enderby Land. Thus one individual was caught, 88 days after marking, more than 500 miles southwest of the place where it was marked, and another had traveled, in 32 days, more than 300 miles to the southeast. Some individuals of this species are unquestionably capable of covering very great distances. A blue whale marked in summer off Bouvet Island, for example, was caught the following summer off

South Georgia (about 1,180 miles from its position of the preceding summer). Most of the animals recovered after one, two, three, or four years were taken, however, in the vicinity of the place where they had been marked originally. It is remarkable that no marked blue whale has as yet been recovered in the winter in tropical latitudes, for this species is hunted at that season (to be sure in small numbers) off the West African coast, in the Indian Ocean not far from Madagascar, and northwest of Australia, as well as on the west coast of South America up to Peru and the Equator. But these individuals are mostly young, and it is possible that the winter migration toward warm waters is less clear-cut for this species than it is for the humpback. The fin whale displays migratory behavior similar to that of the blue whale. In summer it frequents the same Antarctic waters, and in the winter it, too, is found at times in African waters. A young individual marked in February 1935 in the Antarctic, at latitude 65° south, was captured on July 1, 1937, off Saldanha Bay in South Africa, 1,900 miles north of the point where it was marked. As in the preceding species, there is a pronounced tendency for marked individuals to return summer after summer to the same locality, although this rule does not always hold. The humpbacks of the Southern Hemisphere would seem to travel immense distances each year. Figure 81 reproduces one of Rayner's charts and shows the regularity of these movements. In summer these whales frequent Antarctic waters and in winter the tropical latitudes (northwest of Australia and Madagascar), where they breed; the following summer they return very faithfully to the localities of the preceding year, and so on year after year. Some segregation even seems to exist

FIG. 81: *The migration of Antarctic humpback whales in the Indian Ocean. Points of marking and recapture of a few individuals. After Rayner, 1940.*

between the different groups (African, West Australian, New Zealand, Chilean, and Atlantic), which would thus tend to be isolated from one another.

Among the pinnipeds, also, we are acquainted with some remarkable migrators, of which the harp seal is one. This species inhabits the circumpolar waters of the Northern Hemisphere but reproduces in only three very definite localities within its range: the White Sea, the western North

FIG. 82: *Area of distribution and lines of migration toward zones of reproduction (cross-hatched) of the harp seal. After Nansen, in Sivertsen, 1941.*

Atlantic about Jan Mayen, and the vicinity of Newfoundland.[2] A regular migration therefore takes place, bringing the adults in autumn to their breeding-places (fig. 82); the young are born there between the end of January and the beginning of April, and then there is a return migration toward the more northern latitudes, where the summer is spent. In the White Sea Sivertsen marked 171 young seals with numbered aluminum plates attached to their flippers;

[2] One group northwest of the Island and another in the Gulf of Saint Lawrence.

eleven recoveries were made up to 1941, and fig. 83 clearly shows the dispersal of the young animals. In the northern Pacific, Alaska fur seals carry out even more spectacular migrations. This species reproduces only on the Pribilof

FIG. 83: *Some results obtained from markings used in studying the migrations of the harp seal. Nos. 225 and 240 were captured a year after marking, No. 3 eight years later. After Sivertsen, 1941.*

Islands, 200 miles away from the nearest land, where the animals are to be found from May to November. As winter begins, the females and young undertake a journey of nearly 3,000 miles that brings them to the coast of Southern California where they pass the cold season. The males, on the other hand, spend the winter no farther away than the

Gulf of Alaska and the waters south of the Aleutian Islands. Spring brings both sexes back to the Pribilofs. In the Antarctic the crab-eating seal usually remains all winter near the edge of the ice pack, although it has been reported as far away as New Zealand.

The ability to fly enables the bats to move readily from place to place and facilitates migrations over vast distances. The study of these movements has been much advanced by the practice of banding the animals with incomplete metallic rings so attached to the front limb as not to injure the membrane. The large mouse-eared bat and the noctule have been most used in Europe for systematically planned research. Out of 8,295 large mouse-eared bats banded by Eisentraut between 1932 and 1942, 199 were recovered later, and analysis of these recoveries shows that in the spring—March and early April—this species leaves its winter quarters (in Brandenburg), and flies to its summer stations. The latter are located along the arc of a circle extending from the northwest to the northeast (fig. 84). The distances between winter and summer quarters vary a good deal according to the individuals concerned, the maximum being 160 miles, the minimum less than half a mile, and the average between 20 and 50 miles. Great fidelity to the wintering-locality, even to certain exact spots (such as a particular gallery in a cave), is the rule. Out of 355 large mouse-eared bats banded during the winter of 1932–3 and recaptured during the winter of 1933–4, only three had changed locality. Moreover, some individuals were moved late in the winter from their accustomed winter shelter to another some 90 miles away, where they finished their hibernation, but not one of these returned to this place the next year, although many did return to their accustomed winter quarters.

There were not so many recoveries of the noctule—only 19 out of 1,464 that were banded. But here the distances between winter and summer quarters were much

FIG. 84: *Migrations of two groups (A and B) of large mouse-eared bats banded in their winter quarters at Brandenburg, and of four noctules banded in winter at Dresden. After Eisentraut.*

greater, as is witnessed by an individual that was banded at Dresden and recaptured at Kampiai, Lithuania, 470 miles away. An observation made by Bels illustrates again the remarkable ability this species has for making rapid flights over long distances: a noctule banded August 1, 1938, at Haarlem in Holland was recovered on the 29th of the same month near Duffel in Belgium, 90 miles to the south.

213

The record for distance as the crow flies is held at present by a European pipistrelle, which, banded on June 28, 1939, in the province of Dnepropetrovsk, Russia, was recovered by Buresch on September 8, 1939, near Plovdiv in Bulgaria, at a minimum distance of 720 miles!

In North America the red bat and the hoary bat are also great migrators. The first is often seen on the open sea, during its autumn migration southward, and one of them was captured 240 miles off Cape Cod, in August. It is probable that they regularly reach the Bermuda Islands.

In Australia *Pteropus poliocephalus* migrates periodically from Queensland to New South Wales, and in Africa seasonal migrations have been described in *Epomorphus wahlbergi* and *Eidolon helvum*.

THE PROBLEM OF ORIENTATION AND HOMING

WE have only recently become aware of remarkable powers of orientation or direction-finding possessed by wild mammals, as disclosed by marking and banding. Hitherto the homing of an individual experimentally moved far from its home range seemed to be an attribute of migratory birds exclusively. Today there is proof that similar phenomena are to be observed in rodents and bats at least. Future studies will show whether these observations, along with the many cases of domestic dogs [3] finding their way home after being

---

[3] Some of these instances of "finding the way home" are truly remarkable. Soulath (*Zeits. f. Tierpsychol.*, Vol. 6, 1944, p. 147) gives, for example, the case of a dog that was taken 20 miles from home by rail in a special compartment for dogs and returned by itself, making use of the railroad track. The same author cites also the case of another animal that returned home by boat, disembarking only at its destination, although the two-hour passage included several other stops. But visible landmarks quite probably play a large part in homing. In this connection Grzimek (*Zeits. f. Tierpsychol.*, Vol. 5, 1943, p. 481) has made interesting ex-

taken a long distance away, into unfamiliar country, represent isolated occurrences or, on the contrary, reveal a more general faculty. For the present we must patiently gather reliable observations while admitting our ignorance of the physiological mechanisms involved.

Let us begin by surveying some well-established facts. Stickel has recently published the results of an ingenious experiment, which should be systematically repeated. This author worked with white-footed mice at the Patuxent Research Refuge in Maryland. He used the following technique: 22.5 acres of forest were selected in a uniformly wooded area, so that the surroundings were everywhere the same and there could be no possibility of different plant formations serving as landmarks for the animals. Further, the selected zone seemed to be uniformly populated with white-footed mice, so that "vacant spaces" or sparsely populated spots were eliminated as sources of different population pressure. In this experimental area Stickel set up three concentric parallel squares measuring 990, 660, and 330 feet on a side respectively and marked by rows of Sherman live-traps set at regular intervals of 55 feet, as indicated in the accompanying diagram (fig. 85). All the mice taken alive in the traps were marked with metallic ear tags before being released.

The homing experiment was performed at three different times. On the 27th and 28th of August, 1946, all the mice captured were set at liberty where they were caught. On the 29th of August those taken in the outer line of traps

periments on the horse. Five mares were taken (on foot or in vehicles), *blindfolded*, for distances varying from 3 to 10 miles from where they were bred and into territory unknown to them; under these conditions not one succeeded in returning to the stable.

were transferred to the center of the experimental area—
that is, to a distance of 500 to 700 feet—before release,
whereas the individuals taken in the traps of the two inner
quadrilaterals were released at their place of capture, as before. No trapping was done during the five following days,

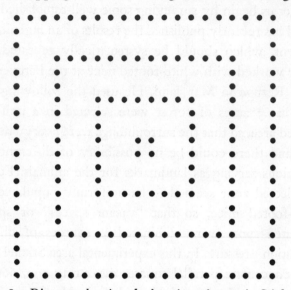

FIG. 85: *Diagram showing the location of traps in Stickel's
experiment.*

so as to leave the population undisturbed before the last
series of trappings, which took place on September 4 to 6.
It will perhaps be supposed that a removal from home of
only 500 to 700 feet would constitute a very slight displacement, but this distance is in reality much beyond the average
normal range of a mouse, which at this season and under
these environmental conditions does not in fact exceed 150
feet for males and 100 feet for females.

The results of this experiment were as follows: out of
27 males thus artificially displaced, 22 (or 82 per cent) re-

turned to their home site where they were recovered between September 4 and 6, two probably returned, one was recaptured 765 feet from its original home range in the wrong direction, and two others were not retaken. Out of 21 females similarly transferred, 13 (or 62 per cent) returned to their home site, one probably returned, another remained near the point of release, and six were not retaken. There were five juvenile individuals that were "displaced" under the same conditions as the adults, none of which were later recaptured. For purposes of comparison, I will mention the fact that 90 per cent of the males and 100 per cent of the females released where they were caught during the first trappings were retaken there during the last period of trapping—which indicates the sensitivity of the method used.

Other authors have also engaged in experimentation of like nature. The Muries, for instance, have obtained some spectacular results. Using the deer mouse, whose individual cruising range is of the order of 100 yards, more or less, they have observed the homing of subjects transported to distances of 100 yards to 2 miles and therefore very probably into unknown territory. More, a young individual of the same species succeeded in regaining its home range after having been carried to a distance of two miles—and that in less than 48 hours! In Austria Wolfgang Schleidt observed the homing of a common redbacked vole from a distance of 700 yards.

Not all rodents would seem capable of such feats. But Hamilton observed the return in less than an hour of a large male meadow vole carried 200 yards from its domicile, and yet this species is of a notably stay-at-home disposition. The same author got positive results with American red squirrels transported more than a mile from their home range, and from eastern chipmunks transported to a distance of 700 paces from their shelters.

The most beautiful experiments in homing, however, have been carried out with bats. The papers of Eisentraut, Norbert Casteret, and Ryberg offer many examples, like those that follow. The last author mentioned obtained many returns of noctules *in a few hours* between Alnarp and Lund (about 6 miles) and between Malmö and Lund (13 miles). The distance between Falsterbo and Lund (28 miles) was covered in 24 hours. The European pipistrelle, on the other hand, was able to accomplish homing flights of only a few miles. The species that at present seems to hold the record for these homing flights is the large mouse-eared bat. In Germany Eisentraut obtained the return of an individual released almost 94 miles away. Casteret has carried out many displacement experiments with the bats of the Tignahustes Cavern in the Hautes-Pyrénées. Several released at 10 miles were already back the next day; out of 65 released at 22 miles, 8 were recovered 3 days later; a few released at 62 miles were back a month later. A few individuals even returned to Tignahustes after having been released at Saint-Jean-de-Luz, 112 miles away from home, on the seashore at Moliets (Landes), 125 miles distant, and at Sète, 165 miles away! It is true that these returns from distant points were very slow and that the large mouse-eared bat is a species that normally accomplishes long journeys, but these performances are remarkable none the less.

How are these mammals able to regain their homes? Visible landmarks unquestionably exist and no doubt they play a predominant part over short distances. It is also probable that they are a factor in migrations. But it must not be forgotten that bats fly almost exclusively at night and that on this account their recognition of topographic features must be limited to twilight hours. Again, it is hard to see what kind of landmarks might be of assistance to small rodents such as deer mice moving about in the uniform, low vegetation of the underbrush. Here the scented trails of their fellows are probably more helpful. There remains the hypothesis of the exploration of unknown territory in chance directions or in a spiral path, until some landmark enables the animal to regain its customary home range. In favor of this explanation is above all the progressive decrease in the percentage of successful returns accompanying increase in distance. This reasoning has validity, and no doubt chance exploration plays a part, as do orientation by visible landmarks and previously familiar scents; but is there not something else?

CHAPTER 8

The Social Life of Mammals

IT might be supposed that in the matter of social behavior two different types of mammals exist: the solitary and the social. This is not true in reality, for a mammal that is strictly solitary throughout its life cycle is inconceivable. There always exists, in fact, a minimum of social relations between the sexes, at the time of mating, and between mother and young during the period of nursing, and some cases are known in which the social relations between individuals are held strictly to this minimum. So it is with the little eastern chipmunk of North America, a species in which the male and female become antagonistic no more than a few minutes after mating and in which the mother and young are associated only as long as they remain together in the nest and for a week after. There is thus no lasting mutual attraction between individuals, and there even seems to be just the opposite of a "need" that would lead the animal to seek the company of its kind.

Sexual relations and family behavior have been surveyed in preceding chapters, and we now have to consider interactions between individuals that live permanently in groups. Without attempting to draw up a classification of mammalian societies, which would of necessity be unsound in the present state of our knowledge, we shall confine ourselves to stating what we know at present about the social behavior of a few species sufficiently studied in this respect, after briefly surveying the means of communication and the social hierarchy.

MEANS OF COMMUNICATION

MUCH has been written on the "language" of wild animals, but it is only in the course of the last twenty years or so that we have begun to understand the nature and function of the means of intercommunication used by mammals. Observation and experiment have revealed the existence of a great many "signals," not only acoustic but also visual and olfactory, that release a characteristic reaction in the individual perceiving them. These sign stimuli of different kinds (sounds, odors, or mimickings) appear to have well-defined functions in the social life of wild mammals, and if divergences exist between different schools of thought as to the interpretation of the observed facts, the reality and importance of the facts are no longer disputed by anyone.

The *acoustic signals* uttered by mammals are not so pleasing to the human ear as are many of the songs and some of the cries of birds, and so it is not surprising that their systematic study has been undertaken only recently and then for very few species. Although their notation encounters the same technical difficulties as that of bird songs, it has still been possible, in a limited number of cases, to analyze the effects of these sounds on the behavior of members

221

of the group, to discover the circumstances under which they are produced, and to gain some idea of their role in the social life of the species.

The California ground squirrel is a gregarious rodent that has been closely studied in recent years by Linsdale and Fitch. The adult animal apparently utters only one simple chirp, and only when in danger. But Fitch's prolonged observations have shown that this familiar chirp varies significantly in pitch, loudness, and inflection according to the occasion. When a squirrel perceives a bird of prey flying in the vicinity it utters a single short syllable of unusual loudness and carrying quality, a *"cheesk,"* and seeks cover. As soon as this signal is perceived by the other squirrels, they pay attention to it and seek their holes while taking up the cry of alarm in turn. If the enemy is a snake, the ground squirrel edges up to it, often coming within a foot or two, examines it, flicks its tail violently from side to side, and gives a peculiar chirp, *"cheet'-ik-irr-irr-irr,"* distinctive in its low, vibrating quality and the series of subdued notes following the loud initial sharp note. This chirping and tail-waving of squirrels that have located a snake serves to attract the attention of others in the vicinity. If a man, dog, or coyote constitutes the danger, the signal generally becomes trisyllabic, *"chwee-chu-chuk."* A still different sound is produced when the danger is less immediate —a *"cheesk-isk-isk-isk-isk,"* with the final syllables blending in a rapid succession. In the case of a mother with young, the female's agitation in the presence of danger that is not immediately threatening is expressed by the prolonged repetition, at intervals of two or three seconds, of a low, melodious note, *"chwërt,"* that is more in the nature of an anxiety symptom than of a signal of alarm. Finally, other sounds, different from the basic chirp, are produced by this species: a low growl that seems to express defiance, a sharp squeal that seems to be a cry of pain and fear, and a high-pitched squeal ending in a trill, given when one squirrel is pursued by others.

Carpenter's researches on the behavior in nature of several species of monkeys afford other examples of auditory signals. The Panama howling monkeys have a vocabulary of at least 15 to 20 different vocalizations, all of which appear to play a very definite part in the behavior of the species. The functions of nine of them seem rather clear. The first is *a voluminous barking roar*, low-pitched and sonorous, uttered by the males of the group in the presence of an enemy, of a rival troop trespassing upon the territory, or of any other disturbance. It has an inhibiting effect on all activities, such as feeding, locomotion, playing, and so on, and the members of the group prepare for attack or defense. The second signal is a *deep, hoarse cluck*, which may be given in series or singly by the leading male before and during the troop's movements; it initiates progression and controls its direction. The third is a *deep, gurgling sound given in a series* by the adult males in the presence of some disturbing factor; it usually precedes the loud roars but seems to affect only the males and not the females or young. The fourth vocalization is a *wail made on inspiration of air, followed by a groan*, sounded by a female whose young one has fallen; it is repeated until the baby is recovered, and it stimulates the males to utter their loud roar. In these circumstances the fallen baby gives a *series of three notes or little cries* that direct the mother and the males toward it.

Another sound is a *purr* of several seconds' duration which a young individual utters in order to obtain coddling from its mother. Finally, the young at play give *little chirping squeals*. The males of the clan produce two other easily recognizable sounds: a *grunting sound* produced when the young play at fighting and one of them utters a cry, the effect of which is to stop the fight; and a *rapidly repeated grunting* that is heard when the group situation involves something new and strange. The function of this latter sound seems to be to attract the attention of the members.

The vocal repertoire of all the mammal species studied so far is, however, rather limited. Thus, observers have found only 3 sounds in the bottlenosed dolphin (McBride and Hebb), 6 in the white whale and the hamster (Schevill and Lawrence, Eibl-Eibesfeldt), 8 in the California ground squirrel and the Senegal bush baby (Fitch, Lowther), 9 in the European red fox, the lion, and the lar gibbon (Tembrock, Guggisberg, Carpenter), 10 in the black-tailed prairie dog (King), 11 in the Camargue wild cattle (Schloeth), 12 in the European badger (Simms), 15 to 20 in the Panama howling monkeys (Carpenter), 20 in the mountain gorilla (Schaller and Emlen), 20 to 30 in the rhesus monkey (Rowell and Hinde), 30 in the Japanese macaque (Itani), and 32 in the chimpanzee (Yerkes and Learned). However, a wide range of intermediate sounds makes available a larger "vocabulary" for expressing small differences of mood. Furthermore, the same vocalization may have different meanings according to the context in which it is given. Thus, a short, sharp *uh-uh* given by a male mountain gorilla when females are quarreling may cause them to subside. If, however, the male emits the same sound without apparent reason, all members of the group first look at him and then face the direction which occupies his attention. In the first case, the sound apparently carries direct meaning; in the second case, the same sound serves only to attract attention to the performer and eventually to permit the communication of further information by means of gestures, facial expressions, or postures (Schaller and Emlen).

All these acoustic signals are innate, though the existence of local differences between populations of the same species suggests that learning also plays a role. The various sounds appear according to a definite schedule in young animals; the barking of the European red fox is, for instance, emitted for the first time around the age of 18 days and the *muf-muf* around 25 days (Tembrock).

The development of light, battery-operated tape recorders and sound spectrographs has opened up almost unlimited opportunities for studying vocal communications among wild mammals, and we may expect great advances in this field.

We must recognize, further, the existence of auditory signals other than vocal. The powerful slapping of the tail on the water by beavers is a most efficient alarm signal; and drumming on the ground with the hind paws is a noise produced under little-understood circumstances by many rodents; such, for example, as Shaw's jird, the lesser Egyptian jerboa, and the fat-tailed gerbil. Tail rattling is similarly used by the dusky-footed wood rat.

Olfactory signals must play an important part in the daily life of wild mammals, but, unfortunately, it is very difficult for us to appreciate the role of odors because of our own mediocre sense of smell. Cutaneous glands are common in mammals,[1] and the accompanying text figures borrowed from Pocock's classic studies will give a better idea of them than would dry descriptions. In the ruminants alone this author described and figured pedal glands (fig. 86) between

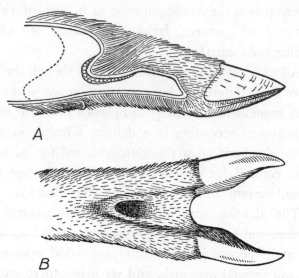

FIG. 86: *Pedal gland of the muntjac,* Cervulus muntjak. *A, median section of the hind foot of young six days old; B, front view of the same foot. After Pocock, 1910.*

the bases of the hoofs, carpal, tarsal, and metatarsal glands whose names alone are enough to show their anatomical positions, and preorbital (fig. 87A and B), inguinal (fig. 87C), retrocornal, occipital, caudal, and preputial glands. Anal glands are common in the carnivores, and the civets have peculiar ones in the perineal region. Some of the secretions of these glands undoubtedly play a part in sexual at-

[1] They are the subject of a recent monograph by Schaeffer (1940). It is an odd fact that these glands are lacking in the primates, excepting the lemurs and the marmoset family.

226

FIG. 87: *Some types of cutaneous glands in the ungulates. A, head of the male* Tetraceros quadricornis; *gl., orifice of the preorbital gland; B, section of this gland; o., orifice; l., flap of skin constituting upper lid of orifice; C, inguinal glands of a male bushbuk: m., nipples; gl., orifices of the glands; s., scrotum. After* Pocock, 1910.

traction,[2] some are employed in marking the territory and the home range (fig. 88), and others are considered to be means of defense. In reality their functions are probably multiple. What is certain is that the scented "trails" and

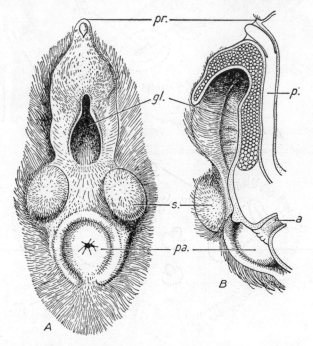

FIG. 88: *Anal gland of the male civet,* Viverra zibethica. *A, inferior view of the anal pouch and glandular area; B, vertical section through the same region. Pa., anal pouch; gl., interglandular space; s., scrotum; p., penis; pr., prepuce. After Pocock, 1915.*

"marks" so important in the lives of wild animals result from the functioning of these glands. Beavers deposit the secre-

[2] J. Le Magnen (*Comptes Rendus Soc. Biol.*, Vol. 165, 1951, pp. 851–60) has shown, for example, that the male white rat is able to perceive and distinguish the odors of males and females of its species and to discriminate between a female in heat and one that is not. The behavior of the female with regard to biological odors is, moreover, clearly different from that of the adult male.

tion of their musk glands on hillocks of mud or projecting objects, and California ground squirrels that of their dorsal glands on stones and twigs. Martens and mongooses smear branches or bark with the product of their anal glands; un-

FIG. 89: *Male* Antilope cervicapra *"marking" a twig by depositing on it the preorbital secretion. After a sketch by Hediger.*

gulates often place the thick secretion of their preorbital (fig. 89) or retrocornal glands on certain trees; many Canidæ mark stones, stumps, stakes, and other projecting objects with their urine mixed with the product of their preputial glands.

That the secretions of the odoriferous glands play various roles is also suggested by the fact that different glands are affected in different ways by sex hormones. The supracaudal gland of the guinea pig is developed only in the adult male, is reduced by castration, and is restored by androgen. The anal glands of the rabbit are very similar in buck and doe, are reduced in both sexes by gonadectomy, and are restored, though somewhat differently, by both œstrogens and androgens. On the other hand, castration does not affect the lateral gland of the short-tailed shrew, which is well developed in males and non-œstrous females.

The extent to which various chemical messages may influence conspecific individuals has been dramatically demonstrated recently. If newly mated female mice are removed from their stud males and exposed to males of a different strain, pregnancy is blocked in about 80 per cent of the cases, through failure of corpus luteum development (Parkes and Bruce). Neither the sight nor the physical contact of the alien males is necessary to bring about the pregnancy block. It is sufficient to place the females in soiled jars recently vacated by males. Conversely, the pregnancy block does not occur in females rendered anosmic by destruction of their olfactory bulbs. The stimuli responsible for this "Bruce effect" are therefore beyond any doubt olfactory.

Visual signals have been studied much less in mammals than in birds. But it is certain that they exist, and all investigations of the hierarchy in social species include mention of characteristic attitudes indicating the rank an individual holds in the society. In many instances it even seems that "threatening" attitudes play a much greater part than real fights.

Certain parts of the fur that sometimes contrast violently in color with the rest of the coat are often made use of as visual signals. The clearest case is that of the "rump

FIG. 90: *Some characteristic expressions of the wolf. A, normal facial expression of an animal of high rank; B, expression of timidity; C, threatening expression; D, suspicious expression. After Schenkel, 1947.*

patches" of the American pronghorn. This animal has long white erectile hairs in the perianal region that are suddenly raised when it is disturbed or frightened; in that state they form two large white rosettes that are visible from a great distance. They probably serve as a "signal of alarm" and as directive marks to other individuals. In a preceding chapter we have described how the European wild rabbit uses the white underside of the tail to attract the female's attention during the nuptial display.

Various positions of the head, ears, and tail, furthermore, have definite meaning. Figures 90 and 91, taken from

A   **B**   **C**   **D**

E   **F**   **G**

FIG. 91: *The expressive function of tail movements in the wolf. A, self-assurance; B, threatening attitude; C (with wagging sidewise), attitude of intimidation; D, normal; E (with wagging sidewise), attitude of submission; F and G, attitudes of acute discomposure. After Schenkel, 1947.*

Schenkel's paper, represent examples of this "sign language"; other instances are given by Backhaus, Hinde and Rowell, Schloeth, Tembrock, and Walther.

THE SOCIAL HIERARCHY

IN the year 1913 the naturalist Schjelderup-Ebbe discovered that there exists in flocks of hens a "pecking order," or hierarchic organization, in which the social ranking depends on the number of pecks or blows with the beak given or received, as well as on the aggressive or submissive attitudes assumed by the individual concerned. The many investigations pursued since then, especially by Allee and his students, have demonstrated the existence of analogous phenomena in many species of domesticated animals. Thus the more or less artificial groupings of hens or white rats are not disorderly assemblages but rapidly become organized

A female marmosa carrying her young.
New York Zoological Society Photo.

A female Virginia opossum carrying her young.
Courtesy of American Museum of Natural History.

An eastern chipmunk hibernating.
Courtesy of American Museum of Natural History.

groups by virtue of the relations of dominance and subordination that are set up among their members.

In what degree are these facts, observed in laboratory rodents or flocks of sheep, peculiar to domesticated species or to life in captivity? How far can they help us toward an understanding of the social component in wild mammals?

To begin with, it is now quite certain that social hierarchies are not peculiar to domesticated animals. This has been shown, for example, by Katz's recent work on the Barbary sheep, carried out on a herd of twelve head—four males, four females, and four young—living in semiliberty on a fenced-in plot of about two acres at the Bronx Zoo in New York. At the beginning of the study, which lasted 53 days, the animals were marked with spots of color in order to make identification easy, and the "rank" of the various members of the group was ascertained as follows: when two individuals were together near the fence of the enclosure awaiting food, they were offered a piece of bread, care being taken to have it equally distant from the two animals. At sight of the bread they moved toward it, but the dominant individual was always the one to get it, after having struck with the head or merely threatened [3] the dominated individual, which thereupon withdrew.

Katz made many repetitions of this test with the various members of the herd and got the following results: Male 1 dominated males 2, 3, and 4; male 2 dominated males 3 and 4; male 3 dominated male 4. Female 1 dominated females 2, 3, and 4; female 2 dominated females 3 and 4; female 3 dominated female 4. Young 1 dominated young 2, 3, and 4;

[3] In the present instance the threat is indicated merely by a sudden twisting movement of the head in the direction of the lower ranking individual.

young 2 dominated young 3 and 4, and young 3 dominated young 4. Further, the males were always dominant with respect to the females, and adults with respect to the young. These results would indicate the existence of a *linear hierarchy* of the simplest kind: Male 1 > male 2 > male 3 > male 4 > female 1 > female 2 > female 3 > female 4 > young 1 > young 2 > young 3 > young 4. This hierarchy or ranking remained very stable throughout the whole course of the tests, since 270 observations out of 272 gave results in conformity with this tabulation.[4] It is noteworthy also that quite apart from this ranking it was always female 1 that acted as leader of the flock when it was frightened by the observer's presence, showing quite clearly that the leader of a group is not necessarily the individual highest in the social scale.

Other examples of hierarchies in wild mammals in captivity are afforded by lions, baboons, and chimpanzees (Yerkes), and even by bottlenosed dolphins.

The second point of importance is the occurrence of unquestionable hierarchies in certain wild species living under natural conditions. Southern's study of the wild rabbit, for example, shows that the whole social organization of the colony during the period of reproduction is based on the territorialism of the females and the dominance of certain of the males. The latter are usually old individuals that are intolerant of competition from young males; they not only chase them and even compel them to go away to try

---

[4] Hierarchies are not always linear; a common arrangement among birds, for example, is the *triangular hierarchy*, where a subject A dominates a subject B while being dominated by a subject C, which is itself subordinated to B. All hierarchies, moreover, undergo change with the passage of time and with the age and physiological state of the subjects. Experimental castration of males reduces their aggressiveness.

their luck in other colonies, but sometimes they fight with them. Southern describes a fight between two males, one of which had ventured too near his rival's mate. After a chase the two adversaries engaged in a furious joust, leaping against each other to a height of three feet. The old dominant males may rule over a section of the warren for several years, as did two animals marked by Southern.

We may consider the existence of a social hierarchy, involving the more or less lasting superiority of certain individuals over others, to be a fairly frequent phenomenon among wild mammals and in no way peculiar to life in captivity. It remains for future research to analyze in detail the relationship between the social hierarchy and territorial behavior, for there seem to be many links between these two manifestations of aggressiveness within the species.

SOME INSTANCES OF SOCIAL LIFE IN MAMMALS

IT is likely that there are mammals of permanent social habit in most of the orders, and doubtless detailed study of the modes of life practiced by exotic species will in the near future provide many new data on this subject. But at the moment we have exact knowledge regarding only a few species of rodents, pinnipeds, ungulates, and primates, to which we shall now turn our attention.

GREGARIOUS RODENTS. The first instance that comes to mind when mammalian societies are under consideration is that of the beavers. In fact these industrious rodents have been the subject of so many books and articles that one might suppose our understanding of their social organization to be well advanced. Unfortunately it is nothing of the kind, for if more or less fictionalized accounts are many, persevering observations are few, and it is no exaggeration to say that a full-scale study of beaver biology is yet to be undertaken.

Bradt, however, has published a considerable series of observations on the American beaver, which serves as a fortunate corrective of previous efforts (that of Warren, for instance). These observations are of interest because they were based on the study of marked [5] individuals living at liberty and because some of them could be followed up for several years. This work makes it evident that the beaver colony—that is, the group frequenting the same body of water,[6] using the same source of food, and maintaining the same dam or series of dams—most commonly consists of a family group comprising 2 adults, the young of the year, and often those of the preceding year. At the age of two years the young, then approaching maturity, are driven away, and the society is thus limited to 12 individuals at most. For example, 42 colonies studied by Bradt were constituted as follows:

CONSTITUTION OF COLONIES	NUMBER OF CASES
1 *female*	1
1 *female and the young of the year*	7
1 *female and the young of the preceding year*	2
2 *females and their young of the year*	1
1 *male*	6
1 *male and* 1 *female*	6
1 *male,* 1 *female, and their young of the year*	9
1 *male,* 1 *female, and the young of the preceding year*	2
1 *male,* 1 *female, their young of the year, and the young of the preceding year*	8

[5] All other marking methods (tagging ears, clipping toenails, etc.) being inconvenient to use for this species, Bradt adopted that of branding the tail with a red-hot iron. Marks so made at various levels on one side or the other or on the upper or under surface last for about one year.

[6] Where, however, they may inhabit more than one house or one burrow.

The history of one of these colonies, followed at House Lake from 1928 to 1933, is especially suggestive. A pair marked in October 1928 had 4 young in May 1929, and 6 others in May 1930, bringing to 12 the number of members of the colony for the latter year. By September of 1931 the 1929 young had disappeared, but 4 of the 6 1930 young remained with the parents and 6 new young were born, the colony thus continuing to consist of 12 members. In May 1932 there were still 12 members: the 2 parents, 6 young a year old, and 4 young of the year. In May 1933 Bradt once again found 12 members: the 2 adults, the 4 1932 young, and 6 newborn of the year. This example shows that the pair of reproducing adults is the nucleus of the social group; in the 42 colonies studied there never was more than one adult male, and his intolerance toward other males of reproductive age explains at once the absence of overlapping in the territories of several colonies and the expulsion of the young when they approach maturity. The males also take the lead in repairing damaged dams, but all the members of the colony share this work. Beaver colonies thus stand as the type of familial societies in which co-operation and co-ordination of activities reach a high degree of perfection.

Almost nothing is known precisely about the social organization of European beaver colonies. We do know that in some localities, where the animals are not in too close contact with man (parts of Norway, the Elbe valley, and Poland, for example), this species is quite capable of building houses and dams like those of the American species. If the Rhone beaver now lives in burrows, it may be in consequence of centuries of contact with civilization; and the case of the female, kept in a park at Parjurade, that before giving birth built a house of branches with a floor and a central opening for escape, shows that under favorable circumstances the characteristic behavior pattern of the species can again be overtly expressed. The colonies of this species are probably constituted like those of its American relatives. Curry-Lindahl, cited by Hainard, believes that in Sweden "a colony consists almost without exception of a single family: parents, young of the year, and young of the preceding year, the latter leaving their parents at two years of age."

The "towns" of the black-tailed prairie dogs are made up of a great many small population units, which King calls "coteries." Generally, each of these contains a single adult male, two or more adult females, yearlings, and the young of the year. Often there are two adult males in a coterie, but one is usually dominant over the other. Prairie dogs within the coterie co-operate with one another and defend the area they occupy against non-members. Cohesion within the coterie is interrupted only during the breeding season (late February to April), when nesting territories are defended temporarily by breeding females. Non-reproducing males and barren females live in separate groups.

The mountain vizcachas of Peru also live in colonies of varying size, numbering from 4 to 75 individuals, among the crags of the high Andean regions wherever water is available. Pearson has recently made a careful study of their biology in the valley of Caccachara, at an altitude of more than 15,000 feet. Like the European marmot, the vizcacha is a strictly diurnal and gregarious animal living in burrows that are often no more than crevices among the boulders with little in the way of furnishings. Most of the colonies consist of family groups that vary in constitution during the course of the year. In July, August, and September a majority of the members of the colony are paired, and the family is made up of an adult male and a parous or pregnant female accompanied by one, two, or three young of different ages;[7] the oldest male offspring may be sexually mature yet still living with the family. When œstrus comes on, the female no longer tolerates the presence of the adult male and chases him out of the burrow while continuing to live with her offspring and even with other females. The evicted males may then join a group living in a special burrow or lead a more or less vagrant life. Sexual promiscuity seems to be the rule in the colony; Pearson saw a male attending several females and several males paying court to one female. When gestation begins, the aggressiveness of the females declines, the adult male is tolerated once more in the burrow, and the family group is re-formed. In the colonies he observed Pearson saw no sign of individual or collective territories defended by their "owners." He noted at most that not every part of the colony's area was common ground; certain individuals, pairs, or families were sometimes seen to occupy exactly the same spot week after week. One family, for instance, always took its sun bath on a particular rock that other members of the colony obviously avoided, although the family in possession never showed any signs of defensive behavior.

We have already discussed the social organization of the wild rabbit warren as disclosed in Southern's beautiful

[7] In this species the young are born one at a time, and a female may give birth two or three times a year.

investigation. Here also the element of stability is provided by the females, which raise their young in their burrows and are jealous in their defense. As for the polygamous males, only certain ones succeed in gaining dominion over the warren and mating with the females. Sexual promiscuity is again the rule in this instance.

THE PINNIPEDS. This order includes the eared seals, the walruses, and the true seals, which are mostly gregarious. Only a few seals, in fact, such as the Ross seal, the leopard seal, and the bearded seal, are truly solitary. All the rest of the species live in groups, but the social structure of these groups is not the same in all cases.

In some instances—all the eared seals, the southern elephant seal, and the North Atlantic gray seal—the polygamy of the males involves the formation of harems during the period of reproduction. Thus the Falkland sea lion, carefully studied by Hamilton, lives in vast herds (unorganized, it would seem) when not reproducing. With the coming of the Antarctic summer, however, the breeding and nonbreeding animals separate, but many of the previous season's pups remain with their mothers until the next are born. The nonbreeding animals repair to certain shores, and among them will be found not only immature individuals and some of the previous season's pups but also idle bulls that have not been able to obtain cows. The breeding herd thus consists of harem bulls, pregnant cows about to give birth, virgin cows, and newborn pups. Each male has a definite number of females (9 on the average), which he jealously defends against the sexual approaches of other males and with which he will copulate soon after the young of the preceding year are born. The male does not allow any of the females of his harem to return to the sea before copulation has taken place, but when all the females have been covered, the harem breaks up. Then the males become less aggressive, and they may be seen sleeping or guarding the young. The reproductive season is in full swing during the first half of January, and the dispersal of the harems begins in early February. The existence of such harems during the reproductive period seems to be general among all the eared seals. Those of the Alaska fur seal are well known, and, as we have seen, the two sexes undertake long migrations in order to keep the rendezvous in the Pribilof Islands.

The harems of the southern elephant seal likewise involve the separation of the females into groups when they go ashore to have their young. Those observed by Matthews in South Georgia contained from 2 to 30 females per male, the average being between 12 and 20. Here again the males having adjacent harems fight violently in defense of their property and drive away bachelor bulls that frequent the beach around the edges of the harems. When one of these bachelors approaches, the harem bull throws back his head, roars while inflating his proboscis, and opening his mouth utters a series of muffled bellows. Usually this display of might is enough to scare off the intruder, but sometimes there is a fight. Then, face to face, the two males rear up as high as they can, mouths open and proboscises inflated, trying to tear at each other with their upper canine teeth. If one of the animals loses his balance while fighting, the other throws himself upon the foe, biting him in the back and neck; the wounds thus inflicted may be six inches across, and the eyes and proboscis are often reached. Usually the wounded animal gives up the fight. The females, for their part, accept any male that approaches them and are in no way faithful to their lord and master. With this species, then, as with the eared seals, there is a territory defended by the male during the period of reproduction, and this territory is strictly limited to the harem.

The gray seal is transitional between the polygamous pinnipeds and the gregarious seals that are sexually promiscuous. This species has been closely studied by Darling on the Treshnish Islands and North Rona, off Scotland, and by Davies on Ramsey Island in the Irish Sea. On the latter island it is the males that arrive first at the breeding-grounds, after the first of August. In September they have established their territories and they are on patrol along the beaches where the females are to come and give birth. The latter reach land three days to three weeks before the birth of their young; during this waiting-period they spend most of their time in the water and as a rule take the initiative in prenuptial play with the males. Individuals of the two sexes face each other and touch each other with their front limbs, the female mounts on the back of the male, and the two animals often swim in circles, one behind the other. The young are born in September and October, and the males copulate with the females shortly after the latter give birth. The important point is that several different males rule in succession over the same harem, without there being any relation between the number of females that compose it and the number of males that succeed one another. Thus at Ogof Colomenod, in 1947, there were 24 females, and Davies observed a succession of 4 males within two months and a half. At Aber Mawr, for 12 females, 3 males succeeded one another within three weeks. On another beach (Ogof Thomas Williams) a single male, to the contrary, maintained a harem of 17 females for six weeks and was seen at least twice chasing away a possible rival. Mutual intolerance between males is therefore rather variable according to the case, and real fights are rare. Bertram rightly considers the gray seal to be a species in which polygamy and harem formation are dying out.

All the other species of seals, though mostly gregarious, seem to be sexually promiscuous, and they never form harems of females protected by a male proprietor.

GREGARIOUS UNGULATES. Gregariousness is extremely frequent in the various families of this vast group, and truly solitary species are the exception. The hyraxes or "conys," the elephants, the horse family, the hippopotami, many of the pig family, most of the Bovidæ, the giraffes, the guanacos, the vicunas, and a majority of the deer family live in groups. Unfortunately the social structure of these herds and its seasonal changes through the course of the year remain unknown in most cases, since but few of the species have been studied from this point of view.

In a good many species the males associate with one or several females only at the rutting period. When this is over, they abandon mate or harem and resume solitary life or else form herds made up of males only. The females and young go their way and form herds occupying a well-defined home range and "controlled" by a female leader. The young follow their mothers for a longer or shorter time according to the species, the young males generally departing just before puberty. These matriarchal associations are able to carry out co-ordinated activities, such as even mutual aid.[8]

The red deer is a good example of this type of society. Darling's observations, made in the Highlands of Scotland, have established the fact that in winter the companies of stags and the groups of hinds have separate and distinct home ranges. The range of the females is really their "home" and they have their young there. That of the males, on the other hand, appears for the most part to be merely a winter retreat. In no case are these home ranges defended against intrusion by other members of the species, and when circumstances are unfavorable several groups may even unite. Here, then, there is no question of true territorial behavior.

In summer the deer move up toward the mountaintops, and several herds that occupy separate home ranges in the winter may unite and graze together. The various groups nevertheless retain their independence.

In autumn, at the time of rut, the males enter the "territory" of the females and fight among themselves as they endeavor to establish their harems. At this time the males evidently dominate the females they have rounded up. But this dominance is real in the sexual sphere only, and in case of danger the females come together again in a compact group under its accustomed female leader, as before the harems were formed.

This annual cycle in itself accents the essential role of the female herds, and a deeper study of the facts only goes to confirm this first impression. Whereas the hind groups are organized and always have a leader of female sex and

---

[8] A striking instance is afforded by the Indian elephants that, according to Sauvel (*Terre et vie*, 1947, p. 29), transported a fatally wounded individual for about forty yards.

reproductive age, the stag companies are less coherent. The latter have no leader, although one individual may fight with the others. An animal may often spend the winter with one group and the summer with another, and the company may sometimes split into age groups. Solitary individuals are generally old, sick, or wounded animals, and it is probable also that some of them are unmated males.

A more or less similar social organization is found in many species of ungulates: elk, ibex, chamois, saiga antelope, pronghorn, topi, Uganda kob, waterbuck, Thomson's gazelle, impala, and, possibly, giraffe.

Unfortunately, in most cases we know very little about the nature and duration of the bonds between the "harem bull" and his females. In some cases the adult male clearly controls his cows and tries to intimidate and chase away any potential rival. In most species a bull's supremacy probably does not last for more than the breeding season. But the adult male vicuna apparently stays with his females all the year round.

A few gregarious Bovidæ do not form harems during the breeding season, but, on the contrary, tend to establish temporary monogamous mateships at rutting time. This is true of the American bison (McHugh) and the Himalayan thar (Anderson). Others, such as the bighorn sheep, are thoroughly promiscuous. Buechner has observed that ewes generally accept more than one ram in rapid succession. Up to 12 males have been seen mating with the same female.

A similar tendency is also found in some deer. The rutting behavior of the Columbian black-tailed deer studied by Dassmann and Taber was also promiscuous. The bucks seek more than one doe, and does accompany more than one buck during a single breeding season. Here there is no pairing or harem formation.

Members of the horse family (zebras, wild horses, and wild asses) do not exhibit a uniform social behavior either. Such African species as Burchell's zebra and related forms live in bands of varying size in which the two sexes are mingled indiscriminately except at the time of rut, when the pairs are briefly isolated. These assemblages appear to have no true leader. Grévy's zebra forms only small herds in which the stallions play no permanent or dominant part, and it is the same with the mountain zebra. The wild asses of Nubia and Somaliland form herds of females accompanied by their young and led by a female; the males join them only at the reproductive periods.[9] Among the Mongolian wild asses it is again the females that form the stable element in the herds; during rut the stallions take possession of 3 or 4 females with their foals and protect them against the advances of other males. The herds of wild horses that formerly existed, on the other hand, were to the best of our knowledge controlled and led by a dominant stallion. Thus we can observe again, in this one family, all the gradations between the loose and leaderless assemblages of the zebras, the matriarchal societies of the wild asses, and the patriarchal societies of the true horses.

TROOP STRUCTURE AMONG MONKEYS AND APES. Notwithstanding their taxonomic position, the numerous species of prosimians, monkeys, and apes may be distributed

---

[9] Among the Indian wild asses, the herds of females, accompanied by their young, live apart from the males for three months after giving birth.

into three broad ethological categories: the so-called solitary species, those living permanently in pairs or small family groups, and those forming large heterosexual troops.

All of the solitary primates are nocturnal animals— such as the mouse lemurs (*Microcebus*), the dwarf lemurs (*Cheirogaleus*), the aye-aye, the *Lepilemur*, the slender loris (*Loris*), the slow loris (*Nycticebus*), the potto (*Perodicticus*), the angwantibo (*Arctocebus*), the bush babies (*Galago*), the tarsier, and the owl monkey (*Aotus*). All these animals are usually found singly, though the young may stay for a time with their mother. At most a small number of adults can be found sleeping together during the day, at least in a few species.

A few arboreal and diurnal primates live in permanent (monogamous?) family groups. Thus, the sifakas (*Propithecus*), the woolly lemurs (*Avahi*), and the indri (*Indri*) live in groups usually formed of an adult male, an adult female, and one or two young (J. J. Petter). The Asiatic gibbons do the same. The lar gibbon, studied in Thailand by Carpenter, forms permanent family groups, made up of the two parents, the young of the year, and a variable number of older but still immature individuals.

Most of the diurnal primates, though, live in large heterosexual groups; in most cases, however, we know nothing about the structure and turnover of these groups. As pointed out by De Vore, the gregarious prosimians, monkeys, and apes can be subdivided into two broad categories. In the arboreal species, the troops have relatively small home ranges and are loosely organized, the males being seldom aggressive and dominance-oriented; among the terrestrial species, on the other hand, the troops generally have larger home ranges and are organized into more rigid social categories based on a hierarchy of dominance. In fact, it is among the terrestrial monkeys that we find the strongest sexual dimorphism, particularly in the morphological features that equip the adult male for effective fighting— larger body size, larger canine teeth, etc. In the first category are the Panama howler monkeys (Carpenter, Collias and Southwick, Altmann), red spider monkeys (Carpenter), red-tail monkeys (Haddow), Indian langurs (Jay), olive colobus (Booth), *Colobus guereza* (Ullrich), and the chimpanzee (Goodall). The various baboons (De Vore, Washburn, Hall) and macaques (Altmann, Itani, Imanishi), are in the second category. The mountain gorilla, though primarily terrestrial, is somewhat peculiar since its groups are more open and less motivated by sex (Schaller and Emlen).

The social organization of all the terrestrial groups so far studied is characterized by relationships of dominance and subordination among the adult and subadult members of the troop. But this hierarchy of dominance is not organized according to an order of rank in which each member of the group occupies a definite position; it rests on a system of classes which bestows on the individual a definite status recognized by all other members as well as certain functions and privileges. Thus, an adult male treats a female the same as any other, one juvenile like all other juveniles, and an infant like other infants. Similarly, an adult female, although her position within the female hierarchy is clearly discriminated by other females, treats adult males as members of a class (De Vore, Itani). When a baboon troop is resting or feeding, the most dominant males occupy the center, with the mothers and the young infants gathered around them, and the groups of young juveniles playing close by. Around this nucleus are the more peripheral members of the troop—the less dominant adult males, older juveniles, and pregnant or œstrus females. A similar organization has been found in Japanese macaques.

In these heterosexual groups lasting male-female relationships are seldom established. During the œstrus, a female generally mates with several males in close succession. In the later part of the œstrus she forms, at most, temporary consort relationships, for some hours or some days, with the dominant adult males. Such sexual promiscuity has been observed among the howler monkeys, *Colobus guereza, Presbytis entellus,* and the chimpanzee, as well as among the South and East African baboons and the mountain gorilla. Groupings suggestive of a harem have been observed only among hamadryas baboons (Kummer and Kurt) and patas monkeys.

There is no reliable evidence that these primates defend any sort of territory. Groups of baboons, langurs, chimpanzees, and gorillas have frequently been seen in close contact with neighboring troops of the same species, with no display of aggression between the groups evident. The "vocal battles" of howlers and the resounding early morning "whoops" of the langurs seem to serve more to identify the membership and the location of the troop than to issue a challenge to neighboring groups. Such cries can thereby function as epideictic (Wynne-Edwards) and spacing mechanisms, without any directly combative connotation.

CHAPTER 9

Mammals and Their Environment

MAMMALS are not mere automata functioning apart from their surroundings. Every one of them is more or less closely adapted to its habitat, and its presence, in turn, has repercussions upon the environment. This environment is, in fact, a living complex, the integration of a whole series of factors —climatic, edaphic (properties of the soil), biotic (fauna and flora), and even psychologic [1]—the effects of which combine to make up the specific environment of each animal.

One need not be a naturalist to realize that species are not distributed at random over the surface of the earth. It is wholly unlikely that chamois or Alpine marmots will be

[1] It is fully justifiable to take account of "psychological" factors, along with other factors of ecological and historical nature, in the study of the distribution of species. There is no lack of instances where climatic and biotic influences, taken alone, are insufficient to explain the selection of certain habitats, and it is with good reason that ornithologists appeal in such cases to "subjective" or "psychological" factors that still elude precise and complete analysis. The recent experiments made by Van. T. Harris at the University of Michigan clearly show that laboratory-bred deer mice do have an innate tendency to select particular kinds of objects in the environment. Each of the two subspecies under test exhibited a definite preference for the type of habitat normally occupied in nature.

250

encountered in western European plains, and there is an equally slight chance of finding moles in a sand dune or red squirrels in a beet field! Each major life zone is made up of a whole series of distinct habitats, and each one of the latter includes many different biotopes or ecological niches supporting a special fauna and flora made up of species that depend, directly or indirectly, upon one another and that compose a kind of community of organisms—a biocœnose —having its own metabolism and undergoing its own evolution.

The ecological requirements of a species are what cause it to inhabit a particular environment. Sometimes these are very strict and sometimes they are not so stringent, and in consequence some species will be highly specialized and others relatively unspecialized; but all have played and are still playing an important part in the evolution of living mammals.

In this chapter we shall go on to examine some aspects of these interactions between organism and environment, never losing sight of the fact that in this field, possibly more than in any other, what we know is only an infinitely small part of what would be important for us to know.

CLIMATIC FACTORS

CLIMATIC factors come first to mind when we try to understand the peculiarities of the geographical distribution of species. But we soon realize that the climates of the meteorologists are wholly inadequate alone to account for the preference many mammals show for some particular habitat. What are certainly much more important for most living creatures than regional climates, based on annual averages from many localities, are the local *micro-climates* of the various biotopes or ecological niches. For a forest rodent, to take an example, what count are temperature, humidity, and light at ground level and beneath the plant cover, and not the atmospheric conditions in a meteorological shelter six feet above open grassland. And the differences between them are far from slight! The micro-climate in our temperate forests is on the whole even more moderate than that of the open air. The extremes of temperature and humidity are not so great, and the average temperature is lower than outside, the average humidity higher; air currents are very slight, and there is less light. Furthermore, considerable differences exist among the various levels or strata within the forest. The micro-climate of even an ordinary cultivated field is very different from the macro-climate of the region that includes it. As for burrows and soil cavities, they have a climate very much their own, and we have already seen that this peculiarity plays an essential part in the life of small desert mammals.

TEMPERATURE. The great majority of mammals being homoiothermal or "warm-blooded"—that is, animals that can keep their inner or body temperature constant—one might suppose that the temperature of their surroundings is but a secondary factor in their ecology.

It is true enough that many species originating in warm countries easily bear in captivity temperatures much lower than those of their native countries, but this is not to say that these species can live and prosper as well in our climate as at home. It is absolutely necessary for the ecologist to distinguish carefully between *lethal* and *optimal* temperatures. Here are some examples: Among laboratory animals the lower critical temperature [2] is $-15°$ C. for the guinea pig, $-25°$ C. for the white rat, $-45°$ C. for the rabbit, and $-160°$ C. for the dog (Giaja). The upper critical temperature, more easily reached than the lower, is $+40°$ C. in dry air for the white rat and $+49°$ C. for the dog (Adolph). Inside these limits the inner body temperature remains nearly constant whatever that of the surroundings may be; a variation, say, of $12°$ C. in the latter changing the internal temperature of a mouse by not more than 0.4 of a degree.[3] But within this range of homoiothermic regulation there is for each species a *thermic optimum* that is alone compatible with the normal course of the life cycle. If we compare the growth of genetically identical white mice, some raised at optimum temperature $(21°-3°$ C.) and others at a higher temperature $(32°$ C.)—all conditions being otherwise equal

[2] The term "critical" is applied to temperatures beyond which the temperature regulation of the organism breaks down.

[3] It should be said, however, that on the whole arctic mammals resist cold better than tropical species and indeed show remarkable endurance. The polar foxes of Greenland, for instance, are able to live in the depth of winter on the icecap. Several were seen during the winter of 1950–1 (September to March) around the Central Ice Cap Research Station of the French Polar Expeditions (70°54′N; 40°42′W), at an altitude of 9,000 feet and more than 280 miles from the nearest ice-free land, with the thermometer ranging below $-50°$ C.; during blizzards the animals took shelter in burrows dug in the snow. Ernst Sorge, a member of the Wegener Expedition, made similar observations at "Eismitte," from the 4th to the 22nd of October, in temperatures reaching $-52°$ C. Scholander and his co-workers failed to reach the lower critical temperature for polar foxes subjected experimentally to cold as extreme as $-80°$ C.! The zone of thermoneutrality in these animals is thus very broad, enabling them to endure excessively low temperatures, at least temporarily.

What accounts for this remarkable resistance to cold? The investigators just mentioned have clearly shown that there is no metabolic adjustment to cold in these species and that the phylogenic adaptation to cold or hot climate has taken place only through factors that regulate the heat dissipation, notably the fur and skin insulation. The ability of limbs and feet to get along with little heat supplied from the central body mass is remarkable indeed.

—we find that the growth of the second group is clearly retarded, sexual maturity comes later, and fertility is lower. The second generation will be almost completely infertile, and, furthermore, all animals raised at 32° are more subject to infections than those raised at 21°–3° C. (Mills). Herter made a study of the "thermotactic optimum" for rodents, and even showed that it is almost constant for a given stock because it is hereditary, being transmitted as a dominant character. These optimum temperatures are more important for the ecologist than are the extremes that may be borne temporarily by adults but in any case do not permit the species to thrive and multiply.[4]

Some mammals are but imperfectly homoiothermic and quite unable to carry on their normal activities when the temperature is too low. These are the monotremes, the sloths, and the bats.[5] The duckbilled platypus and the echidna (monotremes) have an inner temperature that varies slowly with the surrounding temperature. According to Martin as cited by Giaja, the body temperature of an echidna rises 4 to 6 degrees when the outer temperature goes from 5° to 30° C. The internal temperature of the South and Central American three-toed sloth, normally about 32° C., falls to 20° C. when that of the surroundings drops to 10 or 15° C. (Britton and Atkinson). This hypothermy is reversible and is accompanied by a state of torpor

[4] The problem of acclimatizing cattle from temperate regions in the tropics raises questions of great interest from this point of view. The various races are not all alike in this respect, and the underlying causes of these differences are by no means fully understood. For a general review of these matters see Dordick, *Acta Tropica*, Vol. 6, 1949, pp. 221–45.

[5] Certain marsupials and armadillos should probably be added to this list.

that may last for hours. Inversely, mere exposure to the sun at 30–40° C. induces a hyperthermy of 40° C. that is quickly fatal. In consequence the sloth family is physiologically restricted to a limited equatorial habitat of very constant temperature. In the bats the internal temperature of the small species normally varies between 34.4 and 40.6° C., according to the degree of wakefulness (Eisentraut), but this temperature falls very rapidly when the animal is at rest and tends to approach the outer temperature. In regions where the winters are cold, bats must therefore migrate or take refuge in caves, attics, or other enclosed places for hibernation.

There has been much debate about the effects produced by environmental temperatures upon certain morphological characteristics, but in some cases the existence of these relations seems to admit of no doubt. Thus it is with the pigmentation of the fur in Himalayan rabbits, which afford a good example of the interaction of genes and environment in the production of the external characteristics of an animal. In this race of rabbits there is certainly a special genetic color factor that exercises its inhibiting effect on coloration only at certain temperatures; cold prevents it from showing its effect, and the result is a peculiar coat color in adults: wholly white except for the tips of the limbs, the ears, and the muzzle, which are pigmented. This pigmentation of the extremities is probably to be explained by the fact that their temperature is lower than that of the rest of the body. If, indeed, a part of the white fur of an adult is shaved off and the animal is kept at a cold temperature during the regrowth of the hair, a pigmented area will develop. Similarly, the young often show a slight general pigmentation of their first fur as a result of the cooling of the nest during the winter.

In this connection it has long been noted, when related forms of the same species inhabiting different climates are compared, that those in cold regions are usually larger than those in warm regions. This seems rather generally true of the vertebrates and is often referred to as Bergmann's law. This law, however, is far from being absolute, and we even know of animals (such as the raccoons) in which the size of different forms becomes smaller as the latitude inhabited by them becomes higher. Stein has recently shown that the size of the European mole decreases with the altitude; a difference in altitude of only 450 yards can entail an appreciable difference in size. In Central Europe, east of the isotherm of $-8°$ C. in January, the large race is replaced by a smaller one. None the less Bergmann's law is valid for many mammals, and it may be verified even within the compass of a single species. In England, for example, house mice living in cold storage plants where the temperature never rises above $-10°$ C. are always much larger than mice of the same species inhabiting houses or wheat stacks (Laurie); a female has been taken in the cold habitat which weighed 40 grams, whereas 30 grams is the maximum for the others. Again, it has been noted that the species of cold regions show a tendency toward shortening of the extremities (Allen's law); feet, tail, and ears are seen to decrease in length as the observer goes northward. The classical instance of this tendency is furnished by the North American hares and rabbits of the genus *Lepus:* the ears of the antelope jack-rabbit, living in Arizona, are much longer than those of the more northern snowshoe hare and still more markedly so than those of the arctic hare, living in the far north. The North American foxes show the same tendency.

The most generally accepted explanation of these facts is that the increase in size involves a relative decrease in surface area, which reduces heat loss and aids in maintaining homoiothermy. This explanation is based on experimental evidence. It has been shown that if white rats of homozygous stock are raised, at a high temperature (31 to 33.5° C.), each animal will have in two or three months a longer tail, a more developed scrotum, and less weight than those kept at 15 to 20° C. It is also true that rabbits raised at a high temperature have ears longer than normal (Mills). All this promotes the dissipation of heat.

WATER. In all its forms—gaseous, liquid, or even solid —this element plays an important part in mammalian ecology. This is not surprising, for water is by weight the most important constituent of living matter and the constant movement of water within the organism is a fundamental physiological mechanism.

For land mammals water is first of all an essential element in metabolism. But as regards ecology, the main point is that the various groups do not all have the same requirements, and, what is more, that these requirements can be satisfied in very different ways.

Some mammals drink a great deal and in consequence are practically restricted to habitats that provide free water in sufficient quantity. Many African herbivores, for instance, regularly visit water holes or other sources each day at a fixed hour, often coming from considerable distances.

Other animals, in the absence of a temporary or permanent water supply, drink dew or water running down tree trunks or foliage after a rain. There are still more numerous species that can do without free water for longer or shorter periods, finding enough for their needs in the water content of their animal or vegetable food. This is true of many ungulates, rabbits and their relatives, carnivores, and insectivores. On the other hand certain groups—especially among the rodents—can subsist indefinitely and reproduce on a diet of seeds and other almost anhydrous or waterless plant foods. As is to be expected, these groups are predominant in all the desert regions of the Old and New Worlds. The pocket mice and kangaroo rats of the southwestern United States, for instance, are quite able to live exclusively on seeds that have a water content not exceeding 5 to 10 per cent. On this diet they not only fail to lose weight but even grow normally fat. Under the same conditions the white rat rapidly loses 40 to 50 per cent of its weight and is unable to survive in the end. The pocket mice and kangaroo rats have no reserves of water in their tissues, but they excrete urine twice as concentrated as that of other rodents, which makes for a considerable economy in the use of water (Schmidt-Nielsen). This may be called a true physiological adaptation to desert conditions, but it would be risky to generalize on this basis concerning all the other desert small mammals. The southwestern white-throated wood rat, also native to the desert zones, is able to live in such an environment only because of a special peculiarity in its diet. This rodent cannot subsist on anhydrous seeds alone, but it finds the water it needs in the cactus and other succulent plants that compose up to 44 per cent of its food.

Atmospheric humidity is another important ecological factor, particularly for certain species. The small bats, for example, can live only in rather humid air. If the European species are kept in captivity without food or water and with the humidity below 85 per cent, they die in a day or two with their wing membranes partially desiccated. But if the humidity is high, the same species can survive a fast of 30 to 40 days (Nerincx). In the caves used for hibernation the relative humidity is always very high, 75 to 98 per cent. Some insectivores, in particular the moles, also require dampness. Outside their always very humid burrows moles do not live long in a dry atmosphere; in nature they may be forced by prolonged dry spells to emerge from their burrows, and that is quickly fatal.

Variations in relative humidity also affect behavior: the red deer, for example, is extremely sensitive to variations in atmospheric humidity. Although rain has no definite influence on the movements of a herd of deer, a very humid atmosphere reduces travel from place to place, whereas a dry atmosphere has the opposite effect. This is interpreted by Darling as owing to the fact that a warm and humid atmosphere favors the transmission of various scents and is necessary for the proper functioning of the olfactory apparatus. The California ground squirrel retires to its burrow if the humidity of the air is too low or too high (Linsdale). The fact is that a certain optimum humidity is required by all the rodents, and it is noteworthy that whenever the relative humidity is measured inside burrows, a rather high and almost constant figure is obtained.

There are some morphological peculiarities which have been attributed to atmospheric humidity. It is, in fact, rather commonly true that in a group of related forms the coat color darkens as the humidity of the habitat increases; this has been noted in North American insectivores (certain moles), rodents (lemmings), and carnivores. It may be that the enlargement of the tympanic bullæ (rounded projections below the ears) of desert mammals is also correlated with the dryness of the habitat (Heim de Balsac). The cavities of these bullæ are said to contain air of very high humidity, which may check dehydration of the middle ear and the fluid it contains, but this suggestion has still to be investigated experimentally. The occurrence of enlarged bullæ in some marine Cetacea does not accord well with this idea, and in some cases at least the bullæ could act as resonators, facilitating the perception of vibrations in soil or water.

Snow and ice constitute an important and complex ecological factor for mammals living in cold regions. When the winter snow reaches a certain depth, it seriously interferes with the feeding of herbivores and impedes the locomotion of even the largest species. But, on the other hand, it is a poor conductor of heat, and this property helps many species in their struggle to survive low atmospheric temperatures. Arctic hares often let themselves be covered by falling snow and in this way find shelter from the cold. In Siberia there are voles which dig their burrows under deep snow and succeed in remaining active all winter and breeding under these conditions (Formosov). In summer the coolness of glacier snow attracts certain ungulates and hares that come to the locality to get relief from the biting insects that swarm at that season on the tundras.

All the direct or indirect effects of water which we have just been reviewing are, in brief, dependent under

natural conditions upon the annual rainfall. It is not surprising, therefore, that certain isohyetal lines (indicating
equal precipitation) should coincide with the distributional
limits of certain forms of animal life. In the Mediterranean
region of the Old World the isohyetal line 200 marks a
threshold that warm-blooded desert vertebrates scarcely
cross and beyond which to the southward Berber or North
African components of the fauna cannot live (Heim de
Balsac). In east European Russia the distributional limit of
the wild boar corresponds approximately with the limit of
winter snow cover 20 to 30 inches deep (Formosov). Further detailed study of mammalian ecology will doubtless
bring to light more data of this kind.

As for the aquatic mammals, we are but poorly informed about their tolerance of varying physico-chemical
characteristics of the water in which they live, but it is
probably rather wide. We do know that the manatee lives
equally well in fresh, brackish, and salt water, and that seals
in captivity do very well in river water. Along the coasts of
Europe the common seal lives in salt water as well as in
brackish water (Baie de Somme), and it may even ascend
rivers.[6] On the other hand, the European otter, primarily a
fresh water species, readily enters salt water in search of
fish, as has been observed in Scandinavia, Scotland, Brittany
(Sept Iles), and even Morocco.

LIGHT. This factor, still little studied, affects the ecol-

[6] In Canada a local subspecies (*Phoca vitulina mellonæ*) of the
common seal even lives in a fresh water lake in Ungava (New Quebec),
known as Seal Lake; it has probably been evolving there, landlocked,
since the last Glacial Period; that is, for about 5,500 years (Doutt, *Ann.
Carnegie Museum*, Vol. 29, 1943, pp. 61–125). Two distinct forms of the
ringed seal inhabit the fresh water lakes Ladoga and Saina in Finland.
A well-marked species of seal (*Phoca sibirica*) is found in Lake Baikal.

ogy of mammals in many ways. Daily variations in light intensity are fundamental to the nycthemeral or day-and-night rhythm of most species. Diurnal mammals become active at sunrise or sometimes a little before, as do Godet moles (fig. 92). Their activities go on all day and come to an end

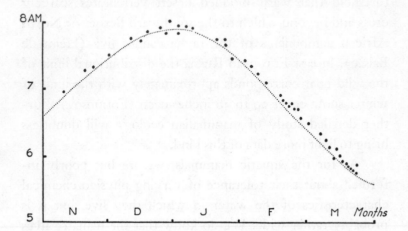

FIG. 92: *Variations in the time at which daily activity begins for the European mole, from November to March, in the vicinity of Rennes, Brittany. Time of sunrise is indicated by the dotted curve. After Godet.*

at twilight. The California ground squirrel will serve as another example. From June to August in Hastings Reserve (California) the squirrels emerge from their burrows between 5.40 and 6 a.m. They carry on their various activities all day long, with maximum intensity always around 8 or 9 a.m. and 4 p.m. They go back underground between 6.40 and 7.30 p.m. These data represent only an average, of course, for other factors, especially temperature and humidity, may modify this timetable. In January the few that do not hibernate come out toward noon to warm themselves in the sun, returning to their burrows by five o'clock at the latest. The strong propensity for sunbathing shown by this species, even in very warm weather, is explained by Linsdale as a method for getting rid of ectoparasites. Twilight and nocturnal species have a contrasting rhythm of activity. The European badger, for example, carefully studied by Neal, does not emerge from its burrow until after sundown, and the time of emergence in summer is later than in autumn or spring. Other factors, such as temperature and periods of full moon, may cause slight variations in this rhythm, but intensity of sunlight remains dominant.

Variations during the month in the intensity of light at night must probably be taken into account, at least in connection with strictly nocturnal species. Harrison observed in the giant forest rat of Malaysia, for example, that the rate of pregnancy showed a bimonthly rhythm that appeared to be in phase with the moon, and which suggested that the greatest number of conceptions occurred near the time of the full moon. Nothing of the kind is found in diurnal rodents of the same region, and Harrison believes that the onset of the period of bright moonlight near the time of full moon has some stimulating effect on conception.

Variation through the year in the length of the days may be even more important, and its effect upon the reproductive period and the molting cycle has already been proved, at least in certain species.

Artificial lengthening of the day can cause the gonads to mature out of season in some mammals. The experiment was performed by Bissonnette on the ferret, from October to March, and he observed an increase in the size of the testes during this period, which is normally the time of testicular involution. Spermatozoa were produced by the experimental animals three months earlier than would ordinarily be the case. In the field vole reduction of the photoperiod from 15 to 9 hours prevents normal reproduction (Baker and Ranson). But many mammals reproduce in the fall rather than in the spring; that is, at a time when the length of day or photoperiod is decreasing regularly. Now, it appears that these species also can react to an experimental change in the photoperiod, and Bissonnette has been able to show that in the goat an artificial reduction in length of day stimulates reproductive activity, whereas an increase is inhibitory. Other evidence in favor of the importance of variation in the length of daily illumination is afforded by the change in the reproductive period experienced by species native to the Northern Hemisphere which are transferred to ecologically comparable regions in the Southern Hemisphere. In Scotland the stag has its rutting period in September and October, but in New Zealand this occurs in March and April; that is, in the austral autumn. The American gray squirrel, introduced into South Africa by Rhodes around 1904, reproduces there in the austral spring and summer (October to January), whereas in North America and in England the reproductive period of the species is from January to July. Factors other than light must be concerned in tropical species, for a seasonal rhythm of testicular activity clearly exists in some forms, such as the flying foxes (*Pteropus*), despite the uniform length of the day in low latitudes.

The influence of variations in the photoperiod on the molting cycle appears equally probable, for certain species at least. This has been discussed above (page 125), and here

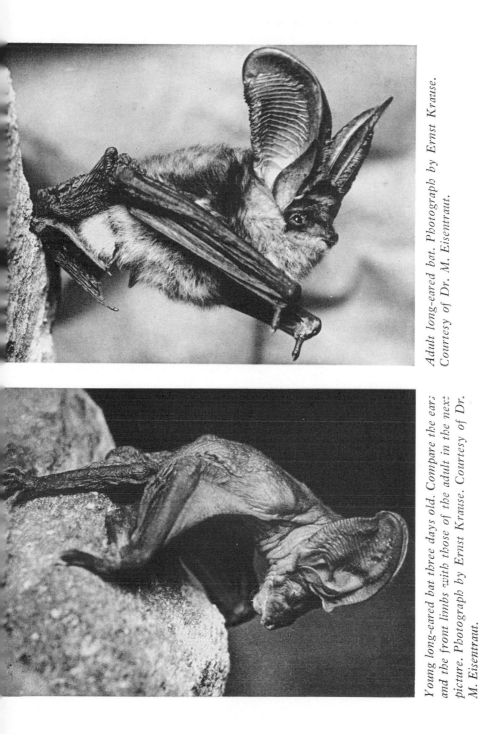

Young long-eared bat three days old. Compare the ears and the front limbs with those of the adult in the next picture. Photograph by Ernst Krause. Courtesy of Dr. M. Eisentraut.

Adult long-eared bat. Photograph by Ernst Krause. Courtesy of Dr. M. Eisentraut.

A harem of Alaska fur seals, Pribilof Islands.
Note the male, the pregnant females, and the few young.
Photography by Dr. Arétas.

we shall only call attention to a few pertinent experiments. Artificial reduction of the photoperiod has been known to bring on an out-of-season molt in two North American Mustelidæ, the Bonaparte weasel and the long-tailed weasel. In the first species the white winter coat followed the brown summer pelage, whereas in the second a light-brown coat spotted with white on the feet was obtained. Artificial lengthening of the day also induced molting in these two species, with a return to the summer coloration. Yet there is great variability from one animal to another in this respect (Bissonnette and Bailey). In the snowshoe hare Lyman has been able to prevent the appearance of the white coat in autumn by exposing the animals to artificial light for 18 hours per day; the same treatment, given in January to animals in winter white, resulted in the appearance of the brown summer coat. It is even possible to keep the hares in dark fur the year round, if the photoperiod is held constantly at 18 hours; but if the illumination is reduced to 9 hours a day, the change to white fur occurs, even when the temperature remains at 21° C.! All these results, along with those of Novikov and Blagodatskaia on the Siberian varying hare (see page 126), are proof of the influence of variations in the daily photoperiod upon the molting cycle, but some species seem to be more sensitive to such changes than others.

ALTITUDE. A good deal is known about the physiological changes produced by altitude (and particularly by artificial reduction in barometric pressure) on man, the dog, and the laboratory rodents. Undoubtedly one of the most important is the increase in the number of red corpuscles in the circulating blood, which adapts the organism to the reduced oxygen pressure that makes all effort distressing to man at high altitudes.

Now, there exist in mountainous regions, and especially on the high plateaus of the Andes and of Central Asia, a number of mammalian species that appear to be remarkably well adapted to these habitats, peculiar as they are. On this account the physiology of these animals is of very special interest, and it seems odd that so few works have been devoted to them.

In 1936 Hall, Dill, and Barron published some observations they made in the Andes on three typical mammals of high altitudes, the llama, the vicuna, and the vizcacha. The first has been domesticated and used as a beast of burden by the natives for thousands of years. The second is a wild species, capable of running at a speed of 30 miles an hour at an altitude of more than 15,000 feet, which these physiologists were privileged to study. Their observations were made on a very tame individual that had been in captivity for some time. As for the vizcachas, the individuals used as standard samples had been captured at an altitude of 12,000 feet.

The researches of Hall and his associates showed that the hemoglobin of these three species has a much greater affinity for oxygen (oxygen capacity) than the hemoglobin in rabbit and sheep blood. This peculiar character, an important advantage for life at high altitudes, would seem to be *hereditary*, since these same authors have also found it in four llamas in the Boston Zoo, three of which were born in that city and the fourth in Hamburg! Furthermore, if we make a comparative study in the sheep and llama of the variation with altitude in the number of red corpuscles per cubic millimeter of blood, we find a great difference between the mammal of the plain and the mammal of the mountain. In the sheep there are 10,530,000 red blood corpuscles per cubic millimeter at sea level and 16,000,000 at 16,050 feet, whereas practically no variation is observable in the llama (11,430,000 at sea level and 11,100,000 at 16,-050 feet).

Is this lack of variation in corpuscle number with altitude in mountain species a fact of general application? It is still too soon to say with certainty, but in support of such a view must be counted Kalabuchov's observation when he transferred to Moscow (altitude 490 feet) twelve long-tailed field mice caught at 5,200 feet in the Caucasus. After seven months at the lower altitude their red-cell count per cubic millimeter had not changed materially, continuing to register between 9,500,000 and 10,600,000.

EDAPHIC FACTORS

THE nature of the soil affects the distribution of mammals in two ways: indirectly, through vegetation whose characteristics depend in large measure upon soil differences, and directly, where fossorial species that spend most of their lives under ground are concerned. We shall mention here only a few examples of the second, or direct, type of soil influence, which has so far been studied only incidentally.

Subterranean rodents and insectivores do not live indiscriminately in any kind of soil, and the difficulties encountered in keeping them in captivity are not all concerned with feeding. They must have proper soil, and the texture of the soil, directly affecting its water and gas content, is possibly more important than its chemical composition.

The observations of Schaerffenberg and of Godet demonstrate the importance of soil aeration in the case of the European mole. This animal cannot live long in captivity if it is confined in wooden boxes containing earth, but it can be kept alive for months if cages of metal screen are used or if the wooden cages are liberally perforated on all sides and filled with fibers of wood. Godet even believes that to provide good aeration is the essential function of the complex system of concentric galleries surrounding the nest. In nature this species invades various biotopes, but a hard and stony soil stops it. Pavlinine's recent marking experiments have shown, for example, that railroad ballast is for this animal a more difficult obstacle to pass than is a stream of water.

Another significant soil factor is humidity. Common voles in France commonly favor clayey, calcareous soils, neither too light nor too heavy and above all not too moist. The Sierra pocket gophers marked by Ingles lived during the summer in meadows where the water table was more than 4.3 feet below ground, exploring the more humid zones only when their nests happened to be located near-by in dryer soil. On the approach of winter the gophers migrated to better-drained land that did not freeze and thus allowed the animals to continue their activities during the less favorable season; the following spring they returned to the meadows. Thus the species carefully avoids damp soils, and a strip of wet ground, even though a narrow one, may form an impassable barrier.

Even for ungulates the soil may constitute an important factor in limiting their geographical distribution. Essential minerals may be insufficient or lacking altogether in some soils, with the result that deficiency diseases cause the rarity or even the extinction of particular species in certain localities. Domesticated cattle furnish good examples of this. When the soil of the region where they are raised is too poor in phosphoric acid and calcium phosphate, disorders due to phosphoric deficiency appear (called aphosphorose), indicated by such symptoms as perversion of the appetite with tendencies toward bone eating, abnormalities in gait, broken bones that are spontaneous or caused by the slightest impact, sexual apathy and disturbances of the œstrus cycle, and so on. Raising stock is practicable in such regions only if the phosphorus content of the soil is artificially increased.

BIOTIC FACTORS

THE relations of mammals with the living environment—the fauna and flora of their habitats—are multifarious; some are secondary, others of dominant influence, but all deserve close study, for they bring us into direct contact with the complex interrelations between the animal and its animal and plant environment.

PHYTOBIOTIC FACTORS. Plants may influence the distribution of mammals in many ways. Obviously, species with a highly specialized vegetable diet cannot occur at all in a given locality unless the particular plant they eat grows there. Koalas without eucalyptus trees are inconceivable, as are giant pandas without bamboo. But such a situation is infrequent, most mammals being rather eclectic in their feeding habits. The white-tailed deer is known, for in-

269

stance, to feed on 614 different plant species in the United States alone (Taylor).

For most mammals, therefore, a continuous supply of plant material, readily available to them at any time of the year, is far more important than the type of vegetation *per se*. The black-tailed deer of western North America provides a good example of the degree to which the plant productivity of different habitats may by itself influence both the animals themselves and their population densities.

Odocoileus hemionus columbianus generally occupies the area lying west of the crests of the Sierra Nevada–Cascade mountain chains, from Santa Barbara County in California to Kodiak Island in Alaska (Taber). Within this range, the deer that occupy areas where snow seldom falls are resident the year round, whereas those that live where snow regularly falls in the winter are migratory. The area in which resident deer are found may be broadly divided into two classes according to their vegetation—the *chaparral* and the *coastal conifer forest*. In the coastal ranges and the Sierra foothills of California, the cool wet winters and hot dry summers favor the establishment of chaparral vegetation where rainfall is moderate. It consists of an association of fire-tolerant shrubs, many of which send up crown sprouts following burning. Chaparral typically forms a closed canopy, so that the understory vegetation is poorly developed. Often associated with chaparral is the oak woodland, which consists of scattered trees with a well-developed herbaceous understory. On the other hand, from northern California to Vancouver Island, the coastal climate, with uniform temperature and heavy rainfall, favors the establishment of the coastal conifer forest. The typical dominant tree is *Pseudotsuga*, but locally other genera are abundant, such as *Sequoia* in the south and *Picea*, *Tsuga*, and *Thuja* in northern areas. This forest is typically closed-canopy, with a poor development of understory vegetation, except at the edges of the openings and along watercourses.

The chaparral provides excellent cover for deer, but it is limited as a source of food. The diet of the deer is composed almost entirely of the leaves and twigs of shrubs, supplemented in some years with acorns. As most chaparral plants are evergreen, their principal growth takes place during a two-month period in the spring. At this time, the foliage is high in crude protein and phosphorus. But during the summer, fall, and winter, the shrubs are almost dormant, and the percentage of crude protein and phosphorus is therefore low. As a result, the resident deer of the chaparral are small animals, the adult male weighing 144 pounds on the average and the adult females 77 pounds. Their reproductive rate is low, only 71 fawns being born per 100 does two years old and older (Taber and Dasmann). The population densities are generally medium, 10 to 20 per square mile.

In the dense, closed-canopy coastal conifer forest, the understory provides most of the food for the deer. Typical forage genera include *Vaccinium*, *Alnus*, *Acer*, *Gaultheria*, *Ribes*, *Sambucus*, *Salix*, and *Rubus*. Shaded by the forest canopy, these plants tend to be low in food value, especially during the winter months. Because of the low quantity and often low quality of the food available to the deer in the mature coastal forest, reproductive rates in these populations, as well as the population density figures (1 to 5 per square mile) appear to be low. But when the coastal forest is burned, or logged, the vegetation of the forest floor responds by increasing dramatically both in quantity and in quality, at least for a few years. As a result, the deer of recently opened coastal forests attain a much higher weight (averaging 167 to 277 pounds for adult males and 103 to 121 pounds for adult females) than those of the chaparral; their reproductive rate is also higher (125 to 140 fawns per 100 does two years old and older), and their population densities reach 40 to 70 per square mile. Even before the white man settled in the area, fire was an important ecological factor in the snow-free coastal forests of that part of northern America. But since the middle of the nineteenth century, fires have been more common and logging, in particular, has become the most important factor in the opening of the forest canopy. The result has been a general increase in the number of these animals during the last decades. In many areas, hunters do not harvest the annual increment and overpopulation results. Then the starvation sequence of lowered reproductive and survival rates ensues, with numerous deaths and damage to the habitat occurring during severe weather.

Much remains to be discovered about the food and cover preferences of the herbivores of the African plains. It is hard to understand, at first sight, how ten to twenty different species of ungulates can live together at the same time and in the same place without entering into competition. Observation of their feeding behavior shows that some of these animals actually exploit, to a certain extent, different types of the plant foods produced by the environment; the black rhinoceros eats thornbushes, the giraffe browses on the foliage of medium-sized acacias, the smaller antelopes graze on young shoots of grass, buffalos eat the coarser grasses, and elephants feed on practically any plant material, from leaves and roots to fruits and coarse grasses. But preferences of the various species may be much more subtle than this. Examining the most recently ingested portion of the stomach contents of topis and blue wildebeests (*Connochaetes taurinus*) that had been grazing together on the short grasses of the Mara district of Kenya, the Talbots found that the topis deliberately chose dry stalks and leaves whereas the blue wildebeests displayed a marked preference for fresh green grass. This preference is so strong that it apparently determines the so-called local migrations of the species. Throughout their study the Talbots observed the Serengeti-Mara wildebeests in, or moving in the direction of, areas where short green grass was available, usually in proximity to surface water, or in areas where it was raining or where rain had fallen within the past twenty-four hours. Since these movements may be up, down, or across the prevailing winds, and they are observed in all seasons and under widely varying conditions of temperature and humidity, the Talbots think it is probable that the primary stimuli for these major herd movements are visual.

These examples show that even slight changes in the vegetation can have far-reaching consequences for the mammalian fauna of an area. Conversely, some mammals play an essential part in the support and evolution of certain plant communities. On the Eurasian steppes, for example, fossorial rodents, such as the boback marmot and the little souslik, work over enormous quantities of earth, bringing it from depths of as much as 15 feet to the surface, where it forms numerous mounds. This earth is quite different in composition from the surface soil. It is richer in mineral salts but is poorer in humus and it is less alkaline, and on it springs up a special vegetation somewhat like that of deserts, which persists until the soil of the mounds has gradually become like the adjoining soil. The xerophytic plants then colonize newly built mounds, and so the cycle continues. In this case the rodents exert a clearly conservative influence, retarding the natural succession of plant formations.

In general the rodents of fossorial habits have a considerable effect, in some regions, upon the evolution of soils. Grinnell has attempted to estimate the amount of earth brought to the surface each year by the pocket gophers of Yosemite National Park, in California, and he arrives at a figure of about 8 tons per acre. Again, Ellison gives an average of 5 tons per acre for the northern pocket gopher in Utah. Formosov also gives large figures for the little souslik of the steppes between the Don and the Volga, estimating the amount of earth collected in mounds on the surface at 100,000 cubic yards per square mile! This means that a very considerable mixing and aeration of the soils has been accomplished. But it all implies some danger to the soils concerned, for under certain conditions such extensive undermining promotes the erosion that sometimes alters the biotope radically.

ZOOBIOTIC FACTORS. We have already referred in passing to the relations between animal species living in the same habitat. And in the next chapter we shall discuss the interrelations between predators and their prey (lynx and snowshoe hare, carnivores and ungulates, etc.), as well as the influence of certain pathogenic organisms on the dynamics of wild populations. We shall therefore do no more here than give some information on the ecological importance of certain blood-sucking insects, on the problem of symbiosis or commensalism, and on the interrelationships between ectoparasites and their hosts.

The blood-sucking insects, in particular the Diptera or two-winged flies, play a very considerable part in the ecology of the ungulates. In analyzing the behavior of red deer in Scotland, Darling lays stress on the role of the Tabanidæ (horseflies and deerflies) as a determining factor in certain seasonal movements. The most dreaded fly (*Hæmatopota pluvialis*) is especially active in bright sunlight on calm, warm days, with maximum activity between the hours of ten and four; this is when it attacks the deer, covering them with bites on face and feet (Darling counted the bites at an average rate of 30 per minute!). These bites are so painful that the deer leave the lowlands and ascend to higher levels in late June, when the flies begin to appear in numbers. Sdobnikov studied the reindeer living at large on the tundras of arctic Russia, and he, too, emphasizes the ecological importance of the Diptera, represented in his case by 9 species of Tabanidæ, 4 Culicidæ (mosquitoes), and some Simuliidæ (black flies); the last are especially partial to the blood-filled young horns of the animals, and when the flies are numerous the horns fail to attain normal size and may even become deformed. Two endoparasitic flies, *Cephenomyia nasalis* and *Œdemagena tarandi,* are also

275

important in reindeer ecology, especially the first, whose larvæ (sometimes numbering a thousand in a single animal!) may bring the host to exhaustion. Several observers in the American Arctic regard mosquito attacks as the determining factor that starts the caribou migrations; this, however, is a doubtful matter.

The blood-sucking Diptera are important for ungulate ecology in regions other than the cold North. As is well known, the African tse-tse fly, carrier of certain protozoan blood-parasites (trypanosomes) that cause animal disease, can prevent the breeding of large mammals in some localities and thus directly modify the habitat in general. Thomas mentions certain parts of Uganda, for example, where the densely populated pasturage was beginning to show the effects of overgrazing and erosion. After the decimation of the cattle by trypanosomiasis, the vegetation recovered and in three years the grass grew a yard high. In the valley of the Kidepo River, along the boundary between the Sudan and Uganda, the stratum of herbaceous plants reached a height of six feet some years after a similar epidemic. Such an alteration of the habitat has, of course, a direct effect on the composition of the fauna with respect to small mammals as well as large ones.

The detailed study of the reciprocal relations between certain species for mutual benefit (called mutualism, symbiosis, or commensalism) should be worth undertaking. But in any case the association of cattle egrets and oxpeckers with the larger ungulates, wild and domesticated, is an established fact. Verheyen has actually seen antelopes, when visited by oxpeckers, stand still, slightly separate their legs, and elevate their tails as if to facilitate the work of these birds.[7] Percival reports that when a rhinoceros is asleep, it is easy to approach it if no oxpeckers are on it but difficult if the birds are there. He adds that they would give the alarm when perched on a rhinoceros but not when they were doing their pecking on cattle. The well-known British ornithologist Moreau, who made a special study of the red-billed oxpecker in East Africa, feels that it is perfectly justifiable in this case to speak of symbiosis.

Another curious case of commensalism is the association, in tropical Africa, of the ratel or honey badger and a bird, the honey guide (*Indicator indicator*). These two vertebrates gain appreciable benefit from their common exploitation of wild bee nests, and Verheyen has recently stated precisely how their association works. The honey guides have the habit of uttering a series of characteristic calls when in the presence of any mammal, even a man; if a ratel hears these calls, it follows the bird and soon discovers the bee tree. What is most remarkable is that the ratel seems evidently capable of evoking the bird's calls by putting itself in plain sight of the bird and whistling softly. But the whole procedure cannot be considered obligatory, for in India the honey badger is quite capable of locating wild bee nests without the aid of a honey guide.

The association between the hippopotamus and a fish (*Labeo velifer*) that nibbles at the abundant organic detritus on the amphibious mammal's hide is not unlike the association between oxpecker birds (Buphagidæ) and big game in the savannas.

[7] The tendency of cattle egrets (*Bubulcus*) to associate themselves with mammals is so strong that Hediger reports seeing them perch, in captivity, on South American capybaras, which are rodents. (See the photograph by Hediger in *Wild Animals in Captivity*, 1950, fig. 26b.)

In certain cases the commensalism is less intimate, as when, for example, it is the burrow of a digging animal that attracts other species living in it. In Europe the burrows of the badger often harbor foxes, rabbits, or rats. In Africa aardvark holes are fancied by wart hogs, porcupines, mongooses, and many other small mammals, and on the high Peruvian plateaus guinea pigs may frequently live in tunnels dug by tuco-tucos.

The role of the many ectoparasites of mammals (fleas, lice, and ticks) as eventual carriers of disease is well known. However, apart from this one aspect the mutual relationships of host and ectoparasite populations have hardly been studied up to now. Yet it appears that a better knowledge of the conditions which favor or prevent the pullulation of these parasites would be well worth the trouble of undertaking such difficult investigations, as they probably have some important ecological implications for the hosts themselves.

Very few wild mammals are completely free of ectoparasites, but the number of them on any one individual varies widely according to the size, age, and state of health of the host, and apparently also according to the time of the year and the size and dispersion of the host populations.

The size of the host animal undoubtedly plays a part in fixing the upper limits of an ectoparasite population. An adult African buffalo killed by Verheyen in the Albert Park played host to 1780 ticks, whereas one of the coyotes studied by Ellis had but 108 fleas on it. In the case of small mammals, it would seem almost impossible for them to harbor as many ectoparasites without becoming seriously ill. However, we must not generalize too quickly. Hopkins found, for example, that small ungulates usually harbor more lice than the large ones.

Age and state of health also seem to be important factors. Young artiodactyls and young primates generally have more lice than adults and healthy animals.

The seasonal changes in the number of ectoparasites in a given host population are very great. But the "peaks" of infestation rarely occur at the same time of the year. For instance, Yeh and Davis have found that the infestation of a rat population in Baltimore by *Xenopsylla cheopis* was at a maximum in summer and autumn, whereas *Nosopsyllus fasciatus* was more abundant in winter and spring.

It is quite possible that the various ectoparasites on the same host enter into interspecific competition. Long ago, Thompson observed an apparent incompatibility between the presence of fleas and the presence of mites or lice on the same rat. These observations have been confirmed by Hopkins, who found that a heavy infestation of mites or lice is usually incompatible with the presence of large numbers of individuals of the other group on the same host specimen. Thus a possible explanation for the absence of lice on bats may be their heavy infestation by mites, fleas, and Diptera.

Another important factor in regulating the size of ectoparasite populations is probably the size and distribution of the host populations themselves. An interesting study by Mohr and Lord shows that among cottontail rabbits in Illinois the size of the flea and tick populations is

279

generally positively related to the size of the populations of their hosts. Furthermore, widely scattered, small habitats support decidedly lower concentrations of ectoparasites than large ones.

The Structure
and Dynamics of
Natural Populations

THE interest of naturalists in the study of wild or natural populations of animals is something comparatively new, for at the beginning of this century very little attention was paid to the structure and dynamics of natural populations, and the difficulties that impeded the study of them seemed insurmountable. Two very different points of view have been influential in bringing about the complete change of opinion which has taken place in our time.

In the first place, the advance of applied zoology has promoted the development of reliable methods of estimating the size of game and rodent populations; without such techniques it would be impossible to check on the efficiency of game-management and pest-control programs.

In the second place, and more recently, theoretical considerations concerning the modes of evolution have given a new impetus to this type of research. As a result of the work of such geneticists as R. A. Fisher, J. B. S. Haldane, and Sewall Wright, population size has emerged as one of the essential factors in evolution. Indeed, as George G. Simpson justly writes, "it is populations, not individuals, that evolve," and when a new characteristic appears by mutation, its chances of spreading through the population vary with the size of that population. Broadly speaking, we may say that in a large population, where mating occurs more or less at random, the chances that a mutation will become established depend first of all on its selective value. On the other hand, in small populations, or in "closed" social groupings within large populations, chance tends to prevail, through genetic drift, which alters gene frequencies in a random or non-directed fashion.

METHODS OF ESTIMATING THE SIZE OF POPULATIONS

TO ascertain the number of any one species living at a given time in a given area is not an easy task. Let it be said at once that none of the methods in current use is rigorously accurate, for all include more or less important sources of error; but the essential point is to be aware of them and to make sure that the technique used is adapted to the case under consideration.

When the country is open enough (tundra, steppe, mountain meadows, prairies, and short-grass savannas) and the animals are of large or medium size, the best way to estimate their numbers is to attempt an actual census, that is, to count all the individuals present in the area under study. This can be done either from the ground or from the air. On the ground, patrols of trained observers "comb" the area at the same time, walking parallel with one another at intervals of, say, 1000 yards. Each observer counts any animal present within 500 yards on either side of him, and the counts of all the patrols are totaled at the end of the day. In this way we have been able to take a census, every two months for two consecutive years, of all the large ungulates living in the 230-square-mile area that forms the western part of the Rwindi-Rutshuru plain, in the Albert National Park, in the Congo (Bourlière and Verschuren). Similar counts can be made from slow, low-flying airplanes or helicopters. The ground to be surveyed is first divided up into small units according to easily recognizable topographical features, such as watercourses, tracks, hills, etc. Then each of these units is inspected by flying up and down it along a series of parallel tracks. The distance between successive tracks depends upon the visibility, the density of animals, and the altitude. In most cases, the observer on either side of the airplane surveys a strip 150 to 400 yards wide, and the altitude maintained is about 400 feet. Large concentrations of animals which cannot be counted accurately in this manner are photographed and the animals later counted from projected slides or paper enlargements. Such was the method used by Stewart and Talbot for their 1961 survey of the Serengeti Plains, in East Africa. Needless to say, the reliability of such counts varies with the experience of the counters and the visibility of the animals, which depends itself upon many factors: height of the grass, density of the cover, time of day, color of the animals, etc. Figures are generally more accurate for large animals than for smaller ones; it is hard to miss an elephant at 500 yards in an open plain, but one can easily overlook a lion lying in a small thicket or even in a clump of grass at 50 yards. On the whole, aerial counts tend to give lower figures than counts made on the ground.

In more closed environments (tree savannas, bush, and forests) and in marshlands, actual censuses cannot be taken and the best approximation is obtained by counting the animals in a sample area, provided this sample is actually chosen at random and surveyed at frequent intervals. The strip-census method is the most often used; it consists of actually counting the number of individuals seen in a given strip through an area, computing the number observed per unit area, and applying this figure to a similar larger area. There are many limitations inherent in such a technique; the track followed by the observer must always be the same and areas where animals are often disturbed by traffic are to be avoided. Consequently, the often used roadside counts cannot in any way be regarded as satisfactory. Furthermore, the width of the counting strip has to take account of the conspicuousness and the flushing distance of the animals to be counted. In the strip censuses we made in the tree savannas of the Albert National Park, for instance, the strip on each side of the track was 300 yards wide for elephants, hippopotami, buffalos, topis, and waterbuck, 150 yards wide for Uganda kobs, bushbuck, wart hogs, giant forest hogs, and large carnivores, and only 5 feet wide for hares. In forest habitats the width of the strip must be reduced considerably.

Obviously, such direct counts are impossible when we want to study small animals and nocturnal animals. In such cases we have to rely on removal methods or capture-recapture techniques.

The most satisfactory but also the most laborious and

costly removal method is the direct capture by hand of all the small mammals present on a certain number of quadrats taken at random in the habitat under study. In the open grasslands of the Garamba National Park, in the Congo, J. Verschuren set up a series of quadrats measuring 50 by 50 yards; then he and his assistants, working from the periphery toward the center, laboriously removed all the vegetation and litter in the area in a single day. All the burrows found in the sample area were excavated and the animals present in them captured. However, this kind of direct removal is possible only in grassy habitats and on suitable soils. In most cases we must rely on "saturation trapping," that is, intensive trapping of a quadrat of, say, one acre for a series of successive nights. The traps are set in a grid, at 50-foot intervals, in a habitat whose vegetation and physiography are uniform. The population estimate may then be made in various ways. The number of animals caught may be cumulatively added to give an estimate when the line levels off; or the number of animals caught per day can be smoothed and extrapolated to zero to give the total for the area. Another graphic method of estimating total population from the results of several consecutive nights of trapping has been developed by Hayne. It consists of plotting the catch per night on a vertical axis against the total number of animals previously removed from the population on a horizontal axis. A straight line is then fitted to the points and extended to the horizontal axis. The value at the point of intersection is the estimate of total population (fig. 93). Unfortunately such techniques have many inherent limitations. The precise area from

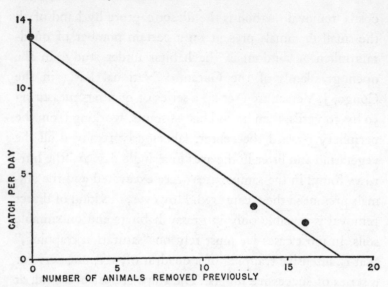

FIG. 93: *Progressive decrease in numbers of adult* Microtus pennsylvanicus *caught per day, as animals were removed from the area at East Lansing, Michigan, June 1948. The slope of the line (−0.71) numerically equals the probability of capture, and indicates that about 7/10 of the animals present at the beginning of a period were trapped during that period. After Hayne (1949).*

which the animals are drawn remains unknown; in all probability it is larger than that of the quadrat. Furthermore, it has been repeatedly demonstrated that once individuals have been removed from a population other individuals tend to move into the area left vacant. Finally, colonial behavior and habitat selection tend to make the distribution of individuals far from random in even a small area.

The capture-recapture method consists of capturing animals in live traps, marking and releasing them, and then recapturing some of them. If we assume that the size of the population remains constant during the period of study, that the sampling and the distribution of the population is random, and that marked and unmarked individuals have an equal chance of being caught, then we can easily estimate the size of the population.

The method depends upon a very simple ratio, first used in connection with wild populations by Petersen, and better known as the Lincoln index. The population (N) is related to the number marked and released (M) in the same way as the total caught at a subsequent time (n) is related to the number of recaptures (m), or:

$$\frac{N}{M} = \frac{n}{m}, \text{ whence: } N = \frac{Mn}{m}$$

Ideally, the marking and releasing should be done at one time (during a single day), and the recapturing as well (on another day). However, frequently so few animals are caught in one day that the method is inapplicable. In these cases it is permissible to group together the captures for a period (a week, for instance) and assume that all were made on the same day. However, the basic assumptions of the capture-recapture method are rarely valid under natural conditions. Even if one is dealing with a small island where immigration and emigration are impossible, during a time of the year (winter, for instance) when births do not occur, one is still faced with the fact that mortality rates are not necessarily the same in the marked

THE *Natural History* OF *Mammals*

and unmarked individuals. In addition, there may be age and sexual differences in the willingness to accept bait and in degree of activity. Further, marked individuals may become trap-shy or, conversely, they may return to live traps time after time, having learned that the traps are ready sources of food. Consequently, the capture-recapture method can be used with confidence only when the behavior and ecology of the species under examination have already been adequately studied. Additional information on the methods of estimating population may be found in the excellent manuals by Davis and Mosby.

THE STUDY OF THE COMPOSITION OF POPULATIONS

TO understand adequately the dynamics and the turnover of natural populations, we must know something about the sex ratios, the age distribution, and the reproductive status of their members.

Usually it is a simple matter to determine the sex of a captive mammal, though there are many exceptions. The long clitoris and the closure of the vaginal opening outside the œstrus period often make the sexing of the mouse and dwarf lemurs very difficult. The same is true of the European mole, while the "scrotal" swelling of the female genitalia of the spotted hyena has given rise to a good deal of wild speculation. In many newborn and sexually immature mammals autopsy may be necessary to ascertain the sex of a given individual. Under field conditions, the sexing of many large mammals is not very difficult owing to the existence of well-developed secondary sexual characteristics (horns, sexual skins, etc.). But this is not so among some groups, such as the zebras, whose scrotums are not very noticeable in wild individuals.

It is generally very difficult to determine the age of mammals, both in captivity and in the wild state. Often the best we can do is to classify the animals into three age groups: the young of the year, yearlings, and adults. This division, crude as it may be, has the advantage of indicating the proportion of reproductive individuals in the total population, a matter of great ecological significance.

In some cases, however, age determination can be made much more precisely. Ungulates whose permanent horns consist of a bony axis covered with a permanent corneous sheath (chamois, ibex, bighorn, etc.) have their age inscribed, so to speak, on their heads. The growth of the horns is retarded or halted during one season of the year, usually a cold or a dry season, resulting in a distinct transverse streak with loosened edges. These "age rings" are generally much less conspicuous than the "ornamental rings" with which they have often been confused in the past. Figure 94, taken from Couturier's monograph, gives an example of the succession of these growth rings on the horns of the chamois. It can be seen that in this species the horns lengthen very rapidly during the first two years and much more slowly thereafter. Thus the rings are far apart near the tip of the horns and often very close together at its base. This is the more usual situation. In the cervids the antlers are regularly shed whole each year and cannot therefore be used for age determination. Furthermore, although older cervids often have larger antlers with more points than the younger individuals, no clear correlation can be made between antler size and age.

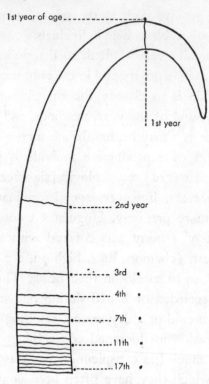

1st year of age

1st year

2nd year

3rd

4th

7th

11th

17th

FIG. 94: *Diagram showing the positions of the age rings on a chamois horn from a male 18 years old. After Couturier.*

Teeth afford very useful age criteria among mammals. The sequence of the loss of the milk dentition and the appearance of the permanent dentition is apparently rather constant within a given population in some species. By observing this sequence in captive animals—or better still, wild animals—of known age, a criterion can be set up for estimating the age of animals of unknown age. The following table, taken from Severinghaus's paper on the Virginia deer, shows the changes that occur in the dental formula from birth to the age of two years:

First week
$$\frac{0-0-0-0}{4-0-0-0}\,^{1}$$

From 1 to 4 weeks
$$\frac{0-0-2-0}{4-0-2-0}$$

From 4 to 10 weeks
$$\frac{0-0-3-0}{4-0-3-0}$$

From 10 weeks to 7 months
$$\frac{0-0-3-1}{4-0-3-1}$$

From 7 months to 13 months
$$\frac{0-0-3-2}{4-0-3-2}$$

From 13 months to 24 months and more
$$\frac{0-0-3-3}{4-0-3-3}$$

For older mammals, in which all the permanent teeth are present, the amount of tooth wear can also be used as a basis for dividing the adult population into various age groups. But this criterion is valid only within the same population, for differences in the principal type of food eaten among various populations of the same species often give rise to differences in tooth wear. The ages of adult hippopotami around Lake Edward have been successfully determined by means of this technique (Longhurst, Bourlière and Verschuren).

In seals and some other mammals (e.g., the moose) the best methods of age determination are based on the structure of the permanent teeth. Variations in the rate of deposition of tooth material are visible as external ridges on the root (Scheffer) and/or as distinct growth layers that

[1] Each dental formula shows the upper teeth above the line and the lower teeth below it. The figures represent the numbers of teeth present on one side of each jaw, in the following order: incisors, canines, premolars, molars.

can be seen in sections of the dentine and cementum (Laws, 1962a). Internal layers are of more value than external annuli because the latter are masked sooner or later by increasing cementum deposition. Dentine layers may cease to be deposited after a number of years owing to closure of the pulp cavity, but they give a valid indication of age for a longer period than the external ridges; in older individuals cementum layers can be used.

The dry weight of the lens of the eye is an excellent indicator of age in the cottontail rabbit, as shown in figure 95, which is based on 92 individuals of known age (Lord). Such a simple method should be tried on many other species. Among the other morphological features which have been used to estimate the age of wild animals, we may mention the earplugs of whales, and the number of

FIG. 95: *The dry-weight, growth-rate curve of the lens of the eye, based on 92 cottontail rabbits of known age. After Lord.*

their corpora albicantia (the scars of the corpora lutea), which are present throughout the life of these large animals (Laws, 1962b), although in smaller mammals they shrink in size and eventually become indistinguishable from the other tissues of the ovaries. Other, less reliable methods have also been proposed—such as the length of the lower row of teeth and the weight of the lower jaw for various voles, and the size and weight of the baculum for many carnivores. These techniques can be correlated with age only in a very rough way and their use is, moreover, restricted to the period of growth.

POPULATION STRUCTURE. As has already been pointed out, a precise knowledge of sex ratios and age distribution is necessary for an understanding of the dynamics of a population. Unfortunately, because of the difficulty of obtaining reliable data, our knowledge in this field is still meager.

SEXUAL COMPOSITION. Most figures concerning the proportions of males and females in natural populations of mammals are unreliable, for those who compiled them frequently did not take into account the fact that the probability of capture is usually not the same for both sexes. This is well exemplified by the European mole. Godfrey and Crowcroft have shown that, even when the sexes are correctly distinguished, trapping during the breeding season can result in an excess of males, which are more active than the females at that time of the year.

Table 8 summarizes some data on the sex ratios of a number of mammals which have been studied recently; in

Table 8. *Percentage of males, at various ages, among populations of wild mammals*

	EMBRYONIC SEX RATIO	SEX RATIO AT BIRTH	IMMATURE SEX RATIO	ADULT SEX RATIO	REFERENCE
MARSUPIALS					
Virginia opposum	43.6 (48)			58.8 (3874)	Petrides, 1949
INSECTIVORES					
Common shrew				49.4 (7196)	Pucek
BATS					
Miniopterus schreibersi		50.0 (1747)			Brosset
Myotis mystacinus				63.5 (2027)	Sluiter et al.
Myotis emarginatus				58.1 (1608)	Bezem et al.
Myotis lucifugus		50.5			Griffin, 1940
Rhinolophus hipposideros				53.2 (1717)	Bezem et al.
PRIMATES					
Alouatta palliata			40.1 (115)	36.3 (368)	Schultz, 1960
Cebus capucinus			53.0 (49)	50.7 (128)	Schultz, 1960
Macaca mulatta				47.4 (1087)	Southwick et al.
LAGOMORPHS					
European wild rabbit	48.5 (394)			43.2 (6917)	Stephens
RODENTS					
Eutamias amoenus				49.4 (694)	Broadbrooks
Deer mouse				57.9 (2147)	Beer et al.
European field vole		50.6			Ranson
Meadow vole				53.0 (1615)	Beer et al.

Muskrat	51.3 (1044)	50.5 (349)		57.8 (4567)	Sather
Brown rat			57.1 (1325)	42.9 (3937)	Schein
Mountain vizcacha				50.9 (9 colonies)	Pearson
CARNIVORES					
Raccoon				58.5 (277)	Petrides, 1950
Mink				70.4 (174)	Petrides, 1950
Urocyon cinereoargentatus				52 (218)	Layne
PINNIPEDS					
Alaska fur seal		51.7 (2172)		53.2 (355)	Scheffer
Bearded seal		51.0 (100)			McLaren
Hawaiian monk seal					Rice
Southern elephant seal		53.2 (5202)			Carrick *et al.*
ARTIODACTYLS					
Hippopotamus	48.6 (35)	54.7 (808)	53.3 (13,046)	47.0 (202)	Longhurst
Mule deer	52.6 (2299)			48.0 (22,362)	Robinette *et al.*; Leopold
European red deer	59.8 (271)	61.5 (117)		35.6	Miller; Darling
Giraffe				71.6 (141)	Bourlière
American bison	52.8 (840)		50.5 (1465)	45.7 (186)	Fuller; McHugh
African buffalo	45.0 (20)			37.1 (5979)	Longhurst; Bourlière
Uganda kob				30.5 (1161)	Bourlière *et al.*
Waterbuck				35.7 (456)	Bourlière *et al.*
Topi				55.0	Bourlière *et al.*
Wildebeest	60.0				Talbot
Impala	42.4 (59)			42.3 (440)	Mossman; Dasmann

most cases the number of specimens examined is given in parentheses after the figures showing the percentage of males in the population. It is readily apparent that the sex ratio in many cases is more or less one male to one female, although some species depart significantly from this rule. There are sometimes decidedly more males than females among newborns and foetuses. "Sexing" the blastocysts before uterine implantation (by making use of the morphological differences between the X and Y chromosomes) in the golden hamster, Lindahl and Sundell found a sex ratio of as high as 64.7 per cent males among the 51 blastocysts they studied only 80 to 90 hours after copulation. Curiously enough, an early predominance of males is often (though not always) found among polygynous ungulates or pinnipeds whose adult populations display a strong predominance of females. Males therefore appear to be more vulnerable to diseases, accidents, and predation; they are also probably more liable to intra-uterine mortality. Chapman and his co-workers have shown that among cows there is a progressive decrease in the proportion of males during the gestation period; among young embryos, 65 per cent were males, while in older ones the sex ratio was at most even. On the other hand, it is well known that inadequate nutrition of the adult female can apparently cause a decline in the number of surviving male offspring; this holds true for mice (Parkes) and mule deer (Robinette *et al.*) as well as for humans (Bernstein). Older mule deer and human mothers also bear significantly fewer male offspring than do younger ones (Robinette *et al.*, Scheinfeld).

AGE COMPOSITION. Knowledge of the age composition of a given population is of prime importance for the geneticist as well as the game manager, as both frequently need to know the size of the effective breeding population. Unfortunately the data pertaining to this aspect of population structure are particularly scanty.

Some of the more accurate observations available concern several of the larger game animals of western Europe and North America. These ungulates breed once a year, are herbivorous, and have a long maximum life span. For these species the data for the construction of life tables are of three kinds: (1) knowledge of the age at death for an adequate and reasonably random sample of the population; (2) knowledge of the fate of individuals of a single cohort, at frequent intervals; and (3) knowledge of the age structure among the living. As Deevey (1947) pointed out, the first and third types of information can be used only if we are prepared to assume that the population is stable in time.

The survival curves of males and females of four species (roe deer, red deer, black-tailed deer, and dall sheep), based on their life tables,[2] are shown in figs. 96 and 97. The data on which these calculations were based were originally published by Evans (1891) for *Cervus elaphus* of the island of Jura off Scotland, by Murie (1944) for *Ovis dalli* of Mount McKinley National Park in Alaska, by Andersen (1953) for Danish *Capreolus capreolus* of the game research station at Kalö, and by Taber and Dasmann (1957) for *Odocoileus hemionus columbianus* of Cali-

[2] The construction of life tables is explained in the manuals by Davis and Mosby.

FIG. 96: *Survival curves for males of five ungulate populations.*

FIG. 97: *Survival curves for females of five ungulate populations.*

fornia. All these populations, except the dall sheep, were hunted.

When we compare these survival curves, we can clearly distinguish some interesting similarities and differences.

1. A very steep initial slope, indicating a high mortality during the first year of life, is found in both sexes of all the species concerned. The actual mortality rate for calves is probably even greater, since their skulls are more easily overlooked and more quickly destroyed than those of adults. This age class is therefore probably underrepresented in most samples.

2. During the second year of life there is little loss among either sex of these species, with two exceptions—among the male roe deer, a species which emigrates, and among the male black-tailed deer of the California chaparral, where some yearlings are killed.

3. During the third year of life there is heavy loss among male and female roe deer and male black-tailed deer from both types of range. The roe deer loss is due to emigration and that of the black-tailed deer to hunting. Among the male dall sheep and the male red deer there is little loss during the third year.

4. From the fourth year onward to old age, the hunted populations (roe deer, black-tailed deer, and red deer) show fairly steep losses among both sexes. The rate of loss tends to decrease in full adulthood in the male black-tailed deer, presumably because these animals, through learning, become less vulnerable to hunting. In the red deer, on the other hand, the rate of loss becomes heavier in full adulthood because of the selection of prime stags by sportsmen.

5. The dall sheep, which is not hunted, shows very little loss from adulthood to nine years of age. If it were not for hunting, the other ungulate populations would probably exhibit survival curves rather similar to those of *Ovis dalli*. However, as Taber and Dasmann (1957) have pointed out, it is doubtful whether they could ever attain as high a survival rate as long as their ranges were fully stocked and starvation was a common cause of death.

6. In old age there tends to be in most cases a steepening of the survival curve; this accelerated loss may be due directly or indirectly to senescence. In dall sheep we know,

for instance, that both the very young and the very old animals were the preferred victims of wolves. Heavily hunted species do not display such a pattern because the high rate of killing permits few individuals to grow old.

On the whole, it seems clear that most of the differences between these various populations of wild ungulates are not inherent in the species, but rather are imposed by environmental conditions. If a roe deer population is fenced in, emigration is prevented but winter mortality due to starvation becomes high. In such a case, it is to be expected that the population dynamics would be different from that found by Andersen in Kalö; the older animals would be competing with younger, physiologically more efficient animals. Similarly, if a herd of dall sheep were not culled by predators, the population would presumably be limited by the food supply and the mortality among prime adults would increase accordingly. Taber and Dasmann are thus correct in pointing out the danger of considering the population dynamics of a given animal under given circumstances to be typical of that species in general.

Other survival curves for wild populations of large mammals are given by Banfield (1955) for the Barren Ground caribou and by Laws (1960, 1962c) for the southern elephant seal and the female fin whale.

All the species of long-lived, slow-breeding mammals considered above show, in most cases, age-specific mortality rates. The situation seems quite different for small mammals, which are both short-lived and fast-breeding. All the species investigated so far appear to have age-constant mortality rates (after very early life).

In his study of the survival rate of wild brown rats on

a Maryland farm, Davis (1948) found, for instance, that no more than about 5 per cent of the rats lived for a year. The same situation applies to the Tulare kangaroo rat; Fitch (1948b) reported that only 4.7 per cent of the *Dipodomys heermani* taken during a four-year live-trapping program had records extending for more than a year. The white-footed mice of the George Reserve in southeastern Michigan likewise have a very low survival rate (Snyder, 1956). With the high rate of mortality of the winter of 1950–51, only one mouse in a thousand could be expected to reach an age of 93 weeks; with the lower rate of the previous winter, 34 mice could be expected to reach 93 weeks, and at least one would probably reach 197 weeks. The mean length of life from birth for such individuals would be 17.4 and 31.5 weeks respectively. Such figures contrast sharply with the potential longevity of six to eight years, recorded in captivity for the same animal.

In the tropical environment of the Malayan jungles, the situation seems to be much the same as in the boreal forests and meadows. Among the 12 species or subspecies of rats studied by Harrison (1956), all had a constant survival rate per month ranging between 0.72 and 0.90, and a mean length of life ranging from 3 to 9 months.

Larger rodents and lagomorphs have a slightly longer mean longevity under natural conditions. Kalabuchov (1933) found that 31.5 per cent of a population of little sousliks in the Caucasus reached the age of one year, and Fitch (1947) reported that 9 to 38 per cent of the cottontail rabbits studied in central California attained an age of one year.

Shrews, on the other hand, appear to be even more

short-lived than rodents. Crowcroft (1956) estimated that the common shrew in England lives at most for only 18 months and that most individuals die before reaching one year of age.

Bats, on the other hand, seem to have a higher survival rate than other mammals of similar size. The life expectancy of a colony of *Myotis mystacinus* ringed by Sluiter and his co-workers (1956) in Holland was 4.4 years, with a maximum life span exceeding 20 years. Bezem *et al.* (1960) also found a life expectancy of 4.5 years and a maximum life span of 20 years for a colony of *Myotis daubentonii*. Such longevities are quite unexpected in such small mammals and are probably related to their very low metabolic rate at rest.

To sum up the available data, it already seems certain that, under natural conditions, small, fast-breeding species, with a low ratio of mean to potential duration of life, show very high, age-constant mortality rates. On the other hand, large, slow-breeding species, with a high ratio of mean to potential duration of life, tend to have age-specific mortality rates. Bats, and perhaps a few other hibernating mammals, form an interesting exception, their life expectancy being much greater than that of continuously active mammals of similar size.

POPULATION DYNAMICS

STABLE populations are probably much less common under natural conditions than the widespread notion of the "balance of nature" would lead us to believe. Small or large oscillations around an "average level" are probably the rule rather than the exception. Every change in the birth rate or the death rate has its repercussions on the density of a population, and factors capable of effecting such changes are very numerous.

FACTORS INFLUENCING THE BIRTH RATE. There are a number of factors capable of affecting the birth rate of wild mammal populations. Moreover, they generally operate in combination with one another, so that it is often impossible to isolate them under natural conditions and we must frequently resort to laboratory experiments under strictly controlled conditions in order to discover them.

The age of the mother has a definite bearing on the number of young produced per unit of time. Figure 98, taken from Höglund's paper on the European varying hare, clearly illustrates this effect. Not only the number of litters per year but also the litter size decreases as the female gets older. The most productive period lies therefore between the ages of 2 and 7 years. Leslie and Ranson have similarly found that the fertility of female field voles raised under optimum conditions is highest between the ages of 12 and 50 weeks. In the Levant vole too, the fertility of the females is at its height between the ages of 150 and 450 days. The same phenomenon apparently occurs also in large ungulates. McHugh has found, for instance, that the incidence of pregnancy declines gradually in the American bison after the age of 12 years, and markedly after 24 years, as shown by the following figures.

AGE OF COW	SIZE OF SAMPLE	PER CENT PREGNANT
2–12 years	70	87
15–18 years	22	77
19–24 years	19	58
25–35 years	14	21

FIG. 98: *Age variation in the litter size (middle curve), the average number of young per female (top curve), and the mean number of litters per year per female (lower curve) in captive European varying hare. After Höglund.*

Nutrition of the female is another factor which can greatly influence the age of puberty, the frequency of birth, the size of the litters produced, and, as already noted, the sex ratio of embryos retained to parturition. Bodenheimer has, for example, compared the number of young produced by female Levant voles kept on different diets during the same length of time (1000 days). Adult females maintained on wheat, barley, and carrots averaged 75 young, while those maintained on carrots alone averaged only 18 young. Moreover, certain food plants may have a peculiarly powerful influence upon the fertility of some small mammals. As long ago as 1934 the Friedmans demonstrated the presence in certain plants (alfalfa, corn, and oats) of a gonadotropic substance that is active in the rabbit, but not in the laboratory rat. Mendelssohn has also been able to increase the summer fertility of captive Levant voles by adding hempseeds to their diet. It is known that severe shortages of food can drastically alter the reproductive cycle of many mammals under natural conditions. Peterson has even reported that the musk ox may not reproduce at all after a very hard winter.

A third factor known to influence birth rates, at least among short-lived, fast-breeding mammals, is population density. Crowcroft and Rowe (1957) established four confined colonies of wild house mice (*Mus musculus*) and provided them with a constant excess of food and water. They started each of these colonies with one male and two females, and allowed the four populations to grow for 18 months, undisturbed by human interference. Each population varied in their rate of increase but reached, at the end of the experiment, a comparable "ceiling." Here the main factor that controlled the size of the populations was the low fecundity of females. Many of the adult females had inactive ovaries and, in one colony, reproduction even ceased entirely after 10 months.

Another example of the influence of population density on fertility is afforded by Kalela's observations on the natural reproductive rate of the vole *Clethrionomys rufocanus* in Finnish Lapland. Here the principal inverse density effect was found in the proportion of young animals attaining sexual maturity and breeding in the summer in which they were born. In 1954, when the season started with a low population, all or almost all of the early-born juveniles of both sexes became mature and bred before the season was out. In 1955, the year of high population, the great majority of young males remained immature, though a considerable proportion of the females became fecund. In one special area, however, where the density was about twice as high as anywhere else in 1955, practically all the young females also failed to breed. In 1956, after a high mortality rate during the previous winter, when the population was even lower than in 1954, the majority of early-born young of both sexes once again became mature and bred in the later part of the summer. Kalela remarks that in this case the regulation of fecundity was, again, not due directly or indirectly to a shortage of summer food, which remained abundant, but to intraspecific intolerance arising from increasing numbers.

The local, seasonal, and year-to-year variations in the age composition of the female population, the abundance and composition of the available types of food, and the population density are sufficient in themselves to account for the frequent differences in fecundity rate so frequently observed between different populations of the same species. But there are probably other, unknown factors which must be taken into consideration. Lord has, for instance, recently found a statistically significant positive correlation between litter size and geographical latitude among six groups of closely related, non-hibernating prey mammals of North America (rabbits, tree squirrels, meadow voles, chipmunks, deer mice, and shrews). On the other hand, two groups of hibernating, fossorial prey species (ground squirrels and pocket gophers) and all the predators with the possible exception of the foxes, showed no relation at all between litter size and latitude. The severity of the winter weather in the higher latitudes has probably been a selective force for larger litters in vegetarian species which are active all the year round. That heredity has to be taken into consideration is also suggested by the findings of Roderick and Storer, who have discovered a significant correlation of $+0.69$ between the mean life span of the dams and the mean size of their litters in 12 inbred strains of laboratory mice.

FACTORS INFLUENCING THE MORTALITY RATE. Many small mammals are endowed with noteworthy powers of reproduction. The young female common voles, which continue to suckle until the seventeenth day after birth, already show a perforated vagina from the eleventh day on and are mated by older males from the thirteenth day on. Correspondingly, litters may be dropped by females from the age of 33 days. Furthermore, under optimal conditions postpartum mating is usual, so that one litter can follow another every 20 days (Frank, 1957). Under these conditions a single female has been able to produce as many as 33 litters within her lifetime, amounting to a total of 127 young. According to Bailey, the female meadow vole can reproduce from the age of 25 days and have up to 17 litters of 6 to 8 young in one year. These few figures give some idea of the enormous reproductive potential of certain small mammals and bring home to us the importance of the mortality factors that are its counterbalance in nature.

These factors may be broadly divided into two main categories: those that depend upon density of population and those that are independent of it. The first category (disease, predation, intraspecific competition) is of especial ecological importance, for on it depends the maintenance of the population at a more or less constant level.

The diseases of free-living mammals are numerous, as shown by McDiarmid's recent study, but under normal conditions the percentage of diseased individuals in a population is generally very low. Elton, Ford, and Baker, for instance, made an extensive investigation of the health and parasites of a natural population of long-tailed field mice near Oxford. They obtained the following figures for the organs more commonly affected.

	NUMBER EXAMINED	NUMBER DISEASED	PERCENTAGE DISEASED
Blood cultures	468	0	0
Liver	989	25	2.6
Lungs	475	2	0.4
Digestive tract	719	2	0.3
Spleen	719	1	0.1
Skin of legs (mite scab)	924	102	11.1
Skin (various lesions)	1156	1	0.1

From this table it is evident that the population as a whole was very healthy, although the occurrence of 41 species of parasites (bacteria and viruses not included) has been reported in this species.

From time to time, however, extremely violent epidemics occur, and these may entail the death of a great many individuals. For example, Villa discovered in Mexico a cave whose floor was completely covered with a continuous carpet of dead bats (*Mormoops megalophylla*); the number of bodies was estimated to be about 100,000 and no survivors were found. In a nearby abandoned mine, many more dead bats were found, only a few surviving. In 1955 most of the 300 crabeater seals wintering on the sea ice of the Crown Prince Gustav Channel in Antarctica died from a contagious disease (probably a virus infection) whose effect was no doubt increased by crowding and partial starvation (Laws and Taylor). The average mortality rate was 85 per cent, but in some places the figure was 97 per cent. Rabies occurs in carnivores (wolves, coyotes), Bang's disease or infectious abortion is found in ungulates, tularemia, salmonellosis, and plague decimate rodents, and so on. Some diseases accidentally or deliberately introduced by man have, at times, almost eradicated certain species from certain environments. Such was the effect of the great epidemic of bovine plague that began in Egypt in 1885 and spread progressively toward the south (Somaliland, 1889; the Congo and Nyasaland, 1892; Zambezi, 1896) to reach the Cape in 1897. It crossed the African continent from north to south in about ten years and killed several hundred thousand buffalos and antelopes, in addition to millions of cattle (Spinage). Following the introduction of myxomatosis into France in 1952, the epidemic spread rapidly all over western Europe, killing in most cases over 99 per cent of the European wild rabbit populations (Bourlière *et al.*, 1956; Thomson and Worden). However, complete extermination of the species seldom occurred, although the population level in most countries is now much lower than before the outbreak and attenuated strains of the virus still kill a number of animals every year.

Besides infectious diseases, the so-called "degenerative" diseases also occur in natural populations of wild mammals, especially among long-lived species. Approximately 75 per cent of the 67 adult baboons studied in Kenya by McGill and his co-workers had some degree of aortic lesions. Marked chronic arthritis has been found in 55 per cent of the skeletons of old wild gibbons examined by Schultz (1961). Whereas dental caries is extremely rare in wild Panama howler monkeys, it was found by the same primatologist in 8 per cent of the adult *Cebus capucinus* and in 10 per cent of the adult red spider monkeys. Nothing is known of the incidence of the various types of cancer among populations of wild mammals.

That accidents are not at all rare in the life of certain arboreal species is proved by the many more or less well-repaired fractures found in every large series of skeletons of wild monkeys and apes. Among 233 wild gibbons, Schultz (1961) encountered healed fractures in only a few older juveniles, but in 28 per cent of the fully grown adults and in 50 per cent of the oldest adults, some of which had as many as seven repaired fractures. Thus the frequency of fractures (and therefore of accidents), as of diseases of bones and teeth, increases markedly with age.

The exact part played by predation in the dynamics of natural populations of mammals remains to be determined. Most of the older naturalists believed that predators had an essential role in holding certain populations of very prolific species at a constant level. As a matter of fact, this does not seem to be true in many cases. The barn owl, for example, is the chief predator on the Levant vole in

Palestine, and the remains of one or sometimes two individuals of this species are found in one regurgitated pellet out of two. Now, an individual owl "exploits," in that part of the Mediterranean area, a hunting terrain of more than 9 square miles on the average around its nest— that is, an area supporting at least 25,000 voles; as one hardly finds more than 600 pellets under each nest, it is therefore probable that the predation pressure of the owl on these voles is very slight. Consequently most modern ecologists, such as Bodenheimer, Elton, and Errington, agree in regarding predation as a mortality factor of secondary importance. There are nevertheless exceptions to this "rule." McCabe and Blanchard have noted the spectacular destruction of local populations of deer mice by a series of weasel raids, and Pitelka (1957) regarded predation as the chief factor which brought about the decline during the microtine cycles he observed in Alaska.

Furthermore, predation may be a much more important factor in controlling population size among slow-breeding ungulates than among prolific rodents. Thus the Talbots have found that large carnivores were responsible for the death of about 45 per cent of the yearling wildebeests they studied in the Serengeti-Mara plains. In Sweden, 15 per cent of the 1031 roe deer found dead in the wild and studied by Borg had also been killed by predators.

Another important cause of death, at least in small mammals, is intraspecific competition, which leads, in addition to a decline in reproduction, to an increase in mortality, especially among young animals. A good example of this phenomenon is shown in fig. 99, which summarizes the results of a recent experiment made by Christian (1959).

311

FIG. 99: *Increasing litter mortality with increasing population size in a confined experimental population of house mice. The vertical lines on the left of the shaded areas represent the number of young born and the lines on the right the number of those which are weaned. The increasingly greater slopes of the lines across the tops of the shaded areas show the increasing litter mortality as population size becomes greater. After Christian.*

Several pairs of house mice were introduced into a large cage having 42 square feet of floor space. Food, water, nests, and shredded-paper nesting material were provided in excess of usage and were well distributed throughout the cage. The population was allowed to grow without interference and censuses were made regularly. When the population growth had essentially ceased, autopsies were performed on all the mice and their controls. (The controls were of the same stock but had been kept as segregated pairs.) The data from the censuses showed that the births per female and infant survival (to weaning) decreased approximately linearly as the logarithm of the population size increased. When the population approached its upper limit, very few young mice were surviving. Those still alive had been weaned too soon and appeared grossly stunted and in very poor condition. The stomachs of nestlings contained very little or no milk, even though observation had shown that there was neither nest destruction nor interference with nursing by other mice to account for these changes. It was found at autopsy that antepartum losses accounted for a reduction of at least 22 per cent in the number of viable embryos as compared with the figure for the control group. In the same period of time, adrenal weight increased approximately 25 per cent in the male mice and 15 per cent in the females in the large populations. The reproductive organs of the adult males were also significantly lighter than those of the control group and spermatogenesis had been partially suppressed. A similar experiment made with a freely growing population of meadow voles yielded essentially similar results, but the maximum population size was considerably less. Other experiments made by Brown, Strecker and Emlen, and Southwick have similarly shown that the growth of confined populations of mice can be self-limited in spite of the abundance of food and other necessities. These results suggest that there is a physiological feed-back system actuated by social competition, which regulates population growth by a progressive suppression of reproduction and infant survival, the latter probably mainly by suppressing lactation.

It is not surprising, then, that the juvenile mortality rate of many small, prolific mammals is so high under natural conditions—88 per cent, for instance, during the first *month* of life was found in a meadow vole population (Getz). On the whole, the smaller and the more prolific a mammal, the greater is its juvenile mortality rate. There are, nevertheless, some interesting exceptions. Even large mammals can have a very high juvenile mortality rate. Among the wildebeests of the Serengeti-Mara area, the Talbots found a first-year mortality rate of the order of 85 per cent, and Scheffer estimated the cumulative natural mortality rate of the Alaska fur seal at 72 per cent up to the beginning of the second year of life. On the other hand, Sluiter *et al.* calculated a mortality rate between birth and the following January of only 21 per cent in the population of whiskered bats they studied in Holland.

Adult annual mortality rates are much lower. The lowest are found in bats (about 20 per cent for *Myotis mystacinus*, Sluiter *et al.*) and in unhunted populations of large ungulates (from 3 to 6 per cent for the African elephant, Bourlière and Verschuren, Buss and Brooks).

POPULATION FLUCTUATIONS. No natural populations remain stable for a long time. Seasonal fluctuations in population densities are the rule in most environments, the more so when we are dealing with species that have high breeding potentials and marked reproductive seasons. In addition to these short-term fluctuations, many mammals show definite variations in population density over a period of years; when the peaks and low points are regularly placed, these multiannual fluctuations are called cycles (fig. 100).

One of the best-known, but until recently least-understood, examples of such multiannual fluctuations is

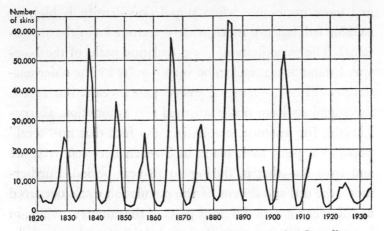

FIG. 100: *Fluctuations in the abundance of the Canadian lynx in the Northern Department of the Hudson Bay Company, from 1821 to 1934. After Elton and Nicholson.*

that of the Norway lemmings. These solitary microtines inhabit the mountains and plateaus of Scandinavia and the Kola Peninsula. Some of their morphological characteristics—the massive "body build," the thick, long, waterproof coat, the broad snout, and the strong feet—make them well adapted to the harsh conditions of arctic life. Active all the year round, they feed mainly on arctic sedges and mosses, in winter digging under the snow to get their food. In the spring they individually undertake local migrations from the heaths in the "lichen belt" of the mountains to lower altitudes, down to the "conifer belt," and return to the mountains during the autumn. Apparently reproduction takes place at any time of the year, even in winter under the snow (Franck, 1962; Curry-Lindahl). These seasonal shifts take place regularly, irrespective of the population density; they are less conspicuous when the population is small or the environment is rich in food resources (at lower altitudes), and more noticeable when population density is high or suitable habitats are more widely scattered (in the mountains). The periodicity of the population peaks of the Norway lemmings was said to be very regular by the older naturalists (Elton), occurring every 3 to 4 years. But recent investigations have not confirmed this assumption. Curry-Lindahl, for instance, emphasizes the fact that no "total" population peak took place in Sweden between 1941–42 and 1959–60—that is, during an 18-year period. Furthermore, the ups and downs of the population cycle occurred at different times in different parts of the country: when, in 1959–60, there was a population peak in central and southern Swedish Lapland, a decline had already set in in the southernmost part of the mountain range. The situation in Alaska, as described by Pitelka, is apparently very similar. The cyclic high in *Lemmus* near Barrow in 1956 was found to extend along the coast only for about 200 miles and inland to distances of no more than 15–50 miles. There was no indication that a similar cycle occurred elsewhere on the arctic Alaskan slope during the same period.

Similar "cyclic" fluctuations are known to occur among populations of many microtines, including the Levant vole in the Middle East (Bodenheimer) and *Microtus brandti* in Mongolia (Dawaa), as well as among American snowshoe hares (MacLulich) and a number of arctic and subarctic carnivores (Elton and Nicholson). Here again the periodicity of the peaks is probably not so regular as is commonly thought. In Mount McKinley National Park, Adolph Murie did not notice any lynx peak between 1927 and 1954, although the rabbits in the area "pyramided" about every ten years.

As shown in fig. 101, increases in carnivore populations follow closely upon increases among the herbivores that are their prey. American and European arctic foxes, which prey mainly on lemmings, show multiannual fluctuations which parallel those of their prey, whereas the foxes of western Greenland, which live on hares, ptarmigan, and

FIG. 101: *The relationship between "good" years in various species of Canadian mammals. After Butler.*

fish in the absence of lemmings, do not show any cyclic fluctuation (Braestrup).

The duration of the interval between consecutive peaks varies with the size and fecundity of the animals. Small, prolific microtines have a short periodicity, 3 to 5 years as a rule. For species of larger size and lower fecundity the intervals are larger, 9 to 11 years, as in the snowshoe hare, the muskrat, and most carnivores.

From the preceding discussion, it is readily apparent that marked multiannual population fluctuations occur mainly in the arctic, in the mountains, and in the steppes and sub-desertic areas—that is, in relatively simple biotic communities. In other areas the richness and complexity of the animal communities seem to act as a buffer against such strong fluctuations in population density. Even in the

Alaskan tundra, Pitelka has noticed that whenever more than one species of lemming was present in a given area, competition apparently acted to keep the size of the populations down and hence to reduce the likelihood of strong fluctuations.

At present there is no general agreement concerning the causes of these multiannual fluctuations. Probably there are many of them. Any temporary increase in the carrying capacity of the environment due to an improvement in climatic conditions or to decreased interspecific competition favors a rise in population levels. On the other hand, epidemics and increases in predation pressure result in lower densities. But the cyclic character, if any, of the multiannual fluctuations can hardly be explained by such more or less random causes. The possibility of a feed-back regulation of population size through socially induced mortality, which we noted earlier, offers a much more attractive alternative.

THE ROLE OF MAMMALS IN TERRESTRIAL BIOTIC COMMUNITIES

IN most of the present-day natural environments, mammals, among all the vertebrates, are the principal consumers of food. This was probably even more true during the Pleistocene era, when most of the mammalian faunas of the world were far more varied than now. It is therefore important to evaluate the size of the mammalian consuming biomass in the various terrestrial habitats, and to try to estimate its annual productivity. The more so, in view of the fact that wild mammals appear in many cases to utilize the plant resources of their environment far more efficiently than do their domestic relatives.

Unfortunately, reliable figures are scarce, but the few we have are very suggestive. In the "primeval forest" of the Pol'ana Mountains in Slovakia, one of the few remaining parcels of the mixed woods which once covered the whole of Central Europe before Neolithic times, Turcek has found the following biomasses (in kilograms per square kilometer):

	BIRDS (74 species)	MAMMALS (28 species)
Herbivores	73.4	503.3
Insectivores	22.7	14.1
Omnivores	14.2	125.4
Carnivores	6.3	17.6
TOTAL	116.6 kg/km²	660.4 kg/km²

Unfortunately, we lack comparable data for other environments, but the following figures, restricted to the dominant group of plant consumers, the ungulates, give at

HABITAT	UNGULATE BIOMASS (in kg per square km)	NUMBER OF SPECIES PRESENT	AREA
Sand desert	5–20	1	Mauretania
Sahellian steppe	80	4	Chad
Steppes of southern Russia	350	1	U.S.S.R.
Arctic tundra	800	1	Canada
North American prairie	3,500	6	Montana
Open mopane wood- land	4,400	15	Southern Rhodesia
Open savanna	4,700	15	Tanganyika
Forest-savanna mosaic	>5,800	>5	Southern Kivu
Acacia savanna	>12,200	>12	Tanganyika
Masai steppe	13,200	18	Kenya
Open plains, with thickets	18,800	11	Western Uganda
Open plains, with thickets	23,500	11	Northern Kivu

least an idea of the magnitude of the total biomass in some open habitats (Bourlière, 1962).

If we add to these figures the (small) biomasses of insectivores, bats, rodents, carnivores, and non-human primates, we can see that the over-all mammalian biomass is, in most cases, incomparably larger than that of the birds, reptiles, or amphibians which share the same environments. Among vertebrates, fishes are the only ones to reach similar figures—but in an entirely different type of environment. In every way mammals have become the dominant terrestrial class in the animal kingdom.

Appendix

SOME readers have suggested that a discussion of certain eco-physiological problems would make *The Natural History of Mammals* a more useful book. However, I have decided to place this material at the end of the book rather than incorporate it into the various chapters, to avoid overloading and perhaps diminishing the clarity of the text. This appendix by no means purports to deal exhaustively with the problems discussed; it simply summarizes briefly the points I have felt to be of particular interest to the field worker.

MAMMALIAN PERCEPTION

MAN has a natural tendency to think that the perceptible world of his mammalian relatives is the same as his own, that a shrew or a whale, a bat or a monkey, perceives its environment in much the same way as he does. Actually nothing is further from the truth. Although very few species have been adequately studied from the point of view of perception, we are now quite certain that to most mammals the outer world looks much different from the way it does to us.

VISION

THE mammalian eye exhibits a profuse adaptive radiation paralleling that of the group itself. It has had to work under a wide range of conditions—in the brightest sunlight and in the faintest moonlight, in the air and under water. On the whole, it has been able to cope with all of these situations. Only in complete and permanent darkness has it given up, as shown by

321

the marsupial mole (*Notoryctes*), the true moles (Talpidæ), the golden moles (Chrysochloridæ), and three rodent groups, the Spalacidæ, the Bathyergidæ, and the "mole" lemming *Ellobius*. Consequently, the eyes of mammals show a wide range of adaptation to the conditions under which the animals live, and rather closely related species living under different conditions may well have quite different vision.

VISUAL ACUITY. The angular distance that must separate two parallel lines before they can be seen individually (the minimum separabile) has been determined experimentally for a number of species.

	VISUAL ANGLE (in minutes)
Man, adult	0.44–0.83
Man, child	0.62
Chimpanzee	0.47
Rhesus monkey	0.67
Capuchin monkey	0.95
Cat	5.5
American opossum	11.0
Albino rat	52.0

There is, thus, a striking difference in visual acuity between the diurnal primates and the few nocturnal mammals so far investigated. Actually this difference is apparently very general. Animals predominantly active by day seem on the whole to be keen-sighted, whereas most nocturnal species do not have sharp vision. A high visual acuity is brought about both by a relatively large eye with long lens-retina distance and by an increase in the relative number of cones. This presumably results in a greater resolving power of the retina. Ground squirrels and prairie dogs, which have extremely sharp eyes, have only cones in their retinae. Some monkeys (marmosets and mangabeys) have many more cones than we do.

The eyes of diurnal animals employ a curious device for

increasing visual acuity, namely, an intra-ocular color filter which absorbs at the blue end of the spectrum and thereby reduces chromatic aberration at the retinal surface. Red oil droplets occur in the cones of certain diurnal marsupials (*Macropus*) and some insectivores; man and most Sciuridæ possess a yellowish lens; and in ground squirrels and prairie dogs the lens is almost orange.

On the other hand, the eyes of nocturnal mammals have a great sensitivity to light due to a preponderance of rods in their retinae, which in turn makes for low visual acuity. The hedgehog, the guinea pig, armadillos, seals, most prosimians, and the owl monkey (*Aotus*) have cone-free retinae; whales, rats, and most nocturnal rodents have only a few cones. However, if the vision of a nocturnal animal makes more use of the length of the rods rather than their diameters, the animal may be able to obtain good resolving power in bright light, provided it has a means of greatly reducing the sensitivity of its eyes under these conditions. This is the role of the slit-shaped pupil (vertical or horizontal) found in many species that are active mainly at night. A device for increasing the sensitivity of the eye in nocturnal animals is the *tapetum lucidum*, a layer of the choroid which causes light penetrating the retina to be reflected back through the visual cells. While this device increases sensitivity, it simultaneously decreases acuity. This reflected light is responsible for the "eyeshine" commonly seen in nocturnal mammals. It must nevertheless be pointed out that not all animals which exhibit eyeshine possess a definite *tapetum*. Choroidal *tapeta* have been found only in a few marsupials (*Dasyurus, Thylacinus*), a single rodent (*Agouti paca*), the carnivores, the seals, the ungulates, the whales, some prosimians, and the owl monkey (*Aotus*).

COLOR VISION. It is not easy to demonstrate that a mammal can discriminate between two color stimuli on the qualitative basis of hue rather than on the quantitative basis of brightness.

Most techniques used by experimenters do not take full account of this distinction and many experimental results are therefore worthless.

Nevertheless, on the basis of the most careful experiments, it seems quite clear that color vision is by no means widespread among mammals, as it is in fishes, reptiles, and birds. It has been established with certainty only for some primates: the chimpanzee, the baboon, the pig-tailed macaque, the rhesus monkey, one mangabey, and the marmoset. The Cebidæ (at least the squirrel monkey, the capuchin monkey, and the spider monkey) can successfully discriminate yellow-green, green, and blue color combinations, but they show deficiencies in the long-wavelength end of the spectrum (Miles). The New World monkeys therefore may have a two-color visual system of the red-blind type, whereas Old World monkeys and apes have a trichromatic system like our own. The few prosimians as yet investigated have yielded only negative results.

For ungulates, the experimental evidence is still controversial. According to Backhaus, the giraffe and the European red deer have color vision, but the nilgai (*Boselaphus tragocamelus*) does not discriminate blue and green from grays of equal brightness. The Indian elephant, on the other hand, has only the most rudimentary color vision, if any (Rensch and Altevogt).

Among carnivores the Mustelidæ that have been carefully studied, the raccoon, and the domestic cat show no evidence of having color vision. For the dog, form and, to a lesser extent, brightness are the important qualities in visual stimuli. Whatever weakly chromatic sensations the dog's cones may afford are rather unsaturated and greatly diluted, with "grayness" stemming from the superabundant rods. To any such semi-nocturnal, rod-rich animal, the richest of spectral lights could at best appear only as delicate pastel tints of uncertain identity (Walls).

For the laboratory rat, the house mouse, the long-tailed

field mouse, the common red-backed vole, the porcupine, and probably all nocturnal rodents, the great weight of evidence is negative. The only rodent with full color vision is the European souslik, whose retina contains only cones; this animal nevertheless displays little interest in colors (Bonaventure).

The hedgehog and the opossum *Didelphis paraguayensis* probably have no color vision at all.

The almost universal color blindness of mammals makes it easier to understand the dullness of their coats, as opposed to the brightness of many fishes, reptiles, and birds. There is no need for an animal to display a bright coat if his social partners do not perceive any hue. It is to be noted that the mammals whose faces, fur, and sexual skins are brightly colored are precisely those whose color vision is similar to man's, namely, the Old World monkeys. In the squirrel family, where the retinae are almost pure-cone, we also find brightly colored animals.

ACCOMMODATION. In mammals the focusing of images is brought about by a change in the curvature of the lens. In order to focus on near objects, the curvature is increased. This is accomplished by relaxing, through muscular effort, a tension which normally exists in the fibers of the suspensory ligaments of the lens. The extent of accommodation may range up to 4 diopters; however, it is usually much less, and sometimes amounts to zero. Among land mammals the ciliary muscle is well developed only in primates, carnivores, and ungulates. In domestic ungulates, this muscle may accomplish nothing, on account of the great size of the lens and the relative weakness of the capsule. Thus the horse, the sheep, and the pig have no accommodation. In many small, large-lensed mammals (e.g., mice) the ciliary muscle consists of but a few fibers, or is even lacking entirely. Some species have interesting substitutes for accommodation. In flying foxes (*Pteropus*) the choroid is beset with innumerable conical eminences which deform the visual-cell layer and therefore place the visual receptors at many different levels. Thus no matter how near or far an object may be, its image falls sharply upon a set of rods standing at a corresponding level on the sides of the choroidal ridges. Mammals which have a single or multiple pin-hole pupil or a structure which produces the effect of one (e.g., a slit pupil lying parallel to an astigmatic axis, as in seals) make use of another substitute, namely, the stenopaic aperture, which produces a fairly sharp image regardless of the distance between the object and the retina. Another substitute for accommodation consists of tilting the retinal surface relative to the visual axis of the eye, whereby objects at various distances can be received in sharp focus. This method is used by the horse, which has no power of accommodation and whose retina is progressively farther from the lens superiorly than it is inferiorly. The animal apparently has only to tilt the eye slightly up or down to receive a sharp retinal image of any object over a considerable distance.

VISUAL ANGLES AND VISUAL FIELD. Most mammals must rely on vision for judging the distance and direction of objects that are beyond the reach of the other senses. However, the volume of space visible to an animal depends on several factors.

The first is the visual angle, in various meridians, of each eye. This angle is surprisingly uniform among mammals, being rarely much greater or much less than 170°. The eye of a sperm whale sees through 125°, a human eye through 150°, and a cat's eye through 200°.

The second factor is the position of the eyes in the head and the ratio of binocular field to total visual field. Binocular (stereoscopic) vision is essential for estimating distances correctly and is therefore of the utmost importance for predators and arboreal mammals which must continually leap from branch to branch. Actually, by and large there is a good correlation between the position of the eyes in mammals and their behavior. Hunters tend toward frontality, whereas the hunted tend to retain laterality of eye position so as to be able to detect an enemy coming from any direction. The width of the binocular field ranges from 140° (in man, apes, and monkeys) to 10° to 40° in lagomorphs and rodents. Intermediate values are found in cats and prosimians (120°), ungulates, Mustelidæ, and Viverridæ (60° to 80°). The bottlenosed whale, the sperm whale, and the Mysticeti (baleen whales) have no stereoscopic vision whatever. Of course, the binocular field of any mammal is narrower above and below than it is straight ahead. Moreover, some animals (e.g., the ungulates) have broad, horizontally oblong pupils which extend the visual field somewhat in the horizontal meridian and hence help to enlarge the binocular field.

The volume of space perceived by an animal's eyes is also influenced by the capacity for reflex and voluntary movements and the location of the area of high resolving power, namely, the *area centralis* or fovea, if one is present. In mammals, the two eyes are never independent but always work in conjunction. This is associated with the fact that most mammals examine objects only binocularly. When the eyes are placed laterally, as in the rabbits, there is usually no *area centralis* and no spontaneous movements at all. Spontaneous eye mobility is greatest in the higher primates, which are the only mammals that possess a fovea. It is fairly well developed in the larger carnivores, but in the ungulates it is far less conspicuous. In binocular vision, whenever the eyes accommodate for a particular distance, they also converge in such a way that the two lines of sight are aimed at a common point. In looking from one object to another which is at a different distance, the extent of convergence either increases or decreases. This amount of convergence, evaluated unconsciously via kinesthetic reception from the internal rectus muscles, is of great help in judging distance.

HEARING

AUDIOGRAMS of human hearing show maximum sensitivity in the range from 800 to 2500 cycles per second with an upper limit around 16,000. The audiograms for other mammals investigated so far, although not always obtained with sufficiently pure tones, have in general a pattern similar to that for man, but with somewhat higher thresholds and often indications of hearing at higher frequencies. A variety of small mammals, mostly rodents, can hear in the range from 6 to 98 kilocycles. For example, a common dormouse was found to have a minimum threshold of 20 kilocycles (Schleidt) and a deer mouse was conditioned over a range from 10 to 65 kilocycles. In studies on the ear of a kangaroo rat cochlear potentials were recorded over a range from 100 to 20,000 cycles per second, with maximum sensitivity at 2000 to 4000 cycles per second (Katsuki and Davis). Rats and guinea pigs hear up to 40 kilocycles, some dogs up to 35 kilocycles, and chimpanzees up to 26 to 33 kilocycles. The ear of some bats is able to perceive high-frequency sounds up to at least 90 kilocycles (Kellog). The use of such sounds in echo-ranging has already been discussed (see Chapter 1).

It is thus evident that what is audible to man is not necessarily the same as what is audible to other mammals; many bats, cetaceans, rodents, and probably also shrews can "hear" at ultrasonic frequencies that we do not perceive.

SMELL

FIELD observations show that many mammals depend on olfaction for locating prey or predators, for determining the sexual condition of their partners, for much of the discrimination of food quality, and also, quite probably, for individual recognition. In most mammals, indeed, a large portion of the forebrain is olfactory and the olfactory organs are highly developed. Only primates and whalebone whales are microsmatic, and toothed whales anosmatic—the olfactory nerves entirely lacking in most of them.

But even in macrosmatic mammals the olfactory powers seem to vary widely from one taxonomic group to another. Carnivores, for example, seem to be more sensitive than rodents, and the ability of dogs to follow trails and to locate underground objects (e.g., truffles) is well known. The mechanism of this superior olfactory power, however, is not quite clear, and the experimental results of various investigators are even somewhat conflicting. Thus Neuhaus concludes that the dog can detect fatty acids in concentrations of 1,000,000 to 1,000,000,000 times lower than can man, whereas Moulton and his co-workers find that, for butyric acid, the dog has an olfactory sensitivity ranging only up to 100 times greater than the lowest threshold reported for this compound in man. Such discrepancies may be due to differences in the techniques used by the various workers, the amount of training given to the dogs, or the different biological significance of the odorants used. It is also to be remembered that olfactory acuity varies with the physiological state of the animal, e.g., hunger or sexual condition. Threshold concentration also varies with temperature and humidity, which alter the volatility of the stimulating compounds. In any case, it is quite possible that the dog's superior sense of smell stems less from an extreme absolute sensitivity of its olfactory receptors than from a better discrimination between different odors thanks to the larger area of its olfactory receptors and a more effective summation of impulses in its large olfactory bulbs.

Despite the many gaps that still exist in our knowledge of the sense organs of mammals, it is already obvious that most of them perceive the outer world in a way very different from our own. Monkeys and apes alone have a sharpness of vision, a color sense, a binocular field, an olfactory power, and a hearing similar to man's. Most other diurnal mammals are color blind, and the nocturnal species have generally so poor a visual acuity that they actually rely more on auditory and olfactory cues than on visual ones. It must nevertheless not be concluded that the perceptible world of these animals is much poorer than that of the more gifted diurnal forms. The superior sense of smell of some carnivores indicates that they perceive, as a compensation, a number of stimuli that will always remain meaningless to us. Moreover, senses completely non-existent in man, such as the "sonar" of bats and porpoises, show that some mammals can perceive in the dark, without any eyes at all, prey and obstacles that would be invisible to us. It is even quite possible that some senses remain to be discovered. The adipose cushion, or "melon," above the snout of toothed whales, which is provided with a number of branches of the trigeminal nerve, may well represent a special means of registering water pressure and flow. The sense of touch may also be far more developed in many mammals than it is in primates. The high degree of development of vibrissae in many active arboreal mammals, marsupials as well as placentals, must have some purpose (Lyne).

ACTIVITY RHYTHMS IN MAMMALS

NO mammal is active at the same rate all the time. Rats and deer, bats and whales, have activity rhythms of alternate sleeping and waking which are generally characteristic of every group and even of every species.

The best-known activity pattern is the 24-hour rhythm, which is controlled, or at least regulated, by sunrise and sunset. Broadly speaking, mammals can be divided into diurnal species, whose feeding, mating, and other activities take place during the day, and nocturnal species, which are active at night and hide during the day. But the activity patterns of animals are seldom as sharply delineated as this. Only the great apes have a monophasic type of sleeping similar to that of man, spending the whole night in the same place or in a temporary "nest." Most of the diurnal ungulates and nocturnal carnivores have, on the other hand, a definitely polyphasic sleeping pattern, in which sleeping periods of limited duration alternate with longer periods of wakefulness. Balch has shown that among adult cattle and sheep, and probably among ruminants in general, short periods of lying at rest are interspersed with periods of standing and rumination. These animals rarely close their eyes and seem even then not to lose consciousness. This peculiarity of ruminants may be related to the need for maintaining the thorax in an upright position for proper functioning of the reticulum and the rumen, and to the requirement of time and consciousness for rumination. Using an "infra-red telescope" (sniperscope) to study the activity pattern of semi-wild roe deer in Czechoslovakia, Bubenik has shown that these animals do not sleep for more than 87 to 236 minutes per night. A giraffe sleeps for no more than 20 minutes and an okapi for about 60 minutes per night (Immelmann and Gebbing). Elephants sleep for 2 to 5 hours (Kurt) and horses for about 7 hours a day. The sleep of seals, porpoises, and whales is also polyphasic, although the sperm whale seems to be a rather deep sleeper; a number of observers have stated that this animal can stay near the surface for hours on end, apparently fast asleep.

Some morphological characteristics can reasonably be interpreted as sleeping adaptations, such as the curious pharyngeal pouches of the walrus (Fay). When these animals sleep in water (in various positions, ranging from nearly horizontal to vertical), the pouches are always inflated. The 25 to 50 liters of air that each of them contains apparently lower the specific gravity of the animals and keep them afloat. The ischial callosities of the baboons are regarded by Washburn as an adaptation to their habit of sleeping in a sitting position.

Superimposed upon the 24-hour rhythm, there is also, particularly in small mammals, a short-term rhythm whose periodicity is apparently determined by body size, metabolism, and the rate of digestion. The actogram of a common shrew recorded by Peter Crowcroft during ten consecutive days (see fig. 102) is a good illustration of this rhythm. It shows clearly about ten distinct bursts of activity per day, from one to two hours' duration, separated by comparable periods of rest. When the ten daily records are added up, as at the bottom of the figure, we can see that the resting periods and the active periods of this particular shrew adhered to similar patterns

FIG. 102: *The activity rhythm of a common shrew. The "blocks" of activity over ten consecutive days are added up at the bottom, showing both a daily and a short-term rhythm. After Crowcroft.*

from one day to the next. This produces "peaks" and "troughs," from which the daily rhythm emerges quite clearly. The major period of maximum activity took place between 8 p.m. and 4 a.m., with a lesser one between 7 a.m. and 11 a.m. But throughout day and night this shrew alternately awoke and slept at rather regular and quite short intervals. Other instances of short-term rhythms in small mammals can be found in the papers of Crowcroft, Davis, Durup, Godfrey, Saint-Girons, and Southern. On the whole, the length of the periods of activity and rest in these short-term rhythms seems to decrease with the size of the animal: about four hours in the brown rat, two and a half hours in the field vole, from three quarters to one and a half hours in the house mouse, and about one hour in the long-tailed field mouse. This suggests that the rhythm is connected with the rate of metabolism—that is, the rate at which the calories taken in are used up by the organism. The smaller the animal, the larger is its relative body surface and the greater its metabolism. Consequently, its food intake must be correspondingly larger and more frequent to keep its internal temperature and its weight constant.

All the 24-hour activity rhythms seem to be geared to the natural rhythm of day and night. If nocturnal animals as different as the wood mouse and the lesser mouse lemur (*Microcebus murinus*) are kept in light-proof rooms, and electric lights are turned on only during the night, so that "night" and "day" are reversed, the animals soon adjust themselves to the new conditions by reversing their 24-hour activity rhythms. As red light is not perceived by these nocturnal mammals, it can be used during the "night" instead of true darkness; in this way the human observer can conveniently study the behavior patterns of many otherwise invisible animals.

Despite the permanent darkness of their underground burrows and nests, European moles also have a basic 24-hour activity rhythm. By fitting a ring containing radioactive cobalt to the legs or tails of these animals, Gillian Godfrey was able to follow from aboveground the movements of a number of moles in a pasture, using a portable Geiger-Müller counter. She was able to show that these moles tended to be inactive in the middle of the day, although there was in fact no time at which all the animals were inactive. It is hard to understand how the daily rhythm of illumination can affect the activity of a blind, subterranean mammal. Perhaps it is through the behavior and vertical migrations of the animals it preys upon.

THE DAILY RATIONS OF MAMMALS

TO understand the ecological significance of the population-density figures of the various mammals living in a particular habitat, the ecologist not only must know the kind of food the different species eat and the time of day or the season at which the food is eaten; he must also know how much food is necessary per day to keep the animals in good health and to enable them to reproduce successfully. This is the only way to estimate correctly the trophic impact of the populations of mammals on the vegetation or on the populations of the animals they prey upon.

Unfortunately, the available data on the daily food intake of wild mammals are scanty and often unreliable. Many observers fail to note either the age of the animals they have studied or their physiological condition. Most mammals eat much more in captivity than in the wild, and therefore tend to fatten considerably. To have some meaning for a field ecologist, the figures must therefore correspond to the average daily food intake necessary to keep an adult animal at its normal weight, without any loss or gain.

Some examples of such daily rations are provided by the table on the next page, in grams (gr) or kilograms (kg) of fresh food per day; the average body weight of the adult is also given, together with the type of diet—vegetable (V), animal (A), or mixed (M).

It is readily apparent from these figures that the smaller the animals the larger, relatively, are their daily food intakes. The tiny shrews eat almost twice their own body weight in small animals per day and the field vole eats daily an amount of grass equal to about 60 per cent of its body weight. On the other hand, the ration of lions and elephants amounts to only 13 per cent and 4 per cent of their body weight respectively.

Table 9. *Daily food intake of adult mammals*

SPECIES	AVERAGE ADULT BODY WEIGHT	AVERAGE DAILY RATION (FRESH WEIGHT)	TYPE OF FOOD
INSECTIVORES			
Suncus etruscus	2.5 gr	4.5–6.7 gr	A
Sorex cinereus	3 gr	4.7 gr	A
Sorex minutus	3.5–4.5 gr	5.5–9 gr	A
Cryptotis parva	4.7 gr	3.6 gr	A
Cryptotis floridana	5 gr	5.5 gr	A
Sorex araneus	8 gr	7–9 gr	A
Blarina brevicauda	21 gr	11.7 gr	A
Talpa europæa	76–93 gr	22–26 gr	A
BATS			
Pipistrellus subflavus	5–6 gr	3.3 gr per hour of flight	A
Myotis lucifugus	8 gr	1 gr per hour of flight	A
Eptesicus fulvus	8–12 gr	2.7 gr per hour of flight	A
Desmodus rotundus	28 gr	45–55 gr per day	Blood
PRIMATES			
Microcebus murinus	60 gr	20 gr	M
Cheirogaleus major	450 gr	250 gr	M
Chimpanzee	45 kg	2 kg	M
CARNIVORES			
Mustela rixosa	57 gr	24 gr	A
Mustela frenata	230 gr	49–77 gr	A
Domestic cat	1600–1900 gr	180 gr	A
Felis leo	150 kg	20 kg	A
RODENTS AND LAGOMORPHS			
Microtus agrestis	30 gr	19 gr	V
Psammomys obesus	65–80 gr	26–58 gr	V
Meriones lybicus	75 gr	5 gr	Seeds
Citellus pygmæus	200–250 gr	20–30 gr	V
Cynomys ludovicianus	1 kg	100 gr	V
Domestic rabbit	1.8–2.2 kg	500 gr	V
Marmota bobac	5.6 kg	600–1000 gr	V
CETACEANS			
Tursiops truncatus	150 kg	9 kg	Fish
Sei whale	25,000 kg	>225 kg	Krill
Blue whale	100,000 kg	>1000 kg	Krill
UNGULATES			
Virginia deer	60 kg	3.5–4.5 kg	V
African dromedary	400 kg	10–40 kg	V
Syncerus caffer	500 kg	30 kg	V
Hippopotamus	1500 kg	100 kg	V
African elephant	3500 kg	150 kg	V

The explanation lies in the higher metabolic rate of the smaller mammals as compared with that of the larger ones. But another basic difference becomes apparent when we compare the daily rations of plant-eaters and flesh-eaters of similar size. The latter often need a greater amount of food per day than the former. This is due mainly to what physiologists call the unequal specific dynamic action (S.D.A.), or calorigenic effect, of the various kinds of foods. When an adult warm-blooded animal takes in a certain amount of energy in its food, a definite percentage of this energy is necessarily and immediately turned into heat. If the animal happens to be in a cold environment, this heat production can be used to maintain its body temperature. But if it lives in a thermoneutral environment—or worse, in a hot environment—the heat production is entirely useless and represents completely "wasted" energy. Now it happens that the calorigenic effect of proteins is far greater (up to 40 per cent of the ingested energy) than that of carbohydrates and fats (about 5 per cent). Therefore, flesh-eaters lose far more calories through S.D.A. than plant-eaters and eat more food daily than the latter for the maintenance of a similar body mass or for performing the same amount of work.

Taxonomic List of Species
Discussed in the Text,
with Common Names

ORDER MONOTREMATA
   Tachyglossus aculeatus   = Australian spiny anteater
   Ornithorhynchus paradoxus = Platypus
ORDER MARSUPIALIA
  Family Didelphidæ
    Didelphis marsupialis   = Virginia opossum
    Didelphis paraguayensis   = South American opossum
    Marmosa isthmica   = Isthmian marmosa
    Marmosa cinerea   = Murine opossum
    Philander philander   = Woolly opossum
  Family Dasyuridæ
    Dasycercus cristicauda   = Crest-tail pouched-mouse
    Dasyurus viverrinus   = Marsupial cat
  Family Myrmecobiidæ
    Myrmecobius fasciatus   = Marsupial banded anteater
  Family Phalangeridæ
    Trichosurus vulpecula   = Silver-gray opossum
    Cercaërtus nanus   = Pigmy opossum
    Petaurus breviceps   = Sugar glider
    Phascolarctos cinereus   = Koala
    Schoinobates volans   = Greater glider-opossum
  Family Phascolomidæ
    Phascolomis hirsutus   = Common wombat
  Family Macropodidæ
    Bettongia lesueur   = Lesueur's rat kangaroo

Bettongia cuniculus	= Tasmanian rat kangaroo
Macropus canguru canguru	= Great gray kangaroo
Macropus canguru major	= Forester kangaroo
Macropus rufus	= Red kangaroo
Protemnodon eugenii	= Dama padamelon
Setonyx brachyurus	= Short-tailed wallaby
Potorous tridactylus	= Dark rat kangaroo
Wallabia rufogrisea	= Brush wallaby

ORDER INSECTIVORA

Family Tenrecidæ
Tenrec ecaudatus	= Tenrec

Family Erinaceidæ
Erinaceus europæus	= (European) hedgehog

Family Soricidæ
Blarina brevicauda	= Short-tailed shrew
Crocidura leucodon	= Bicolor white-toothed shrew
Neomys fodiens	= European water-shrew
Sorex araneus	= Common shrew

Family Talpidæ
Condylura cristata	= Star-nosed mole
Talpa europæa	= European mole
Scalopus aquaticus	= Eastern mole

ORDER CHIROPTERA

Family Noctilionidæ
Noctilio leporinus	= Fish-eating bat

Family Rhinolophidæ
Rhinolophus ferrumequinum	= Greater horseshoe bat
Rhinolophus hipposideros	= Lesser horseshoe bat

Family Desmodontidæ
Desmodus rufus	= Vampire bat

Family Vespertilionidæ
Barbastella barbastellus	= Barbastelle
Eptesicus fuscus	= Big brown bat
Eptesicus serotinus	= Serotine
Lasiurus borealis	= Red bat
Lasiurus cinereus	= Hoary bat
Myotis daubentoni	= Daubenton's bat
Myotis grisescens	= Gray myotis
Myotis keenii	= Keen bat
Myotis lucifugus	= Little brown bat
Myotis myotis	= Large mouse-eared bat
Myotis mystacinus	= Whiskered bat

Myotis sodalis	= Indiana myotis
Myotis subulatus	= Small-footed myotis
Nyctalus noctula	= Noctule
Pipistrellus pipistrellus	= European pipistrelle
Pipistrellus subflavus	= Eastern pipistrelle
Plecotus auritus	= Long-eared bat

Family Molossidæ
| *Tadarida cynocephala* | = Florida free-tailed bat |

ORDER PRIMATES

Family Lemuridæ
Microcebus murinus	= Lesser mouse lemur
Cheirogaleus sp.	= Dwarf lemurs
Lemur catta	= Ring-tailed lemur

Family Indridæ
Propithecus verreauxi	= Sifaka
Indri indri	= Indri
Avahi laniger	= Woolly lemur

Family Daubentoniidæ
| *Daubentonia madagascar-*
iensis | = Aye-aye |

Family Lorisidæ
Arctocebus calabarensis	= Angwantibo
Loris tardigradus	= Slender lori
Nycticebus coucang	= Slow lori
Perodicticus potto	= Potto
Galago senegalensis	= Senegal bush baby

Family Tarsiidæ
| *Tarsius spectrum* | = Tarsier |

Family Cebidæ
Aotus trivirgatus	= Owl monkey
Cebus capucinus	= Capuchin monkey
Alouatta palliata	= Panama howling monkey
Ateles geoffroyi	= Red spider monkey

Family Callithricidæ
| *Callithrix jacchus* | = Common marmoset |

Family Cercopithecidæ
Erythrocebus patas	= Patas monkey
Cercopithecus ascanius *schmidti*	= Redtail monkey
Cercopithecus cephus	= Mustached white-nosed monkey or guenon
Macaca fuscata	= Japanese macaque

Macaca mulatta	= Rhesus monkey
Macaca sinica	= Toque monkey
Papio doguera	= Olive (East African) baboon
Papio cynocephalus	= Yellow baboon
Papio hamadryas	= Hamadryas (or sacred) baboon
Papio comatus	= Chacma baboon
Colobus abyssinicus	= Black-and-white guereza
Procolobus verus	= Olive colobus monkey
Presbytis entellus	= Common Indian langur

Family Pongidæ

Gorilla gorilla	= Gorilla
Hylobates concolor	= Black gibbon
Hylobates lar	= Lar gibbon
Pan paniscus	= Lesser chimpanzee
Pan troglodytes	= Chimpanzee
Pongo pygmæus	= Orangutan

ORDER EDENTATA

Family Myrmecophagidæ

Myrmecophaga tridactyla	= Giant anteater
Tamandua tetradactyla	= Three-toed anteater

Family Bradypodidæ

Bradypus tridactylus	= Three-toed sloth
Cholœpus hoffmanni	= Two-toed sloth

Family Dasypodidæ

Dasypus novemcinctus	= Texas armadillo
Priodontes giganteus	= Giant armadillo

ORDER PHOLIDOTA

Family Manidæ

Manis crassicaudata	= Indian pangolin
Manis javanica	= Sumatra pangolin

ORDER LAGOMORPHA

Family Leporidæ

Lepus alleni	= Antelope jackrabbit
Lepus americanus	= Snowshoe hare
Lepus arcticus	= Arctic hare
Lepus californicus	= Blacktail jackrabbit
Lepus europæus	= European hare
Lepus timidus	= Varying hare
Oryctolagus cuniculus	= European wild rabbit
Sylvilagus floridanus	= Eastern cottontail

ORDER RODENTIA

Family Sciuridæ

Atlantoxerus getulus	= Barbary ground squirrel
Citellus beecheyi	= California ground squirrel
Citellus pygmæus	= Little souslik
Citellus tridecemlineatus	= Thirteen-lined ground squirrel
Cynomys ludovicianus	= Blacktail prairie dog
Glaucomys volans	= North American flying squirrel
Marmota bobak	= Boback marmot
Marmota marmota	= Alpine marmot
Marmota monax	= Woodchuck
Ratufa indica	= Indian giant squirrel
Sciurus carolinensis	= American gray squirrel
Sciurus fremonti	= Fremont chickaree
Sciurus hudsonicus	= American red squirrel
Sciurus niger	= Eastern fox squirrel
Sciurus vulgaris	= European red squirrel
Tamias striatus	= Eastern chipmunk

Family Geomyidæ

Geomys bursarius	= Plains pocket gopher
Thomomys monticola	= Sierra pocket gopher
Thomomys talpoides	= Northern pocket gopher

Family Heteromyidæ

Dipodomys agilis	= Pacific kangaroo rat
Dipodomys ingens	= Giant kangaroo rat
Dipodomys merriami	= Merriam kangaroo rat
Dipodomys ordii	= Ord kangaroo rat
Dipodomys venustus	= Santa Cruz kangaroo rat
Perognathus fasciatus	= Wyoming pocket mouse

Family Castoridæ

Castor canadensis	= American beaver
Castor fiber	= European beaver

Family Pedetidæ

Pedetes cafer	= Spring haas

Family Cricetidæ. Subfamily Cricetinæ.

Cricetus cricetus	= Hamster
Mesocricetus auratus	= Golden hamster
Neotoma albigula	= White-throated wood rat
Neotoma fuscipes	= Dusky-footed wood rat

Oryzomys palustris	= Rice rat
Peromyscus boylei	= Brush mouse
Peromyscus leucopus	= White-footed mouse
Peromyscus maniculatus	= Deer mouse
Sigmodon hispidus	= Hispid cotton rat

Family Cricetidæ. Subfamily Microtinæ.

Arvicola terrestris	= Water vole
Clethrionomys gapperi	= Boreal red-backed vole
Clethrionomys glareolus	= Common red-backed vole
Dicrostonyx grœnlandicus	= Greenland collared lemming
Dicrostonyx hudsonicus	= Hudson Bay collared lemming
Lemmus lemmus	= Norway lemming
Lemmus trimucronatus	= Brown lemming
Microtus agrestis	= Field vole
Microtus arvalis	= Common vole
Microtus guentheri	= Levant vole
Microtus montanus	= Mountain vole
Microtus nivalis	= Snow vole
Microtus ochrogaster	= Prairie meadow vole
Microtus pennsylvanicus	= Meadow vole
Ondatra zibethica	= Muskrat
Phenacomys longicaudus	= Red tree mouse
Synaptomys cooperi	= Lemming mouse

Family Cricetidæ. Subfamily Gerbillinæ.

Gerbillus (Dipodillus) dasyurus	= Wagner's gerbil
Gerbillus gerbillus	= Lesser Egyptian gerbil
Meriones shawi	= Shaw's jird
Pachyuromys duprasi	= Fat-tailed gerbil

Family Spalacidæ

Spalax leucodon	= Lesser mole rat

Family Muridæ

Acomys cahirinus	= Cairo spiny mouse
Apodemus sylvaticus	= Long-tailed field mouse
Cricetomys gambianus	= African giant rat
Lemniscomys barbarus	= Zebra mouse
Micromys minutus	= Harvest mouse
Mus musculus	= House mouse
Rattus manipulus	= Manipur rat
Rattus mülleri	= Giant forest rat

Rattus norvegicus	= Brown (Norway) rat
Rattus rattus	= Black rat
Family Gliridæ	
Dryomys nitedula	= Forest dormouse
Eliomys quercinus	= Garden dormouse
Glis glis	= Fat dormouse
Muscardinus avellanarius	= Common dormouse
Family Zapodidæ	
Zapus hudsonicus	= Meadow jumping mouse
Family Dipodidæ	
Dipus ægyptius	= Lesser Egyptian jerboa
Dipus sagitta	= Northern three-toed jerboa
Stylodipus tellum	= Thick-tailed three-toed jerboa
Family Hystricidæ	
Hystrix indica	= Indian crested porcupine
Family Erethizontidæ	
Erethizon dorsatum	= American porcupine
Family Hydrochœridæ	
Hydrochœrus hydrochœrus	= Capybara
Family Dasyproctidæ	
Dasyprocta punctata	= Agouti
Family Chinchillidæ	
Lagidium peruanum	= Mountain vizcacha
Family Capromyidæ	
Myocastor coypus	= Nutria
Family Ctenomyidæ	
Ctenomys brasiliensis	= Tuco tuco
Family Echymyidæ	
Pröechimys semispinosus	= Spiny rat
ORDER CETACEA	
Suborder Odontoceti	
Delphinapterus leucas	= White whale
Hyperoodon rostratus	= Bottlenosed whale
Orcinus orca	= Killer whale
Physeter catodon	= Sperm whale
Tursiops truncatus	= Bottlenosed dolphin
SUBORDER MYSTICETI	
Balæna mysticetus	= Greenland right whale
Balænoptera borealis	= Finback whale
Balænoptera musculus	= Blue whale
Balænoptera physalus	= Fin whale

Megaptera nodosa	= Humpback whale
Rachianectes glaucus	= Gray whale

ORDER CARNIVORA. SUBORDER FISSIPEDIA.

Family Canidæ

Alopex lagopus	= Arctic fox
Canis aureus	= Golden jackal
Canis latrans	= Coyote
Canis lupus	= Wolf
Lycaon pictus	= African hunting dog
Nyctereutes procyonides	= Raccoon dog
Vulpes bengalensis	= Bengal fox
Vulpes corsak	= Corsak fox
Vulpes fulva	= American red fox
Vulpes regalis	= Northern plains red fox
Vulpes vulpes	= European red fox

Family Ursidæ

Melursus ursinus	= Sloth bear
Thalarctos maritimus	= Polar bear
Ursus americanus	= Black bear
Ursus arctos	= Brown bear
Ursus horribilis	= Grizzly bear

Family Procyonidæ

Ailuropoda melanoleuca	= Giant panda

Family Mustelidæ. Subfamily Mustelinæ.

Gulo gulo	= Wolverine
Martes pennanti	= Fisher
Martes zibellina	= Sable
Mustela cicognanii	= Bonaparte weasel
Mustela erminea	= Stoat (ermine)
Mustela frenata	= Long-tailed weasel
Mustela nivalis	= Weasel
Mustela putorius	= Polecat
Mustela vison	= Mink
Pœcilictis lybica	= Libyan striped weasel

Family Mustelidæ. Subfamily Mellivorinæ.

Mellivora capensis	= Honey badger

Family Mustelidæ. Subfamily Melinæ.

Meles meles	= European badger

Family Mustelidæ. Subfamily
  Mephitinæ.
  Conepatus inca = Andean skunk
  Mephitis macroura = Hooded skunk
  Mephitis mephitis = Striped skunk
  Spilogale putorius = Prairie spotted skunk
Family Mustelidæ. Subfamily
  Lutrinæ.
  Enhydra lutris = Sea otter
  Lutra canadensis = American otter
  Lutra lutra = European otter
Family Viverridæ. Subfamily
  Viverrinæ.
  Viverra civetta = West African civet
Family Viverridæ. Subfamily
  Hemigalinæ.
  Chrotogale ownstoni = Indo-Chinese civet
Family Viverridæ. Subfamily
  Herpestinæ.
  Herpestes urva = Crab-eating mongoose
  Herpestes vitticolis = Striped necked mongoose
Family Hyænidæ
  Crocuta crocuta = Spotted hyena
  Hyæna hyæna = Striped hyena
  Proteles cristatus = Aardwolf
Family Felidæ
  Acinonyx jubatus = Cheetah
  Felis leo = Lion
  Felis manul = Pallas's cat
  Felis mearnsi = Ocelot
  Felis pardus = Leopard
  Felis viverrina = Fishing cat
  Lynx canadensis = Lynx
ORDER CARNIVORA. SUBORDER PIN-
  NIPEDIA.
Family Otariidæ
  Callorhinus ursinus = Alaska fur seal
  Zalophus californianus = California sea lion
  Otaria byronia = Falkland sea lion
Family Odobenidæ
  Odobenus rosmarus = Walrus

Family Phocidæ
Cystophora cristata	= Hooded seal
Erignathus barbatus	= Bearded seal
Halichœrus grypus	= Gray seal
Hydrurga leptonyx	= Leopard seal
Leptonychotes weddelli	= Weddell's seal
Lobodon carcinophagus	= Crab-eating seal
Mirounga leonina	= Southern elephant seal
Monachus monachus	= Monk seal
Ommatophoca rossi	= Ross seal
Phoca grœnlandica	= Harp seal
Phoca hispida	= Ringed seal
Phoca vitulina	= Common seal

ORDER TUBULIDENTATA

Family Orycteropidæ
Orycteropus afer	= Aardvark

ORDER PROBOSCIDEA

Family Elephantidæ
Elephas maximus	= Indian elephant
Loxodonta africana	= African elephant

ORDER SIRENIA

Family Trichechidæ
Trichechus latirostris	= Florida manatee

ORDER PERISSODACTYLA

Family Equidæ
Equus asinus somalicus	= Somali wild ass
Equus burchelli	= Burchell's zebra
Equus grevyi	= Grevy's zebra
Equus hemionus hemionus	= Mongolian wild ass
Equus hemionus khur	= Indian wild ass
Equus zebra	= Mountain zebra

Family Rhinocerotidæ
Diceros bicornis	= Black rhinoceros
Rhinoceros unicornis	= Great one-horned rhinoceros

ORDER ARTIODACTYLA

Family Suidæ
Hylochœrus meinertzhageni	= Giant forest hog
Phacochœrus æthiopicus	= Wart hog
Sus scrofa	= Wild boar

Family Tayassuidæ
Tayassu tajacu	= Collared peccary

Family Hippopotamidæ
  Chœropsis liberiensis = Pigmy hippopotamus
  Hippopotamus amphibius = Hippopotamus
Family Camelidæ
  Camelus bactrianus = Camel
  Lama vicugna = Vicuna
Family Cervidæ
  Alces americana = Moose
  Capreolus capreolus = Roe deer
  Cervus canadensis = Elk
  Cervus elaphus = Red deer
  Odocoileus hemionus = Mule deer
  Odocoileus virginianus = White-tailed deer
  Rangifer caribou = Caribou (reindeer)
Family Giraffidæ
  Giraffa camelopardalis = Giraffe
  Okapia johnstoni = Okapi
Family Antilocapridæ
  Antilocapra americana = Pronghorn
Family Bovidæ. Subfamily
  Bovinæ.
  Bison bison = American bison
  Boselaphus tragocamelus = Nilgai
  Boocercus eurycerus = Bongo
  Bos banteng = Banteng
  Bos gaurus = Gaur
  Bos sauveli = Kouprey
  Syncerus cafer = Cape buffalo
  Taurotragus oryx = Eland
  Tragelaphus scriptus = Bushbuck
Family Bovidæ. Subfamily
  Cephalophinæ.
  Cephalophus sp. = Duikers
Family Bovidæ. Subfamily
  Hippotraginæ.
  Addax nasomaculatus = Addax
  Adenota kob thomasi = Uganda kob
  Alcelaphus caama = Cape hartebeest
  Connochætes gnou = White-tailed gnu
  Connochætes taurinus = Wildebeest
  Damaliscus korrigum = Topi
  Hippotragus equinus = Roan antelope

Hippotragus niger = Sable antelope
Kobus defassa = Defassa waterbuck
Redunca redunca = Reedbuck

Family Bovidæ. Subfamily
Antilopinæ.

Æpyceros melampus = Impala
Antidorcas marsupialis = Springbok
Gazella dama = Dama gazelle
Gazella granti = Grant's gazelle
Gazella thomsonii = Thomson's gazelle
Litocranius walleri = Waller's gazelle (gerenuk)
Ourebia ourebi = Oribi

Family Bovidæ. Subfamily
Caprinæ.

Ammotragus lervia = Barbary sheep
Capra ibex = Ibex
Hemitragus jemlahicus = Tahr
Ovibos moschatus = Musk ox
Ovis canadensis = Bighorn sheep
Ovis dalli = Dall sheep
Rupicapra rupicapra = Chamois
Saiga tatarica = Saiga antelope

Bibliography

THE FOLLOWING LIST is not a complete bibliography of the subject. It is limited to those titles which, in my opinion, will best serve the needs of the field worker. To save space, the titles of the papers (but not the books) have been abbreviated and translated into English, the original language being indicated by a capital letter—F for French, G for German, R for Russian, and S for Spanish. The titles of the most often quoted journals or serials have been abbreviated in the following way:

H.d.Z.	Kukenthal's *Handbuch der Zoologie*
J.M.	*Journal of Mammalogy*
J.W.M.	*Journal of Wildlife Management*
M.	*Mammalia*
P.Z.S.	*Proceedings of the Zoological Society of London*
Z.f.S.	*Zeitschrift für Saugetierkunde*
Z.f.T.	*Zeitschrift für Tierpsychologie*
Z.G.	*Der Zoologische Garten*

As this list contains titles that have not been referred to in the text, a number has been assigned to each reference and a subject index has been compiled for each major taxonomic group and topic (see pages 385 ff.).

1. Adams, L. (1959). *Ecol. Monogr.*, 29:141–70 (Population ecology of snowshoe hares in northwestern Montana).
2. Adolph, E. F. (1947). *Physiology of Man in the Desert.* New York, Interscience, XIII + 357 pp.
3. Adolph, E. F. (1948). *Amer. Jour. Physiol.*, 155:266–77 (Tolerance to cold and anoxia in infant rats).
4. Allee, W. C. (1950). *Colloques Internationaux du CNRS,*

34:157–81 (Dominance and hierarchy in vertebrate societies).

5. Allen, G. M. (1938–1940). *The Mammals of China and Mongolia.* New York, American Museum of Natural History, xxv + 1350 + xxvi pp. Mainly taxonomic.

6. Allen, G. M. (1939a). *Bats.* Cambridge, Harvard University Press, x + 368 pp.

7. Allen, G. M. (1939b). *Bull. Mus. Comp. Zool.*, 83:1–763 (Check list of African mammals). Somewhat out of date.

8. Altmann, M. (1952). *Behaviour*, 4:115–43 (Social behavior of *Cervus canadensis*).

9. Altmann, M. (1956). *Trans. 21st. N. Amer. Wildlife Conference*, 538–45 (Comparative social behavior of four ungulates).

10. Altmann, M. (1958). *Animal Behaviour*, 6:155–59 (Social integration of the moose calf).

11. Altmann, M. (1959). *J.M.*, 40:420–24 (Rutting behavior of the moose).

12. Altmann, M. (1960). *Zoologica*, 45:35–39 (Role of juvenile elk and moose in the social dynamics of their species).

13. Andersen, J. (1953). *Danish Rev. Game Biol.*, 2:127–55 (Analysis of a roe deer population).

14. Andersen, J. (1961). *Terre et Vie*, 1961:41–53 (Ecology of the roe deer in Denmark).

15. Anderson, J. A., and Anderson, J. B. (1961). *New Zealand Deerstalkers Assoc., Spec. Publ.* 2, 36 pp. (Himalayan thar in New Zealand).

16. Anderson, J. W. (1954). *Science*, 119:808–09 (Production of ultrasonic sounds by rats).

17. Ansell, W. F. H. (1960a). *P.Z.S.*, 134:251–74 (Breeding of large mammals in Northern Rhodesia).

18. Ansell, W. F. H. (1960b), *Mammals of Northern Rhodesia.* Lusaka, Govt. Printer, xxxi + 155 + 24 pp. Excellent regional check list, keys for identification, and data on ecology and life history.

19. Antonius, O. (1937). *Z.f.T.*, 1:259–89 (Social behavior of Equidae. G).

20. Antonius, O. (1951). *Die Tigerferde. Die Zebras.* Frankfurt, Schops, 148 pp.

21. Arlton, A. V. (1936). *J.M.*, 17:349–71 (Ecology of the mole).

22. Armitage, K. B. (1962). *Animal Behaviour*, 10:319–31 (Social behavior of *Marmota flaviventris*).

23. Arvola, A., Ilmen, M., and Koponen, T. (1962). *Arch. Soc. Vanamo*, 17:80–101 (Aggresive behavior and sounds produced by *Lemmus lemmus*).

24. Asdell, S. A. (1946). *Patterns of Mammalian Reproduction.* Ithaca, Comstock, x + 437 pp.

25. Backhaus, D. (1959). *Z.f.T.*, 16:445–67, 468–77 (Color vision in ungulates. G).

26. Backhaus, D. (1960). *Z.f.T.*, 17:345–50 (Fighting attitudes of *Equus quagga.* G).

27. Backhaus, D. (1961). *Beobachtungen an Giraffen in Zoologischen Gärten und freier Wildbahn.* Brussels, Institut des Parcs Nationaux du Congo, 202 pp., figs.

28. Backhouse, K. M., and Smart, P. J. G. (1961). *P.Z.S.*, 136:197–200 (Wave-riding in porpoises).

29. Baker, H. G., and Harris, B. J. (1957). *Evolution*, 11:449–60, 5 pls. (Pollination of *Parkia* by bats).

30. Baker, J. R., and Ranson, R. M. (1932). *Proc. Roy. Soc.*, (B) 110:313–22 (Influence of light on the breeding of the field mouse).

31. Balch, C. C. (1955). *Nature*, 175:940 (Sleep in ruminants).

32. Banfield, A. W. F. (1954). *Wildlife Management Bulletin*, Ottawa, Series 1, No. 10, 79 + 112 pp. (Population ecology and life history of the Barren Ground caribou).

33. Banfield, A. W. F. (1955). *Canad. Jour. Zool.*, 33:143–47 (Life table for the Barren Ground caribou).

34. Bannikov, A. G. (1954). (*Mammals of the People's Republic of Mongolia*). Moscow, USSR Academy of Sciences, 669 pp. A great deal on biology. Text in Russian.

35. Bannikov. A. G. (1958). *M.*, 22:152–60 (Ecology and behavior of *Equus przewalskii.* F).

36. Bannikov, A. G. (1963). *Die Saiga Antilope.* Wittenberg Lutherstadt, Ziemsen, 143 pp.

37. Bannikov, A. G. (1961). *Terre et Vie*, 1961:86–100, 1 pl. (Ecology of the wild ass. F).

38. Bannikov, A. G., Jirnov, L. V., Lebiedieva, L. S., and Fandieiev, A. A. (1961). (*Biology of the Saiga Antelope*). Moscow, 336 pp. In Russian.

39. Barbour, T. (1932). *Quart. Rev. Biol.*, 7:307–12 (Roosting habits of bats).

40. Barnett, S. A. (1963). *A study in Behaviour.* London, Methuen, XIII + 288 pp.

41. Bartholomew, G. A. (1952). *Univ. Calif. Publ. Zool.*, 47:369–

472 (Reproductive and social behavior of the northern elephant seal).

42. Bartholomew, G. A. (1959). *Animal Behaviour*, 7:163–71 (Mother-young relations and the maturation of pup behavior in the Alaska fur seal).

43. Bartholomew, G. A., and Cade, T. J. (1957). *J.M.*, 38:60–72 (Hibernation and æstivation in *Perognathus longimembris*).

44. Bartholomew, G. A., and Cary, J. R. (1954). *J.M.*, 35:386–92 (Locomotion in pocket mice).

45. Bartholomew, G. A., and Caswell, H. H., Jr. (1951). *J.M.*, 32:155–59 (Locomotion in kangaroo rats).

46. Bartholomew, G. A., and Collias, N. E. (1962). *Animal Behaviour*, 10:7–14 (Vocalizations of the northern elephant seal).

47. Bartholomew, G. A., and Hudson, J. W. (1960). *Bull. Mus. Comp. Zool.*, 124:193–208 (Æstivation in *Citellus mohavensis*).

48. Beach, F. A. (1939). *J.M.*, 20:315–22 (Maternal behavior of *Marmosa cinerea*).

49. Beach, F. A. (1945). *Amer. Nat.*, 79:523–41 (Current concepts of play in animals).

50. Beach, F. A. (1947). *Psychol. Reviews*, 54:297–315 (Evolutionary changes in the physiological control of mating behavior in mammals).

51. Beach, F. A., and Jaynes, J. (1956). *J.M.*, 37:177–80 (Maternal retrieving in rats).

52. Beer, J. R., Frenzel, L. D., and MacLead, C. F. (1958). *Amer. Midland Natur.*, 59:518–24 (Sex ratio of Minnesota rodents).

53. Bela, B. (1934). *Terre et Vie*, 1934:323–33 (Life history of *Spalax hungaricus*. F).

54. Bels, L. (1939). *De Levende Natuur*, 1939:289–99 (Migrations of *Nyctalus noctula*. In Dutch).

55. Benson, S. B. (1939). *Univ. Calif. Publ. Zool.*, 40:1–70 (Concealing coloration of desert rodents in S.W. United States).

56. Bernstein, I. S. (1962). *Animal Behaviour*, 10:1–6 (Response to nesting material of wild-born and captive-born chimpanzee).

57. Bertram, G. C. L. (1940). *British Graham Land Expedition, 1934–1937, Sci. Reports*, 1:1–139 (Biology of the Weddel and crabeater seals).

58. Bezem, J. J., Sluiter, J. W., and Van Heerdt, P. F. (1960). *Arch. Néerl. Zool.*, 13:511–39 (Population statistics of Dutch bats).

59. Bissonnette, T. H. (1936). *Quart. Rev. Biol.*, 11:371–86 (Sexual periodicity).

60. Bissonnette, T. H. (1941). *Physiol. Zool.*, 14:379–83 (Experimental modifications of the breeding cycle in goats).

61. Bissonnette, T. H., and Bailey, E. E. (1944). *Ann. New York Acad. Sci.*, 45:221–60 (Experimental modification of moults and changes in coat color in weasels by controlled lighting).

62. Blair, W. F. (1940). *Amer. Midland Natur.*, 24:273–305 (Prairie deer mouse populations in southern Michigan).

63. Blair, W. F. (1953). *Advances in Genetics*, 5:1–41 (Population dynamics of small mammals. A review).

64. Bloedcl, P. (1955). *J.M.*, 36:390–99 (Hunting methods of fish-eating bats).

65. Bobrinskoy, N., Kuznetzov, B., and Kuziakin, A. (1944). (*Mammals of the USSR*). Moscow, Sovietskaya Nauka, 440 pp. Range maps. Text in Russian.

66. Bodenheimer, F. S. (1949a). *Physiol. Comp. Oekol.*, 1:376–89 (Ecological and physiological studies on some rodents of Israel).

67. Bodenheimer, F. S. (1949b). *Problems of Vole Populations in the Middle East. Report on the population dynamics of the Levant vole* (Microtus guentheri). Jerusalem, Research Council of Israel, pp. 1–77.

68. Bonaventure, N. (1959). *C. R. Soc. Biol.*, 153:1594–97 (Color vision in *Citellus citellus*. F).

69. Booth, A. H. (1957). *P.Z.S.*, 129:421–30 (Natural history of the olive colobus monkey, *Procolobus verus*).

70. Borg, K. (1962). *J.W.M.*, 26:133–36 (Predation on roe deer in Sweden).

71. Bourdelle, E. (1934). *Bull. Mus. Nat. Hist. Nat.*, 1934:329–39 (Locomotion of the giraffe. F).

72. Bourlière, F. (1947). *M.*, 11:111–15 (Longevity of small mammals in the wild. F).

73. Bourlière, F. (1948). *Terre et Vie*, 1948:65–68 (Reproduction and growth of *Cricetomys gambianus*. F).

74. Bourlière, F. (1950). *Colloques Internationaux du CNRS*, 34: 71–79 (Classification of the patterns of social grouping among vertebrates. F).

75. Bourlière, F., editor (1956). *Terre et Vie*, 1956:121–290 (IUCN symposium on myxomatosis).

76. Bourlière, F. (1962). *Terre et Vie*, 1962:150–60 (Censuses of large ungulates in various African parks. F).

77. Bourlière, F., Petter, J. J., and Petter-Rousseaux, A. (1956). *Mem. Inst. Sci. Madagascar*, A, 10:303–04 (Variations of central temperature among prosimians. F).

78. Bourlière, F., and Verschuren, J. (1960) *Introduction à l'écologie des ongulés du parc national Albert*. Brussels, Institut des Parcs Nationaux du Congo, 158 pp.

79. Bradt, G. W. (1938). *J.M.*, 19:139–52 (Beaver colonies in Michigan).

80. Braestrup, F. W. (1941). *Meddelelser om Grönland*, 131, No. 4:1–101 (Ecology of arctic foxes in Greenland).

81. Brambell, F. W. R. (1947–48). *J. Exp. Biol.*, 23:332–46 (Sterility and prenatal mortality in wild rabbits).

82. Brandborg, S. M. (1955). *State of Idaho, Dept. Fish and Game, Bull.* 2, 142 pp. (Life history of the mountain goat).

83. Brehm, A. (1912–16). *Brehms Tierleben. Die Saugetiere*. 5th edition, revised by L. Heck and M. Hilzheimer. Leipzig. These four volumes contain much on the life histories of mammals.

84. Britton, S. W. (1941). *Quart. Rev. Biol.*, 16:13–34, 190–207 (Form and function in the sloth).

85. Britton, S. W., and Atkinson, W. E. (1938). *J.M.*, 19:94–99 (Poikilothermism in the sloth).

86. Broadbrooks, H. E. (1958). *Misc. Publ. Mus. Zool. Univ. Michigan*, 103:1–42, 3 pls. (Life history of *Eutamias amœnus*).

87. Brooks, A. C. (1961). *Colonial Research Publications*, No. 25, VI + 147 pp. (Life history and distribution of Thomson's gazelle in Tanganyika).

88. Brosset, A. (1961). *M.*, 25:413–52 (Hibernation in Indian bats. F).

89. Brosset, A. (1962). *M.*, 26:176–213 (Bat reproduction in western and central India. F).

90. Brown, D. H., and Norris, K. S. (1956). *J.M.*, 37:311–26 (Co-operation among adult dolphins).

91. Brown, R. Z. (1953). *Ecol. Monogr.*, 23:217–40 (Social behavior, reproduction, and population changes in the house mouse).

92. Bubenik, A. B. (1960). *M.*, 24:1–66 (Activity patterns in the roe deer. F).

93. Buechner, H. K. (1950). *Amer. Midland Natur.*, 43:257–354 (Life history and ecology of the pronghorn).

94. Buechner, H. K. (1960). *Wildlife Monographs*, 4:1–174 (Ecology of the bighorn sheep).

95. Buechner, H. K. (1961). *Science*, 133:698–99 (Territorial behavior in the Uganda kob).

96. Burbank, R. C., and Young, J. Z. (1934). *Jour. Physiol.*, 82:459–67 (Temperature changes and winter sleep of bats).

97. Burckhardt, D. (1958). *M.*, 22:226–44 (Social behavior of the red deer in the Swiss National Park. F).

98. Buresch, I. (1941). *Schr. Bulgar. Akad. Wiss.*, 61:51–72 (Bat migration. G).

99. Burger, M. (1959). *Z.G.*, N.F., 24:434–506 (Fur-cleaning among hares and rodents. G).

100. Burkholder, B. L. (1959). *J.W.M.*, 23:1–11 (Movements of a wolf pack in Alaska).

101. Burrell, H. (1927). *The Platypus.* Sydney, VII + 227 pp.

102. Burt, W. H. (1940). *Misc. Publ. Mus. Zool. Univ. Michigan,* 45:1–58 (Territorial behavior and populations of small mammals in southern Michigan).

103. Burt, W. H. (1943). *J.M.*, 24:346–52 (Territoriality and home range concepts in mammals).

104. Burt, W. H., and Grossenheider, R. P. (1952). *A Field Guide to the Mammals, Giving Field Marks of All the Species Found North of the Mexican Boundary.* Boston, Houghton Mifflin, XXI + 200 pp. Excellent plates.

105. Burton, A. C., and Edholm, O. G. (1955). *Man in a Cold Environment.* London, Arnold, XIV + 273 pp.

106. Buss, I. O. (1961). *J.W.M.*, 25:131–48 (Food habits and social behavior of the African elephant).

107. Buss, I. O., and Brooks, A. C. (1962). *Terre et Vie,* 1962:175–82 (Population dynamics of Uganda elephants. F).

108. Butler, L. (1953). *Canad. J. Zool.*, 31:242–62 (Population cycles in Canadian mammals).

109. Buytendijk. E. J. J. (1920). *Arch. Néerl. Physiol.*, 1920:434–57 (Olfactory acuity of the dog. F).

110. Cabrera, A. (1957–1961). *Catalogo de los mamiferos de America del Sur.* Buenos Aires, Rev. Mus. Argent. Cien.

Nat., Zool., 4, xxii + 732 pp. The basic check list for Latin America.

111. Cabrera, A., and Yepes, J. (1940). *Mamiferos sud-americanos. Vida, costumbres y descripción.* Buenos Aires, Comp. Argent. de Editores, 370 pp. The best introduction for the Latin American subcontinent. Excellent plates.

112. Cahalane, V. H. (1942). *J.W.M.*, 6:338–52 (Caching and recovery of food by the western fox squirrel).

113. Cahalane, V. H. (1947). *Mammals of North America.* New York, Macmillan, x + 682 pp. Mainly life histories.

114. Carpenter, C. R. (1934). *Comp. Psychol. Monogr.*, 10, 2:1–168 (Behavior of the howling monkeys).

115. Carpenter, C. R. (1935). *J.M.*, 16:171–80 (Behavior of red spider monkeys).

116. Carpenter, C. R. (1940). *Comp. Psychol. Monogr.*, 16, 5:1–212 (Behavior of the lar gibbon).

117. Carpenter, C. R. (1942). *Jour. Comp. Physiol.*, 33:133–62 (Sexual behavior of rhesus monkeys).

118. Carpenter, C. R. (1958). *H.d.Z.*, 8, 10, 11:1–32 (Social behavior of wild monkeys and apes. G).

119. Carrick, R., *et al.* (1962). *C.S.I.R.O. Wildlife Research*, 7:89–206 (Ecology and behavior of unexploited populations of the southern elephant seal).

120. Carter, T. D., Hill, J. E., and Tate, G. H. H. (1946). *Mammals of the Pacific World.* New York, Macmillan, xvi + 227 pp. Good introduction.

121. Casteret, N. (1938–39). *M.*, 3:29–34 and 4:1–9 (Homing of bats in S.W. France. F).

122. Chasen, F. N. (1940). *Bull. Raffles Museum*, 15, xx + 209 pp. (Check list of Malaysian mammals).

123. Chowdhury, D. R., and Sadhu, D. P. (1961). *Nature*, 189:491 (Evaporation through the skin of Indian zebu cattle).

124. Christian, J. J. (1959). In *Comparative Endocrinology*, edited by A. Gorbman, pp. 71–97 (Roles of endocrine and behavioral factors in the growth of mammalian populations).

125. Clarke, C. H. D. (1940). *Nat. Mus. Canada, Bull.* 96:iv + 135 pp. (Mammals of the Thelon game sanctuary).

126. Clarke, R. (1956). *Discovery Reports*, 28:237–98 (Sperm whales of the Azores. Ecology and behavior).

127. Cockrum, E. L. (1955). *Trans. Kansas Acad. Sci.*, 58:487–511 (Reproduction in North American bats).

128. Cockrum, E. L. (1962). *Introduction to Mammalogy*. New York, Ronald Press, viii + 455 pp.

129. Cockrum, E. L., and Hayward, B. J. (1962). *Natural History*, 71, No. 8:38–43 (Pollination of the saguaro cactus by bats).

130. Collias, N., and Southwick, C. (1952). *Proc. Amer. Phil. Soc.*, 96:143–56 (Population density and social organization in howling monkeys).

131. Cott, H. B. (1940). *Adaptive Coloration in Animals*. London, Methuen, xxxii + 508 pp.

132. Courrier, R. (1927). *Arch. Biol.*, 37:173–334 (Secondary sexual characters of some seasonally reproducing mammals. F).

133. Couturier, M. A. J. (1938). *Le Chamois* (Rupicapra rupicapra L.). Grenoble, Arthaud, xi + 857 pp.

134. Couturier, M. A. J. (1954). *L'Ours brun*, Ursus arctos L. Grenoble, the author, xi + 905 pp.

135. Couturier, M. A. J. (1961). *Terre et Vie*, 1961:54–73 (Ecology of the chamois and the ibex in the W. Alps. F).

136. Cowan, I. M., and Brink, V. C. (1949). *J.M.*, 30:379–87 (Natural game licks in Canada).

137. Crandall, L. S. (1958). *H.d.Z.*, 8, 10, 8:1–8 (Behavior of the platypus. G).

138. Criddle, S. (1930). *J.M.*, 11:265–80 (Life history of the prairie pocket gopher).

139. Crowcroft, P. (1954). *P.Z.S.*, 123:715–29 (Activity patterns of British shrews).

140. Crowcroft, P. (1956). *P.Z.S.*, 127:285–92 (Life span of the common shrew).

141. Crowcroft, P. (1957). *The Life of the Shrew*. London, Reinhart, viii + 166 pp.

142. Crowcroft, P., and Rowe, F. P. (1957). *P.Z.S.*, 129:359–70 (Growth of laboratory populations of the wild house mouse).

143. Cuénot, L. (1907). *Comptes Rendus Soc. Biol.*, 62:174–76 (Caudal autotomy among rodents. F).

144. Curio, E. (1955). *Z.f.T.*, 12:459–62 (Transport of the young in *Apodemus flavicollis*. G).

145. Curry-Lindahl, K. (1962). *J.M.*, 43:171–84 (Irruption of *Lemmus lemmus* in Sweden during 1960).

146. Darling, F. F. (1937). *A Herd of Red Deer. A Study in Animal Behaviour*. Oxford, Oxford University Press, x + 215 pp.

147. Darling, F. F. (1947). *Natural History in the Highlands and*

Islands. London, Collins (Life history of the Atlantic gray seal on pp. 217–231).

148. Dasmann, R. F., and Mossman, A. S. (1962). *J.M.*, 43:375–95 (Population studies of impala).

149. Dassmann, R. F., and Taber, R. D. (1956). *J.M.*, 37:143–64 (Social life of the Columbian black-tailed deer).

150. Davies, J. L. (1948). *P.Z.S.*, 119:673–92 (Gray seals of Ramsey Island).

151. Davis, D. E. (1945). *J.M.*, 26:119–27 (Home range of Brazilian mammals).

152. Davis, D. E. (1948). *Ecology*, 29:437–48 (Survival of wild brown rats on a Maryland farm).

153. Davis, D. E. (1953). *Quart. Rev. Biol.*, 28:373–401 (Rat populations).

154. Davis, D. E., editor (1956). *Manual for Analysis of Rodent Populations*. Division of Vertebrate Ecology. School of Hygiene and Public Health, Johns Hopkins University, Baltimore, III + 82 pp., figs.

155. Davis, D. E., and Golley, F. B. (1963). *Principles in Mammalogy*. New York, Reinhold, XIII + 335 pp.

156. Davis, D. H. S. (1933). *J. Anim. Ecol.*, 2:232–38 (Activity rhythm of the short-tailed vole).

157. Davis, R., and Cockrum, E. L. (1962). *Science*, 137:341–42 (Repeated homing by a female *Antrozous pallidus*).

158. Davis, W. B. (1938). *J.M.*, 19:338–42 (Relation of size of pocket gophers to soil and altitude).

159. Dawaa, N. (1961). *Z.f.S.*, 26:176–83 (Biology of *Microtus brandti* in Mongolia. G).

160. Deevey, E. S. (1947). *Quart. Rev. Biol.*, 22:283–314 (Life-tables for natural populations of animals. A review).

161. Degerböl, M. (1927). *Videnskab. Meddelel. Dansk. Naturhist. Foren.*, 84:195–202 (Storing up of worms by moles).

162. Degerböl, M. (1940). *Mammalia*, in *Zoology of the Faroes*, 3, pt. 2, fasc. 65:1–133.

163. Degerböl, M., and Möhl-Hansen, U. (1943). *Meddelelser om Grönland*, 131, No. 11:1–40 (Breeding and molts of the collared lemming).

164. De Vore, I. (1961). *The Social Organization of Baboon Troops*. Unpublished Ph.D. thesis, University of Chicago, 181 pp.

165. Dice, L. R. (1947). *Contr. Lab. Vert. Biol. Univ. Michigan*,

34:1–20 (Effectiveness of selection by owls of deer mice which contrast in color with their background).

166. Dieterlen, F. (1959). *Z.f.T.*, 16:47–103 (Ethology of the golden hamster. G).

167. Dieterlen, F. (1962). *Z.f.T.*, 19:191–222 (Care of the young in *Acomys cahirinus.* G).

168. Ditmars, R. L., and Greenhall, A. M. C. (1935). *Zoologica,* 19:53–76 (The vampire bat).

169. Dunn, L. H. (1933). *J.M.*, 14:188–99 (Carnivorous habits of the spear-nosed bat).

170. Durup, H., and Saint Girons, M. C. (1958). *M.*, 22:505–24 (Activity pattern of the common red-backed vole. F).

171. Dusi, J. L. (1949). *J.W.M.*, 13:295–98 (Determination of food habits).

172. Eayrs, J. T., and Moulton, D. G. (1960). *Quart. J. Exp. Psychol.*, 12:90–98 (Olfactory acuity of the rat).

173. Eibl-Eibesfeldt. I. (1950). *Z.f.T.*, 7:327–55 (Maturation of behavior patterns and play in the European badger. G).

174. Eibl-Eibesfeldt, I. (1951a). *Z.f.T.*, 8:370–400 (Maturation of behavior of the European red squirrel. G).

175. Eibl-Eibesfeldt, I. (1951b). *Z.f.T.*, 8:400–23 (Observations on captive *Meriones persicus.* G).

176. Eibl-Eibesfeldt, I. (1953). *Z.f.T.*, 10:204–54 (Behavior of the hamster. G).

177. Eibl-Eibesfeldt, I. (1956). *Z.f.T.*, 21:132–34, 135–37. (Innate feeding behavior of *Sciurus vulgaris* and the polecat. G).

178. Eibl-Eibesfeldt, I. (1957). *H.d.Z.*, 8, 10, 6:1–26 (Expressive attitudes among mammals. G).

179. Eibl-Eibesfeldt, I. (1958). *H.d.Z.*, 8, 10, 13:1–88 (Behavior of Rodentia. G).

180. Eisenberg, J. F. (1963). *Univ. Calif. Publ. Zool.*, 69:IV + 100 pp. (Behavior of meteromyid rodents).

181. Eisentraut, M. (1928). *Z.f.S.*, 3:142 (Burrows of the hamster. G).

182. Eisentraut, M. (1933). *Z.f.S.*, 8:47–69 (Biological observations on some Chaco mammals. G).

183. Eisentraut, M. (1936). *Z. f. wiss Zool.*, 148:159–88 (The flight of bats. G).

184. Eisentraut, M. (1937). *Die deutsche Fledermäuse, eine biologische Studie.* Leipzig, Schops, 184 pp.

185. Eisentraut, M. (1943). *Zool. Anz.*, 144:20–32 (Bat banding in Germany. G).

186. Eisentraut, M. (1945). *Biologia generalis*, 18:327–435 (Biology of the Megachiroptera. G).

187. Eisentraut, M. (1950). *Zool. Jahrb.*, 79:114–77 (Feeding habits of Microchiroptera. G).

188. Eisentraut, M. (1956). *Der Winterschlaf mit seinem ökologischen und physiologischen Begleiterscheinungen.* Jena, Fisher. 160 pp.

189. Elder, J. H. (1935). *Amer. J. Physiol.*, 112:109–15 (Upper limit of hearing in chimpanzees).

190. Ellerman, J. R., and Morrison-Scott, T. C. S. (1951). *Checklist of Palaearctic and Indian Mammals, 1758–1945*. London, British Museum (Nat. Hist.). 810 pp. The most recent check list.

191. Ellerman, J. R., Morrison-Scott, T. C. S., and Hayman, R. W. (1953). *Southern African Mammals, 1758–1951. A Reclassification.* London, British Museum (Nat. Hist.) 363 pp. Check list and keys.

192. Ellis, L. L., Jr. (1955). *Ecology*, 36:12–18 (Ectoparasites of some Oklahoma mammals).

193. Ellison, L. (1946). *Ecology*, 27:101–14 (Pocket gophers and soil erosion on mountain ranges).

194. Elton, C. (1942). *Voles, Mice and Lemmings: Problems in Population Dynamics.* Oxford, Oxford University Press, 496 pp.

195. Elton, C., and Nicholson, M. (1942). *J. Anim. Ecol.*, 11:96–126, 215–44 (The ten-year cycle of the muskrat and the lynx in Canada).

196. Enders, R. K. (1935). *Bull. Mus. Comp. Zool.*, 78:385–502 (Life histories of Barro Colorado mammals).

197. Errington, P. L. (1946). *Quart. Rev. Biol.*, 21:144–77, 221–45 (Predation and vertebrate populations).

198. Evans, H. (1891). *Some Accounts of Jura Red Deer.* Derby, Francis Carter, pp. 1–38.

199. Fairfield, J. (1948). *Amer. Jour. Physiol.*, 155:355–65 (Effects of cold on infant rats).

200. Farner, D. S. (1961). *Annual Reviews Physiol.*, 23:71–96 (Photoperiodicity).

201. Fay, F. H. (1960). *M.*, 24:361–71 (Pharyngeal pouches of the walrus as sleeping adaptations).

202. Felten, H. (1956). *Natur und Volk*, 86:53–57 (Bats eating scorpions. G).

203. Feniuk, B. K., and Kazantzeva, J. M. (1937). *J.M.*, 18:409–26 (Ecology of *Dipus sagitta*).
204. Fisher, E. M. (1939). *J.M.*, 20:21–36 (Habits of the sea otter).
205. Fisher, E. M. (1940). *J.M*, 21:132–37 (Early life of a sea otter pup).
206. Fitch, H. S. (1947). *Calif. Fish Game*, 33:159–84 (Ecology of the cottontail rabbit in central California).
207. Fitch, H. S. (1948a). *Amer. Midland Natur.*, 39:513–96 (Ecology of the California ground squirrel).
208. Fitch, H. S. (1948b). *J.M.*, 29:5–35 (Habits of the Tulare kangaroo rat).
209. Fleay, D. (1944). *Victorian Naturalist*, 61:8–14, 29–37, 54–57, 74–78 (Breeding of the platypus in captivity).
210. Flower, S. S. (1931). *P.Z.S.*, 1931:145–234 (Longevity of mammals in captivity).
211. Flower, S. S. (1948). *P.Z.S.*, 117:680–88 (Duration of life of elephants).
212. Formosov, A. N. (1928). *Ecology*, 9:449–60 (Role of mammals in the steppe biotic community).
213. Formosov, A. N. (1946). *Mater. Flore Faune URSS, Ser. Zool.*, 5:1–141 (The snow cover as a limiting factor for mammals and birds. R).
214. Formosov, A. N. (1961). *Terre et Vie*, 1961:116–29 (Influence of gregarious rodents on the soils and vegetation of Eurasian steppes. F).
215. Foster, W. E. (1960). *Lammergeier*, 1:25–35 (Life history of *Ceratotherium simum*).
216. Frank, F. (1957a). *Z.f.S.*, 22:1–44 (Life history of *Micromys minutus*. G).
217. Frank, F. (1957b). *J.W.M.*, 21:113–21 (Causes of microtine cycles in Germany).
218. Frank, F. (1962). *Z. Morphol. Ökol. Tiere*, 51:87–164 (Biology of *Lemmus lemmus*. G).
219. Fuller, W. A. (1960). *Arctic*, 13:2–19 (Behavior of the wood bison).
220. Fuller, W. A. (1961). *Terre et Vie*, 1961:286–304 (Ecology of the American bison).
221. Gauthier-Pilters, H. (1958). *M.*, 22:140–51 (Social behavior of the dromedary. F).
222. Gauthier-Pilters, H. (1961). *M.*, 25:195–280 (Ecology of the dromedary in the N. Sahara. F).

223. Gee, E. P. (1953). *J. Bombay Nat. Hist. Soc.*, 51:765–72 (Behavior of *Rhinoceros unicornis* in Assam).

224. Getz, L. L. (1960). *Amer. Midland Natur.*, 64:392–405 (Population study of *Microtus pennsylvanicus*).

225. Geyer, R. P., Geyer, B. R., Derse, P. H., Zinkin, T., Elvehjem, C. A., and Hart, E. B. (1947). *Jour. Nutrition*, 33:129–42 (Growth of rats kept under conditions preventing coprophagy).

226. Giaja, J. (1938). *L'Homéothermie*. Paris, Hermann, 70 pp.

227. Godet, R. (1951). *Bull. Soc. Zool. France*, 75:107–28 (Ecology and behavior of the European mole. F).

228. Godfrey, G., and Crowcroft, P. (1960). *The Life of the Mole*. London, Museum Press, 152 pp.

229. Goodall, J. (1963). *Nat. Geogr.*, 124:272–308 (Field observations on the chimpanzees).

230. Gorbman, A., and Bern, H. A. (1962). *A Textbook of Comparative Endocrinology*. New York, Wiley, xiv + 468 pp.

231. Gould, E. (1955). *J.M.*, 36:399–407 (Feeding efficiency of insectivorous bats).

232. Gould, J., and Morgan, C. T. (1942). *J. Comp. Psychol.*, 34: 321–29 (Auditory sensitivity in the rat).

233. Grassé, P., editor (1955). *Traité de Zoologie. 17. Mammifères. Les Ordres: anatomie, éthologie, systématique*. Paris, Masson, 2300 pp. The most recent treatise, to be completed by two more volumes on comparative morphology.

234. Gray, J. (1953). *How Animals Move*. Cambridge, Cambridge University Press, xii + 114 pp.

235. Gregg, R. M., Jamison, E., Wilkie, R., and Radinsky, T. (1929). *J. Comp. Psychol.*, 9:379–95 (Color blindness in dogs, cats, and raccoons).

236. Grether, W. F. (1940). *J. Comp. Psychol.*, 29:167–92 (Color vision in the chimpanzee).

237. Griffin, D. R. (1940). *J.M.*, 21:181–87 (New England cave bats).

238. Griffin, D. R. (1945). *J.M.*, 26:1–15 (Travels of banded cave bats).

239. Griffin, D. R. (1959). *Listening in the Dark*. New Haven, Yale University Press, xvii + 413 pp.

240. Griffin, D. R., Webster, F. A., and Michael, C. R. (1960). *Animal Behaviour*, 8:141–54 (Echo location of flying insects by bats).

241. Griffo, J. V., Jr. (1961). *Amer. Midland Natur.*, 65:257–89 (Homing in the cotton mouse).

242. Grinnell, J. (1923). *J.M.*, 4:137–49 (Burrowing rodents as agents in soil formation in California).

243. Groome, J. R. (1940). *P.Z.S.* (A), 110:37–42 (Seasonal modifications of the interstitial tissue of the testis in *Pteropus*).

244. Grzimek, B. (1956). *Z.f.T.*, 13:143–50 (Hippopotamus behavior).

245. Guiraud, M. (1948). *M.*, 12:54–66 (Life history of the wart hog).

246. Haas, G. (1959). *Z.f.T.*, 16:218–42 (Innate movements in the Barbary sheep. G).

247. Haddow, A. J. (1952). *P.Z.S.*, 122:297–394 (Ecology of *Cercopithecus ascanius schmidti*).

248. Hafez, E. S. E., editor (1962). *The Behaviour of Domestic Animals*. London, Baillère, Tindall and Cox, XIV + 619 pp. An excellent book of interest for all mammalogists.

249. Hainard, R. (1961–62). *Les Mammifères sauvages d'Europe*. Neuchâtel and Paris, Delachaux and Niestlé. 2 volumes. These excellent books are full of original observations.

250. Hall, E. R., and Kelson, K. R. (1959). *The Mammals of North America*. New York, Ronald, xxx + 1083 + 79 pp. Covers Central America and the West Indies. No biology.

251. Hall, F. G., Dill, D. B., and Guzman Barron, E. S. (1936). *Jour. Cell. Comp. Physiol.*, 8:301–13 (Comparative physiology in high altitudes).

252. Hall, K. R. L. (1962). *P.Z.S.*, 139:181–220, 283–327 (Feeding habits, locomotion, and sexual behavior of *Papio ursinus* in South Africa).

253. Hamilton, J. E. (1934). *Discovery Reports*, 8:269–318 (Life history of *Otaria byronia*).

254. Hamilton, W. J., Jr. (1937). *Ecology*, 18:255–63 (Activity and home range of *Microtus pennsylvanicus*).

255. Hardy, G. A. (1949). *Canad. Field Natur.*, 63:86–87 (Squirrel cache of fungi).

256. Harlow, H. F., and Harlow, M. K. (1961). *Natural History*, 70, No. 10, pp. 48–55 (Maternal deprivation in monkeys).

257. Harlow, H. F., and Harlow, M. K. (1962). *Scientific American*, 207, No. 5, pp. 136–46 (Social deprivation in monkeys).

258. Harms, J. W. (1956). *Primatologia*, 1:661–722 (Pregnancy and parturition in monkeys and apes. G).

259. Harris, V. T. (1952). *Contr. Lab. Vert. Biol. Univ. Michigan*, 56:1–53 (Experimental study of habitat selection by races of *Peromyscus maniculatus*).

260. Harrison, J. L. (1952). *Nature*, 170:73–74 (Moonlight and the pregnancy of Malayan forest rats).

261. Harrison, J. L. (1956). *Bull. Raffles Mus.*, 27:5–26 (Survival rates of Malayan rats).

262. Hartman, C. G. (1920). *Anat. Record*, 19:251–61 (Parturition in the Virginia opossum).

263. Hartman, C. G. (1933). *Quart. Rev. Biol.*, 8:185–93 (Survival of spermatozoa in the female genital tract of the bat).

264. Hartman, C. G. (1952). *Possums*. Austin, University of Texas Press, xiii + 174 pp.

265. Hauchecorne, F. (1927). *Zeits. f. Morphol. Ökol. Tiere*, 9:439–571 (Food of the European mole. G).

266. Hawkins, A. E., and Jewell, P. A. (1962). *P.Z.S.*, 138:137–65 (Food consumption of shrews and moles).

267. Hayne, D. W. (1949). *J.M.*, 30:399–411 (Methods for estimating population from trapping records).

268. Hayne, D. W. (1949–50). *J.M.*, 30:1–18 and 31:26–39 (Calculation of size of home range).

269. Hediger, H. (1940). *Verhandl-schweiz. naturforsch. Ges.*, 120:174–76 (Parturition in the American bison. G).

270. Hediger, H. (1948). *Physiol. Comp. Oecol.*, 1:46–62 (Raising of the European hare in captivity. G).

271. Hediger, H. (1949). *Bijdragen tot de Dierkunde*, 28:172–84 (Territorial behavior among mammals. G).

272. Hediger, H. (1950). *Wild Animals in Captivity: An Outline of the Biology of Zoological Gardens*. London, Butterworth, ix + 207 pp.

273. Hediger, H. (1951). *Observations sur la psychologie animale dans les parcs nationaux du Congo belge*. Brussels, Institut des Parcs Nationaux du Congo, 196 pp.

274. Hediger, H. (1958). *H.d.Z.*, 8, 10, 9:1–28 (Behavior of marsupials. G).

275. Hediger, H., and Kummer, H. (1961). *H.d.Z.*, 8, 10, 8a:1–8 (Behavior of the Tachyglossidae. G).

276. Heim de Balsac, H. (1936). *Biogéographie des mammifères et des oiseaux de l'Afrique du Nord*. Supplément 21 au Bull. Biol. France Belgique, 446 pp.

277. Heim de Balsac, H. (1951). *Rev. Mycol.*, 16:238–41 (Mammals eating mushrooms. F).

278. Heimburger, N. (1959). *Z.f.T.*, 16:104–13 (Marking of territory among Canidae. G).

279. Heptner, V. G., Nasimovitsch, A. A., and Bannikov, A. G. (1961). (*The Mammals of the Soviet Union*). Vol. 1, 776 pp. (Ungulates). The most modern textbook, to be completed in three volumes. Contains much on biology. Text in Russian. German translation in progress.

280. Herlant, M. (1934). *Bull. Acad. Roy. Belgique* (5), 20:359–66 (Experimentally induced ovulation in hibernating bats, F).

281. Herter, K. (1936). *Zeits. vergl. Physiol.*, 23:605–50 (Thermotactic optimum of rodents. G).

282. Herter, K. (1938). *Die Biologie der europäischen Igel.* Leipzig, Schops, 222 pp.

283. Herter, K. (1957). *H.d.Z.*, 8, 10, 10:1–50 (Behavior of the Insectivora. G).

284. Herter, K. (1959). *Iltisse und Frettchen.* Wittenberg Lutherstadt, Ziemsen, 112 pp.

285. Hewer, H. R. (1960). *M.*, 24:400–21 (Breeding behavior of the gray seal).

286. Hildebrand, M. (1959–61). *J.M.*, 40:481–95 and 42:84–91 (Locomotion of the cheetah).

287. Hinde, R. A., and Rowell, T. E. (1962). *P.Z.S.*, 138:1–21 (Communication by postures and facial expressions in the rhesus monkey).

288. Höglund, N. H. (1957). *Viltrevy*, 1:267–82 (Reproduction of the European varying hare. In Swedish).

289. Holdenried, R., Evans, F. C., and Longanecker, D. S. (1951). *Ecol. Monogr.*, 21:1–18 (Host-parasite-disease relationships in a mammalian community).

290. Hooper, E. T. (1941). *Misc. Publ. Mus. Zool. Univ. Michigan*, 51:1–47 (Mammals of the lava fields of New Mexico).

291. Hopkins, G. H. E. (1949). *P.Z.S.*, 119:387–604 (Host associations of the lice of mammals).

292. Horner, B. E. (1947). *J.M.*, 28:31–36 (Paternal care in *Peromyscus*).

293. Horton, G. P. (1933). *J. Comp. Psychol.*, 15:59–73 (Hearing in the guinea pig).

294. Howard, W. E. (1949). *Cont. Lab. Vert. Biol. Univ. Michigan*, 43:1–50 (Dispersal, inbreeding, and longevity of prairie deer mice).

295. Howard, W. E. (1957). *J.M.*, 38:516–17 (Food consumption of small carnivores).

296. Howard, W. E., and Childs, H. E., Jr. (1959). *Hilgardia*, 29: 277–58 (Ecology of pocket gophers).
297. Howell, A. B. (1944). *Speed in Animals; Their Specialization for Running and Leaping.* Chicago, University of Chicago Press, 270 pp.
298. Imaizumi, Y. (1960). *Coloured Illustrations of the Mammals of Japan.* Osaka, Hoijusha, 196 pp. Excellent plates. Text in Japanese.
299. Imanishi, K. (1960). *Current Anthropology*, 1:393–407 (Social life of the Japanese macaque).
300. Immelmann, K., and Gebbing, H. (1962). *Z.f.T.*, 19:84–92 (Sleep in the giraffe and the okapi. G).
301. Ingles, L. G. (1949). *J.M.*, 30:343–50 (Ground water and snow as limiting factors for pocket gophers).
302. Ingles, L. G. (1957). *J.M.*, 38:263–64 (Innate feeding behavior of the coatimundi).
303. Innis, A. C. (1958). *P.Z.S.*, 131:245–78 (Social and reproductive behavior of the giraffe).
304. Innis Dagg, A. (1962). *J.M.*, 43:88–97 (Role of the neck in the movements of the giraffe).
305. Irving, L. (1939). *Physiol. Reviews*, 19:112–34 (Respiration in diving animals).
306. Irving, L. (1942). *Trans. New York Acad. Sci.*, 5:11–16 (Heart and circulation during diving).
307. Irving, L., and Krog, J. (1954). *Jour. Appl. Physiol.*, 6:667–80 (Body temperature of arctic birds and mammals).
308. Irving, L., Scholander, P. F., and Grinnell, S. W. (1941). *Jour. Cell. Comp. Physiol.*, 17:145–68 (Respiration of the porpoise).
309. Irving, L., Scholander, P. F., and Grinnell, S. W. (1942a). *Jour. Cell. Comp. Physiol.*, 18:283–97 (Heart rate of diving seals).
310. Irving, L., Scholander, P. F., and Grinnell, S. W. (1942b). *Amer. Jour. Physiol.*, 135:557–66 (Blood pressure of diving seals).
311. Itani, J. (1954). *Japanese Monkeys in Takasaki-Yama.* Tokyo, Kokunsha (In Japanese. Quoted after the partial translation of J. E. Frisch).
312. Itani, J. (1959). *Primates*, 2:61–93 (Paternal care in Japanese macaques).
313. Jaeger, P. (1954). *Bull. Inst. fr. Afrique Noire*, A, 16:796–821 (Pollination of the baobab by bats. F).

314. Jameson, E. W., Jr., and Brennan, J. M. (1957). *Ecol. Monogr.*, 27:45–54 (Environmental analysis of some ectoparasites of small forest mammals).

314a. Jay, P. (1963). *Terre et Vie*, 17:50–65 (Field observations on the common Indian Langur; see also contribution in 468 and 537a).

315. Jettmar, H. M. (1926). *Z.f.S.*, 1:13–22 (Burrows of trans-Baikal mammals. G).

316. Johnson, C. E. (1921). *J.M.*, 2:87–89 (The "hand stand" habit of the spotted skunk).

317. Kachkarov, D. N., and Korovine, E. P. (1942). *La Vie dans les déserts.* Paris, Payot, 361 pp.

318. Kalabuchov, N. J. (1933). *Rec. Trav. Sci. Univ. Moscou.*, 1: 29–33 (Life span of *Citellus pygmæus* in the Caucasus. R).

319. Kalabuchov, N. J. (1937). *J. Anim. Ecol.*, 6:254–72 (Altitude adaptations of rodents).

320. Kalela, O. (1957). *Ann. Acad. Scient. Fenn.*, A, IV, No. 34, pp. 1–60 (Regulation of reproductive rate in subarctic populations of *Clethrionomys rufocanus*).

321. Kalela, O. (1961a). *Ann. Acad. Sci. Fenn.*, A, IV, 55:1–62 (Seasonal change of habitat of *Lemmus lemmus*).

322. Kalela, O. (1962b). *H.d.Z.*, 8, 10, 3:1–40 (Migrations of mammals. G).

323. Katsuki, Y., and Davis, H. (1954). *J. Neurophysiol.*, 17:308–16. (Electrophysiology of the ear of the kangaroo rat).

324. Katz, I. (1949). *Zoologica*, 34:9–18 (Behavioral interactions in a captive herd of Barbary sheep).

325. Kaufmann, J. H. (1962). *Univ. Calif. Publ. Zool.*, 60, No. 3 (Ecology and social behavior of the coati on Barro Colorado Island, Panama).

326. Kayser, C. (1961). *The Physiology of Natural Hibernation.* Oxford, Pergamon, VII + 325 pp.

327. Kellog, W. N. (1961). *Porpoises and Sonar.* Chicago, University of Chicago Press, XIV + 177 pp., 8 pls., 25 figs.

328. Kenyon, K. W. (1960). *M.*, 24:431–44 (Territorial behavior in the Alaska fur seal).

329. King, J. A. (1955). *Contr. Lab. Vertebrate Biol. Univ. Michigan*, 67:1–123 (Social behavior and population dynamics of the black-tailed prairie dog).

330. Kirchshofer, R. (1958). *Z.f.S.*, 23:33–49 (Ecology and behavior of *Gerbillus nanus garamantis*. G).

331. Koenig, L. (1957). *Z.f.T.*, 14:510–21 (Marking of territory in the Alpine marmot. G).

332. Koenig, L. (1960). *Z.f.T.*, 17:427–505 (Ethology of *Glis glis*. G).

333. Koford, C. B. (1957). *Ecol. Monogr.*, 27:153–219 (Ecology and behavior of the vicuna in Peru).

334. Koford, C. B. (1958). *Wildlife Monographs*, 3:1–78 (Relationships of the prairie dog with plants, soils, and land use). See also *Terre et Vie*, 1961:327–41.

335. Kolosov, A. M. (1935). *Bull. Soc. Natur. Moscou, Ser. Biol.*, 44:165–77 (Biology of the korsak fox. R).

336. Koponen, T., Kokkonen, A., and Kalela, O. (1961). *Ann. Acad. Sci. Fenn.*, A, IV, 52:1–30 (Spring migration of *Lemmus lemmus*).

337. Krieg, H., and Rahm. U. (1961). *H.d.Z.*, 8, 10, 12:1–48 (Behavior of Xenarthra and Pholidota. G).

338. Kriszat, G. (1940). *Zeits. f. Morphol. Ökol. Tiere*, 36:446–511 (Sense organs and biology of the European mole. G).

339. Kritzler, H. (1952). *J.M.*, 33:321–34 (The pilot whale in captivity).

340. Krumbiegel, I. (1953–55). *Biologie der Saugetiere*. Krefeld and Baden Baden, Agis, 844 pp. A somewhat uncritical compilation. To be used with caution.

341. Kummer, H., and Kurt, F. (1963). *Folia Primatologica*, 1:4–19 (Social life of free-living Hamadryas baboons).

342. Kurt, M. (1960). *M.*, 24:258–72 (Sleep in elephants. F).

343. Lataste, F. (1887). *Documents pour l'éthologie des mammifères*. Bordeaux, 659 pp. Also published, in parts, in *Actes Soc. Linn. Bordeaux*, Vols. 40, 41, and 43.

344. Laurie, E. M. O., and Hill, J. E. (1954). *List of Land Mammals of New Guinea, Celebes and the Adjacent Islands, 1758–1952*. London, British Museum (Nat. Hist.), 175 pp. The basic check list.

345. Laws, R. M. (1953–56). *Falkland Islands Dependencies Survey, Sci. Rep.*, 8, 13, and 15, 62 + 88 + 66 pp. (Natural History of the southern elephant seal).

345a. Laws, R. M. (1959). *Norks Hvalfangst-Tidende*, 9:425–52 (Accelerated growth in seals).

346. Laws, R. M. (1960). *Norsk Hvalfangst-Tidende*, 10–11:466–76, 520–42 (The southern elephant seal at South Georgia).

347. Laws, R. M. (1962a). *Z.f.S.*, 27:129–46 (Age determination of pinnipeds).

348. Laws, R. M. (1962b). *Discovery Reports*, 31:327-485 (Reproduction, growth, and age of southern fin whales).
349. Laws, R. M. (1962c), in Le Cren, E. D., and Holdgate, M. W. *The Exploitation of Natural Animal Populations*, pp. 137-58 (Population dynamics of southern stocks of baleen whales).
350. Laws, R. M., and Taylor, R. J. T. (1957). *P.Z.S.*, 129:315-324 (Mass mortality of crabeater seals).
351. Layne, J. N. (1958). *J.W.M.*, 22:157-63 (Reproduction of the gray fox).
352. Lechleitner, R. R. (1958). *Amer. Midland Natur.*, 60:145-55 (Behavior of the black-tailed jack rabbit).
353. Legouix, J. P. (1957). *M*, 21:396-404 (Hearing in mammals. A review. F).
354. Leitch, I., Hytten, F. E., and Billewicz, W. Z. (1959). *P.Z.S.*, 133:11-28 (Maternal and neonatal weights in mammals).
355. Leslie, P. H., and Ranson, R. M. (1940). *J. Anim. Ecol.*, 9:27-52 (Mortality, fertility, and rate of natural increase of a laboratory population of *Microtus agrestis*).
356. Leyhausen, P. (1956). *H.d.Z.*, 8, 10, 21:1-34 (Behavior of the cats. G).
357. Lindahl, P. E., and Sundall, G. (1958). *Nature*, 182:1392 (Sex ratio before uterine implantation in the golden hamster).
358. Lindemann, W. (1955). *Behaviour*, 8:1-45 (Behavior development of the lynx. G).
359. Lipkow, J. (1954). *Zeits. f. Morphol Ökol. Tiere*, 42:333-72 (Lateral gland of the golden hamster).
360. Lockley, R. M. (1961). *J. Animal Ecol.*, 30:385-423 (Social behavior of the European wild rabbit).
361. Löhner, L. (1926). *Pflügers Archiv.*, 212:84-94 (Olfactory acuity of police dogs. G).
362. Lord, R. D., Jr. (1959). *J.W.M.*, 23:358-60 (The lens as an indicator of age in cottontail rabbits).
363. Lord, R. D., Jr. (1960). *Amer. Midland Natur.*, 64:488-99 (Litter size and latitude).
364. Lyman, C. P. (1942). *Proc. New England Zool. Club*, 19:75-78 (Control of coat color in the varying hare by daily illumination).
365. Lyman, C. P., and Dawe, A. R., editors. (1960). *Mammalian Hibernation*. Proceedings of the First International Symposium on Natural Mammalian Hibernation, May 13-15, 1959. *Bull. Mus. Comp. Zool.*, 124:1-549.

366. Lyne, A. G. (1959). *P.Z.S.*, 133:79–133 (Vibrissae in marsupials).
367. McBride, A. F., and Hebb, D. O. (1948). *J. Comp. Psychol.*, 41:111–23 (Behavior of the bottlenosed dolphin).
368. McBride, A. F., and Kritzler, H. (1951). *J.M.*, 32:251–66 (Pregnancy, parturition, and postnatal behavior of the bottlenosed dolphin).
369. McCabe, T. T., and Blanchard, B. (1950). *Three Species of Peromyscus.* Santa Barbara, Rood Associates, v + 136 pp.
370. McDiarmid, A. (1962). *Diseases of Free-Living Animals.* Rome, FAO Publications, Agricultural Series, No. 57, 119 pp.
371. McGill, H. C., Jr., Strong, J. P., Holman, R. L., and Werthessen, N. T. (1960). *Circulation Research*, 8:670–79 (Arterial lesions in wild Kenya baboons).
372. McHugh, T. (1958). *Zoologica*, 43:1–40 (Social behavior of the American buffalo).
373. McLaren, I. A. (1958). *Jour. Fish. Res. Bd. Canada*, 15:219–27 (Growth and reproduction of the bearded seal).
374. MacLulich, D. A. (1957). *Univ. Toronto Stud., Biol. Ser.*, 43:1–36 (Population fluctuations in *Lepus americanus*).
375. Macpherson, R. K. (1960). *Physiological Responses to Hot Environments.* London, H. M. Stationery Office, xv + 323 pp.
376. Malbrant, R. (1952). *Faune du Centre Africain Français (Mammifères et Oiseaux)*, 2nd edition. Paris, Lechevalier, 616 pp. Mammals on pp. 15–221. Biological data on the larger species.
377. Malbrant, R., and Maclatchy, A. (1949). *Faune de l'équateur africain français.* 2, *Mammifères.* Paris, Lechevalier, 323 pp. Keys for identification; life-history data for large species.
378. Malmo, R. B., and Grether, W. F. (1947). *J. Comp. Physiol. Psychol.*, 40:143–47 (Red blindness in *Cebus* monkeys).
379. Marlow, B. J. (1962). *Marsupials of Australia.* Brisbane, Jacaranda Press, 141 pp. Excellent introduction.
380. Matthews, L. H. (1929). *Discovery Reports*, 1:233–96 (Natural history of the elephant seal).
381. Matthews, L. H. (1939). *P.Z.S.*, 109:43–56 (Habits of the spotted hyena).
382. Matthews, L. H. (1944). *P.Z.S.*, 113:117–20 (Parturition in the kangaroo).

383. Matthews, L. H. (1952). *British Mammals.* London, Collins, xii + 410 pp. Essentially biological.

384. Meyer, D. R., Miles, R. C., and Ratoosh, P. (1958). *J. Neurophysiol.,* 17:289–94 (Absence of color vision in the cat).

385. Meyer-Holzapfel, M. (1956). *H.d.Z.,* 8, 10, 5:1–36 (Play in mammals. G).

386. Meyer-Holzapfel, M. (1957). *H.d.Z.,* 8, 10, 17:1–28 (Behavior of the bears. G).

387. Miles, R. C. (1958a). *J. Comp. Physiol. Psychol.,* 51:152–54 (Color vision in the marmoset).

388. Miles, R. C. (1958b). *J. Comp. Physiol. Psychol.,* 51:328–31 (Color vision in the squirrel monkey).

389. Miles, R. C., Ratoosh, P., and Meyer, D. R. (1956). *J. Neurophysiol.,* 19:254–58 (Absence of color vision in the guinea pig).

390. Miller, W. C. (1932). *Proc. Roy. Phys. Soc.,* 22:99–101 (Sex ratio of Scottish red deer).

391. Mills, C. A. (1945). *Ann. New York Acad. Sci.,* 46:97–105 (Influence of environmental temperatures on warmblooded animals).

392. Minchin, K. A. (1937). *Records S. Austral. Mus.,* 6:1–3 (Weaning of a young koala).

393. Mohr, C. O. (1947). *Amer. Midland Natur.,* 37:223–49 (Tables of equivalent populations of North American mammals).

394. Mohr, C. O., and Lord, R. D., Jr. (1960). *J.W.M.,* 24:290–97 (Relationships between ectoparasite populations and rabbit populations).

395. Mohr, E. (1941). *Zool. Anzeig.,* 135:48–65 (Caudal autotomy and tail regeneration among rodents. G).

396. Mohr, E. (1956). *H.d.Z.,* 8, 10, 22:1–20 (Behavior of the Pinnipedia. G).

397. Mohres, F. P. (1952). *Zeits. vergl. Physiol.,* 34:547–88 (Echo location of Rhinolophidae. G).

398. Moore, J. C. (1956). *Amer. Mus. Novitates,* No. 1811, pp. 1–24 (Observations on manatees).

399. Morrison, P. R., Pierce, M., and Ryser, F. A. (1957). *Amer. Midland Natur.,* 57:493–501 (Food consumption of shrews).

400. Mosby, H. S., editor. (1960). *Manual of Game Investigational Techniques.* Ann Arbor, The Wildlife Society, xx + 345 pp.

401. Mossman, A. S., and Mossman, H. W. (1962). *Science,* 137:869 (Fetal sex ratio in impala).

402. Moulton, D. G., Ashton, E. H., and Eayrs, J. T. (1960). *Animal Behaviour,* 8:117–28 (Olfactory acuity of the dog).

403. Moulton, D. G., and Eayrs, J. T. (1960). *Quart. J. Exp. Psychol.,* 12:99–109 (Olfactory acuity of the rat).

404. Müller, H. (1954). *Rev. Suisse Zool.,* 61:451–53 (Behavior development of *Mustela erminea.* G).

405. Murie, A. (1944). *The Wolves of Mount McKinley.* Washington, Fauna of the Nat. Parks., xx + 258 pp.

406. Murie, A. (1961). *A Naturalist in Alaska.* New York, Devin-Adair, xi + 302 pp.

407. Murie, O. J. (1935). *North Amer. Fauna,* 54:1–93 (Alaska-Yukon caribou).

408. Murie, O. J. (1940). *J.M.,* 21:119–31 (Notes on the sea otter).

409. Murie, O. J. (1951). *The Elk of North America.* Washington, Wildlife Management Institute, x + 376 pp.

410. Murie, O. J., and Murie, A. (1931). *J.M.,* 12:200–09 (Travels of *Peromyscus*).

411. Neal, E. (1948). *The Badger.* London, Collins, xv + 158 pp.

412. Nerincx, E. (1944). *Bull. Mus. Roy. Hist. Nat. Belgique,* 20(19):1–24 (Ecology and behavior of bats in Belgium. F).

413. Neuhaus, W. (1953–56). *Zeits. vergl. Physiol.,* 35:527–52, 38: 238–58, 39:25–43 (Olfactory acuity of the dog. G).

414. Nevo, E. (1961). *M.,* 25:127–44 (Ecology of *Spalax ehrenbergi* in Israel).

415. Nice, M. M., Nice, C., and Ewers, D. (1956). *J.M.,* 37:64–74 (Behavior development in snowshoe hares and red squirrels).

416. Nolte, A. (1955). *Z.f.T.,* 12:77–87 (Ethology of *Macaca radiata* in S. India. G).

417. Novick, A. (1958). *J. Exp. Zool.,* 137:443–62 (Orientation in Old World Megachiroptera).

418. Novikov, B. G., and Blagodatskaya, G. I. (1948). *Dokl. Akad. Nauk SSSR,* 61:577–80 (Protective seasonal coloration. R).

419. Odum, E. P. (1959). *Fundamentals of Ecology.* 2nd edition. Philadelphia and London, xvii + 546 pp. By far the best textbook on the subject.

420. Ognev, S. I. (1928–50). (*The Mammals of Eastern Europe and Northern Asia*). Moscow, USSR Academy of Sciences, Vols. 1–7. A ninth volume has been published by A. G. Tomilin in 1957, dealing with the cetaceans. The whole

set is still unfinished. Contains much on biology. Text in Russian. English translation underway in Israel.

421. Osgood, W. H. (1943). *Field Mus. Nat. Hist., Zool.,* 30:1–268 (Taxonomy of Chilean mammals).

422. Palmer, R. S. (1954). *The Mammal Guide. Mammals of North America, North of Mexico.* New York, Doubleday, 384 pp. Excellent summary of the life histories, but poor plates.

423. Parkes, A. S. (1924). *Sci. Prog.,* 18:426–35 (Factors governing mammalian sex ratio).

424. Parkes, A. S., and Bruce, H. M. (1961). *Science,* 134:1049–54 (Olfactory stimuli in mammalian reproduction).

425. Parry, D. A. (1949). *Brit. Jour. Exp. Biol.,* 26:24–34 (The swimming of whales).

426. Pavlinine, V. N. (1948). *Zool. Zjur.,* 27:555–62 (Marking of European moles in the Ural Mountains. R).

427. Pearson, O. P. (1942). *J.M.,* 23:159–66 (Poisonous saliva of *Blarina brevicauda*).

428. Pearson, O. P. (1944). *Amer. Jour. Anat.,* 75:39–93 (Reproduction in *Blarina brevicauda*).

429. Pearson, O. P. (1948). *J.M.,* 29:345–73 (Life history of the mountain viscacha in Peru).

430. Pearson, O. P. (1951). *Bull. Mus. Comp. Zool.,* 106:117–76 (Mammals of the Peruvian highlands. Biological data).

431. Pearson, O. P. (1959). *Mem. Mus. Hist. Nat. Javier Prado,* 9:1–56 (Biology of the subterranean *Ctenomys* in Peru).

432. Pengelley, E. T., and Fisher, K. C. (1957). *Nature,* 180:1371–72 (Internal seasonal clock and hibernation in *Citellus lateralis*).

433. Peterson, R. L. (1955). *North American Moose.* Toronto, University of Toronto Press, xi + 280 pp.

434. Petrides, G. A. (1949). *J.M.,* 30:364–78 (Sex and age determination in the opossum).

435. Petrides, G. A. (1950). *Amer. Midland Natur.,* 43:355–82 (Sex and age ratios in furred animals).

436. Petter, J. J. (1962). *Mem. Mus. Nat. Hist. Nat.,* A, 27:1–146 (Ecology and behavior of Madagascar lemurs. F).

437. Petter-Rousseaux, A., and Bourlière, F. (1959). *Comptes Rendus Soc. Biol.,* 153:226–28 (Experimental modification of the breeding cycle of *Microcebus murinus* through modification of the photo-period. F).

438. Petzsch, H. (1936). *Beitrage zur Biologie, inbesondere Fort-*

pflanzungsbiologie des Hamsters (Cricetus cricetus L).
Leipzig, Schops, 83 pp.

439. Pilters, H. (1954). *Z.f.T.,* 11:213–303 (Behavior of the New World Tylopods in captivity. G).

440. Pilters, H. (1956). *H.d.Z.,* 8, 10, 27:1–24 (Behavior of the Tilopoda. G). See also Gauthier-Pilters.

441. Pimlott, D. H. (1961). *Terre et Vie,* 1961:246–65 (Ecology of moose in North America).

442. Pitelka, F. (1957). *Biology Colloquium Proceedings, Oregon State College,* 18:73–88 and *Cold Spring Harbor Symposia of Quantitative Biology,* 22:237–51 (Microtine cycles in Alaska).

443. Player, I. C., and Feely, J. M. (1960). *Lammergeier,* 1:3–24 (Life history of *Ceratotherium simum*).

444. Pocock, R. I. (1910). *P.Z.S.,* 1910:840–985 (Specialized cutaneous glands of ruminants).

445. Pocock, R. I. (1915). *P.Z.S.,* 1915:131–49 (Feet and glands of the Viverrinae).

446. Porsch, O. (1932). *Oesterr. bot. Zeits.,* 80:31–44 (Pollination of *Crescentia* by bats. G).

447. Poulton, E. B. (1929). *P.Z.S.,* 1929:277–303 (Prey of British insectivorous bats).

448. Prater, S. H. (1947). *The Book of Indian Animals.* Bombay, Nat. Hist. Soc., xxxii + 263 pp. Excellent introduction; biological data. A new, revised edition, with beautiful color plates by P. Barruel, is in preparation.

449. Prosser, C. L., and Brown, F. A., Jr. (1961). *Comparative Animal Physiology.* 2nd edition. Philadelphia, Saunders, ix + 688 pp.

450. Pruitt, W. O., Jr. (1957). *Saug. Mitteil.,* 5:18–27 (Survey of the Soricidae).

451. Pruitt, W. O., Jr. (1958). *Arctic,* 10:130–38 (Bioclimate of some taiga mammals).

452. Pruitt, W. O., Jr. (1960). *Biological Papers,* Univ. of Alaska, 3:1–43 (Ethology of the Barren Ground caribou).

453. Pucek, M. (1959). *Acta Theriologica,* 3:93–104 (Venom of the European water shrew).

454. Pucek, Z. (1959). *Acta Theriologica,* 3, 43–73 (Sex ratio in the common shrew).

455. Rahm, U. (1961). *H.d.Z.,* 8, 10, 23:1–8 (Behavior of Tubulidentata. G).

456. Rainey, D. G. (1956). *Univ. Kansas Publ., Mus. Nat. Hist.,*

8:535–646 (Life history and ecology of *Neotoma flori-dana*).

457. Ramakrishna, P. A. (1950). *J.M.*, 31:274–78 (Parturition in certain Indian bats).

458. Rand, A. L. (1935). *J.M.*, 16:89–104 (Habits of some mammals of Madagascar).

459. Rand, R. W. (1955). *P.Z.S.*, 124:717–40 (Reproduction in the female *Arctocephalus pusillus*).

460. Raspopov, M. P., and Issakov, U. A. (1934). *(Biology of Hares and Squirrels: Their Diseases)*. Moscow, 140 pp. Text in Russian.

461. Rayner, G. W. (1940–48). *Discovery Reports*, 19:245–84 and 25:31–38 (Results of whale-marking in Antarctica).

462. Reed, C. A., and Carr, W. H. (1949). *J.M.*, 30:79–80 (Use of cactus as protection by the hooded skunk).

463. Reed, C. E. (1946). *Jour. Comp. Psychol.*, 39:185–206 (Copulatory behavior of small mammals).

464. Reichstein, H. (1959). *Zool. Jahrb., Abt. Syst. Oekol. Geogr. Tiere*, 86:367–82 (Population ecology of the field vole. G).

465. Reichstein, H. (1960). *Z.f.S.*, 25:150–69 (Home range and territory in the common vole. G).

466. Rensch, B., and Altevogt, R. (1953). *Z.f.T.*, 10:119–34 (Color vision in the Indian elephant. G).

467. Reynolds, V. (1963). *Folia Primatologica*, 1:95–102 (Field observations on chimpanzees).

468. Rheingold, H. L. (1963). *Maternal Behavior in Mammals*. New York, Wiley, viii + 349 pp.

469. Rice, D. W. (1960). *J.M.*, 41:376–85 (Population dynamics of the Hawaiian monk seal).

470. Richard, P. B. (1958). *M.*, 22:566–74 (The European beaver's use of its feet in cleaning its fur. F).

470a. Richard, P. B. (1959). *Comptes Rendus Acad. Sci.*, 248:1424–26 (Reingestion in the European beaver. F).

471. Robinette, W. L., Gashwiller, J. S., Low, J. B., and Jones, D. A. (1957). *J.W.M.*, 21:1–16 (Differential mortality by sex and age among mule deer).

472. Robinson, P. F. (1959). *Science*, 130:502–03 (Metabolism and tolerance to heat of *Meriones unguiculatus*).

473. Rochon-Duvignaud, A. (1943). *Les Yeux et la vision des Vertébrés*. Paris, Masson, 719 pp.

474. Roderick, T. H., and Storer, J. B. (1961). *Science*, 134:48–49 (Correlation between litter size and life span in mice).

475. Rosenzweig, M. R., Riley, D. A., and Krech, D. (1955). *Science*, 121:600 (Echo location in the rat).

476. Roth-Kolar, H. (1957). *Z.f.T.*, 14:362–75 (Ethology of the agouti. G).

477. Russell, C. P. (1932). *Ecol. Monogr.*, 2:1–46 (Seasonal migrations of mule deer).

478. Ryberg, O. (1947). *Studies on Bats and Bat Parasites*. Stockholm, Svensk Natur, XVI + 330 pp.

479. Saint-Girons, M. C. (1957). *M.*, 21:69–76 (Food consumption of *Suncus etruscus*. F).

480. Saint-Girons, M. C. (1959). *M.*, 23:245–76 (Activity patterns of small rodents. F).

481. Salman, D. H. (1949). *Physiol. Comp. Oecol.*, 1:95–109 (Home range of cottontails).

482. Sanderson, I. T. (1940). *Trans. Zool. Soc. London*, 24:623–725 (Mammals of the Cameroons forest).

483. Sather, J. H. (1958). *Wildlife Monographs*, 2:1–35 (Biology of the muskrat).

484. Sauvel, R. (1949). *Terre et Vie*, 1949:89–109 (Life history of the kouprey. F).

485. Schäfer, E. (1937). *Z.G.*, N.F., 9:122–39 (Ecology and behavior of *Equus kiang* in Tibet. G).

486. Schaffer, J. (1940). *Die Hautdrüsenorgane der Saugetiere*. Vienna and Berlin, Urban und Schwarzenberg, VIII + 464 pp.

487. Schaller, G. B. (1963). *The Mountain Gorilla. Ecology and Behavior*. Chicago, University of Chicago Press, XVII + 431 pp. A first-rate life history.

488. Schaller, G. B., and Emlen, J. T., Jr. (1962). *Terre et Vie*, 1962:115–32 (Ecology and social behavior of the mountain gorilla).

489. Scheffer, V. B. (1950). *Science*, 112:309–11 (External ridges on the roots of the teeth of pinnipeds as an indication of age).

490. Scheffer, V. B. (1958). *Seals, Sea Lions and Walruses. A Review of the Pinnipedia*. Stanford, Stanford University Press, X + 179 pp.

491. Scheinfeld, A. (1943). *Human Fertility*, 8:33–42 (Factors influencing the sex ratio).

492. Schenkel, R. (1947). *Behaviour*, 1:81–129 (Facial expressions and expressive attitudes of the wolf. G).

493. Schleidt, W. M. (1951). *Z.f.T.*, 8:132–37 (Homing of *Evotomys glareolus.* G).

494. Schleidt, W. M. (1951–52). *Experientia*, 7:65–66, and *Die Naturwiss.*, 39:69–70 (Reactions of voles and mice to high-frequency sounds. G).

495. Schloeth, R. (1961). *Z.f.T.*, 18:574–627 (Social behavior of the Camargue wild cattle. G).

496. Schmidt, F. (1943). *Naturgeschichte des Baum- und Steinmarders.* Leipzig, Schops, 258 pp.

497. Schmidt-Nielsen, B., Schmidt-Nielsen, K., Brokaw, A., and Schneiderman, H. (1948). *Jour. Cell. Comp. Physiol.*, 32:331–60 (Water conservation in desert rodents).

498. Schmidt-Nielsen, B., Schmidt-Nielsen, K., Houpt, T. R., and Jarnum, S. A. (1956–57). *Amer. Jour. Physiol.*, 185:185–94 and 188:103–12 (Water balance and temperature regulation in the camel).

499. Schneider, K. M. (1930). *Z.G.*, *N.F.*, 3:305–14 (Reproductive behavior of the Indian elephant. G).

500. Scholander, P. F., Hock, R., Walters, V., and Irving, L. (1950). *Biol. Bull.*, 99:259–71 (Adaptation to cold in arctic and tropical mammals and birds).

501. Schönholzer, L. (1959). *Zool. Garten*, 24:345–434 (Drinking behavior of captive mammals. G).

502. Schouteden, H. (1948). *Faune du Congo Belge et du Ruanda Urundi. 1. Mammifères.* Tervuren, Musée du Congo, VIII + 331 pp. Taxonomy only.

503. Schultz, A. H. (1956). *Primatologia*, 1:887–964 (Postembryonic age changes in primates).

504. Schultz, A. H. (1960). *P.Z.S.*, 113:337–90 (Age changes and variability in the skulls and teeth of Central American monkeys).

505. Schultz, A. H. (1961). *Viking Fund Publications in Anthropology*, 31:58–90 (Factors influencing the social life of primates).

506. Scott, J. P. (1950). *Ann. New York Acad. Sci.*, 51:1009–21 (Social behavior of dogs and wolves).

507. Scott, J. P. (1958). *Animal Behavior.* Chicago, University of Chicago Press, XI + 281 pp. A good, well-balanced introduction.

508. Scott, T. G. (1943). *Ecol. Monogr.*, 13:427–79 (Food coactions of the northern plains red fox).

509. Seitz, A. (1950). *Z.f.T.*, 7:1–46 (Inborn behavior patterns among Canids).

510. Seitz, A. (1959). *Z.f.T.*, 16:747–71 (Behavior development of *Canis aureus*. G).

511. Severinghaus, C. W. (1949). *J.W.M.*, 13:195–216 (Age criteria of white-tailed deer).

512. Shadle, A. R. (1944). *Jour. Comp. Psychol.*, 37:145–49 (Play of American porcupines).

513. Shadle, A. R. (1946). *J.W.M.*, 10:159–62 (Copulation in the American porcupine).

514. Shadle, A. R., and Po-Chedley, D. (1949). *J.M.*, 30:172–73 (Rate of penetration of a porcupine spine).

515. Shadle, A. R., Smelzer, M., and Metz, M. (1946). *J.M.*, 27:116–21 (Sex reactions of the American porcupine).

516. Shaw, W. T. (1936). *J.M.*, 17:337–49 (Cone-storing by the western pine squirrel).

517. Shaw, W. T. (1944). *J.M.*, 15:275–86 (Harvesting and storing of seeds by the giant kangaroo rat).

518. Sheldon, W. G. (1950). *J.W.M.*, 14:33–42 (Denning habits and home range of red foxes).

519. Shorten, M. (1954). *Squirrels*. London, Collins, xii + 212 pp.

520. Shortridge, G. C. (1934). *The Mammals of South West Africa. A Biological Account of the Forms Occurring in That Region*. London, Heinemann, xxv + 779 pp. A most useful compilation.

521. Siebenaler, J. B., and Caldwell, D. K. (1956). *J.M.*, 37:126–28 (Co-operation among adult dolphins).

522. Simpson, G. G. (1949). *The Meaning of Evolution: A Study of the History of Life and Its Significance for Man*. New Haven, Yale University Press, xv + 364 pp. A brilliant synthesis.

523. Simpson, G. G. (1953). *The Major Features of Evolution*. New York, Columbia University Press, xx + 434 pp.

524. Sivertsen, E. (1941). *Hvalradets Skrifter*, 26:ix + 166 pp. (Biology of *Phoca groenlandica*).

525. Skoczen, S. (1961). *Acta Theriologica*, 5:23–43 (Food storage of the European mole).

526. Slijper, E. J. (1956). *Hvalradets Skrifter*, No. 41:1–62 (Gestation and birth in aquatic mammals).

527. Slijper, E. J. (1960). *H.d.Z.*, 8, 6, 3:1–108 (Parturition among mammals. G).

528. Slijper, E. J. (1962). *Whales*. London, Hutchinson, 475 pp.

529. Sludsky, A. A. (1956). *The Wild Boar. Ecology and Economic Importance.* Alma-Ata, Kazakhstan Academy of Sciences, 218 pp. Text in Russian.

530. Sluiter, J. W., Van Heerdt, P. F., and Bezem, J. J. (1956). *Arch. Néerl. Zool.,* 12:63–88 (Population statistics of *Myotis mystacinus*).

531. Smith, C. F. (1948). *Trans. Kansas Acad. Sci.,* 51:313–15 (Burrow of *Geomys bursarius*).

532. Smith, J. M., and Savage, R. J. G. (1956). *Jour. Linn. Soc.* (Zool.), 42:603–22 (Locomotory adaptations in mammals).

533. Snyder, D. P. (1956). *Misc. Publ., Mus. Zool. Univ. Michigan,* 95:1–33 (Survival rates and population fluctuations of the white-footed mouse).

534. Sokolov, I. I. (1959). (*Ungulate Mammals. Orders Perissodactyla and Artiodactyla*). *Fauna of the USSR,* Vol. 1, No. 3, 640 pp. Moscow, USSR Academy of Sciences. Much about biology. A basic text for northern Asiatic ungulates. Text in Russian.

534a. Sokolov, I. I. (editor). *Mammals of the U.S.S.R.* Moscow and Leningrad, U.S.S.R. Academy of Sciences, 2 volumes, 2001 pp. The only modern field guide to the mammals of the U.S.S.R. Text in Russian.

535. Southern, H. N. (1948). *Behaviour,* 1:173–94 (Sexual behavior of the European wild rabbit).

536. Southern, H. N. (editor). *The Handbook of British Mammals.* Oxford, Blackwell, xxi + 465 pp. An excellent book.

537. Southwick, C. H. (1955). *Ecology,* 36:212–25, 624–34 (Population dynamics and regulation in house mice populations).

537a. Southwick, C. H. (editor) (1963). *Primate Social Behavior.* New York, Van Nostrand, vi + 191 pp. An anthology of some of the best field studies.

538. Southwick, C. H., Beg, M. A., and Siddiqi, M. R. (1961). *Ecology,* 42:538–47, 698–710 (Population survey of rhesus monkeys in India).

539. Spinage, C. A. (1962). *African Wild Life,* 16:55–60 (Rinderpest and faunal distribution patterns in Africa).

540. Steiniger, F. (1950). *Z.f.T.,* 7:356–79 (Social behavior of the wild Norway rat. G).

541. Stephens, M. N. (1952). *P.Z.S.,* 122:417–34 (The wild rabbit in western Wales).

542. Stewart, D. R. M., and Talbot, L. M. (1962). *East Afric. Agric. Forest. Jour.*, 28:58–60 (Census of wildlife on the Serengeti, Mara, and Loita plains).

543. Stickel, L. F. (1949). *Amer. Midland Natur.*, 41:659–64 (Homing of *Peromyscus*).

544. Strecker, R. L., and Emlen, J. T. (1953). *Ecology*, 34:375–85 (Regulatory mechanisms in house mouse populations).

545. Summerhayes, V. S. (1941). *Jour. Ecol.*, 29:14–48 (Effect of voles on vegetation).

546. Taber, F. W. (1945). *J.M.*, 26:211–26 (Life history of the nine-banded armadillo).

547. Taber, R. D. (1961). *Terre et Vie*, 1961:221–45 (Ecology of the black-tailed deer).

548. Taber, R. D., and Dasmann, R. F. (1958). *The Black-Tailed Deer of the Chaparral.* State of California, Dept. Fish and Game, Game Bulletin 8, 163 pp.

549. Talbot, L. M., and Talbot, M. H. (1963). *Wildlife Monographs*, 12:1–88 (Wildebeeste ecology in Western Masailand).

550. Talbot, L. M., and Talbot, M. H. (1962). *East Afric. Agric. Forest. Jour.*, 28 January: 131–38 (Food preferences of some East African wild ungulates).

551. Tate, G. H. H. (1947). *Mammals of Eastern Asia.* New York, Macmillan, xiv + 366 pp. A most useful introduction.

552. Tavolga, M. C., and Essapian, F. S. (1957). *Zoologica*, 42:11–31 (Reproductive behavior of the bottlenosed dolphin).

553. Taylor, W. P., editor (1956). *The Deer of North America. The White-Tailed Mule and Black-Tailed Deer, Genus Odocoileus. Their History and Management.* Washington, Wildlife Management Institute, xix + 668 pp. A basic book for anyone interested in the ecology of the deer.

554. Tembrock, G. (1957a). *H.d.Z.*, 8, 10, 15:1–20 (Behavior of the European red fox. G).

555. Tembrock, G. (1957b). *Z.G.*, N.F., 23:289–560 (Ethology of the European red fox. G).

556. Tembrock, G. (1958). *Zool. Beitr.*, N.F., 3:423–96 (Play in the European red fox. G).

557. Tembrock, G. (1959a). *Tierstimmen. Eine Einführung in die Bioakustik.* Wittemberg-Lutherstadt, Ziemsen, 286 pp.

558. Tembrock, G. (1959b). *Z.f.T.*, 16:351–68 (Social hierarchy in the European red fox. G).

559. Tembrock, G. (1960). *Saug. Mitteil.*, 8:150–54 (The vocal repertoire of the European red fox. G).

560. Tevis, L. (1950). *J.M.*, 31:40–65 (Summer behavior of beavers).

561. Tevis, L., Jr. (1952). *J.M.*, 33:198–205 (Autumn foods of chipmunks and golden-mantled ground squirrels).

562. Thomson, G. B. (1938). *J. Anim. Ecol.*, 7:71–73, 328–32 (Censuses of ectoparasites of Ceylonese and Javanese rats).

563. Thomson, H. V., and Worden, A. N. (1956). *The Rabbit.* London, Collins, xii + 240 pp.

564. Thomson, W. K. (1949). *J.W.M.*, 13:313 (Moose courting behavior).

565. Troughton, E. (1947). *Furred Animals of Australia.* New York, Scribners, xxvii + 374 pp. A somewhat old-fashioned book, still useful for lack of any modern handbook on Australia.

566. Trumler, E. (1959). *Z.f.T.*, 16:478–88 ("Expression movements" in the horse family. G).

567. Turcek, F. J. (1953). *Bull. Inter. Acad. Tchèque Sci.*, 53:81–105 (Biomasses of the mammal and bird faunas in the forests of the Polana Mountains).

568. Tyndale-Biscoe, C. H. (1959). *Nature*, 183:471–72 (Reingestion in lagomorphs).

569. Ullrich, W. (1961). *Z.G., N.F.*, 25:305–68 (Ethology and social behavior of *Colobus guereza* in Tanganyika. G).

570. Vaipio, P. (1950). *Evolution at the Population Level with Special Reference to Game Animals.* Helsinski, Papers on Game Research, Vol. 5, pp. 1–176.

571. Van den Brink, F. H. (1956). *Die Säugetiere Europas.* Hamburg, Parey, 225 pp. A field guide with excellent plates and range maps.

572. Varlet, F. (1949). *Notes Africaines*, 1949:100 (Elephant salt licks. F).

573. Vellard, J. (1950). *Trav. Inst. Franc. Etudes Andines*, 2:19–38 (Resistance of *Conepatus inca* to rattlesnake poison. F).

574. Venables, U. M., and Venables, L. S. (1955). *P.Z.S.*, 125:521–32 (Social and reproductive behavior of the common seal).

575. Verheyen, R. (1951). *Contributions à l'étude éthologique des Mammifères du parc national de l'Upemba.* Brussels, Institut des Parcs Nationaux du Congo, 161 pp. Many observations on the life histories of a great many species.

576. Verheyen, R. (1954a). *Monographie éthologique de l'hippo-*

potame. Brussels, Institut des Parcs Nationaux du Congo, 91 pp.

577. Verheyen, R. (1954b). *Bull. Inst. Roy. Sci. Nat. Belgique,* 30, 43:1–19 (Life history of the African elephant. F).

578. Verschuren, J. (1957). *Ecologie, biologie et systématique des Cheiroptères.* Exploration du Parc National de la Garamba, Brussels, 7:1–473.

579. Vestal, E. H. (1938). *J.M.,* 19:1–36 (Biotic relations of the wood rat).

580. Vibe, C. (1950). *Meddelelser om Grönland,* 50, No. 6:1–116 (Marine mammals of the Thule district).

581. Villa, B. (1955). *An. Inst. Biol. Univ. Mex.,* 26:547–52 (Mass mortality in the bat *Mormoops megalophylla.* S).

582. Villa, B., and Cockrum, E. L. (1962). *J.M.,* 43:43–64 (Migration in the guano bat).

583. Wahlstrom, A. (1928–29). *Z.f.S.,* 3:284–94 and 4:157–85 (Biology of *Sorex vulgaris* and *Crocidura leucodon.* G).

584. Walls, G. L. (1942). *The Vertebrate Eye and Its Adaptive Radiation.* Cranbrook Institute of Science, Bull. No. 19, XIV + 785 pp.

585. Walther, F. (1958). *Z.f.T.,* 15:340–80 (Fighting and mating behavior in antelopes. G).

586. Walther, F. (1960). *Z.f.T.,* 17:188–210 (Mating behavior in the okapi. G).

587. Washburn, S. L. (1957). *Amer. J. Phys. Anthropol.,* 15:269–76 (Ischial callosities of Old World monkeys as sleeping adaptations).

588. Washburn, S. L., and De Vore, I. (1961). *Viking Fund Publications in Anthropology,* 31:91–105 (Social behavior of *Papio doguera* in East Africa). See also *Scientific American,* 204 (6):62–71.

589. Weber, M. (1927–28). *Die Saugetiere.* Jena, Fisher. 2 vols. Second edition of a classic morphological work by H. M. de Burlet and O. Abel.

590. Webster, F. A., and Griffin, D. R. (1962). *Animal Behaviour,* 10:332–40 (Role of the flight membranes in insect capture by bats).

591. Welles, R. E., and Welles, F. B. (1961). *The Bighorn of Death Valley.* Washington, Fauna of the National Parks of the United States, xv + 242 pp.

592. Wells, L. J. (1935). *Anat. Record,* 62:409–47 (Seasonal sexual rhythm of *Citellus tridecemlineatus*).

593. Wever, E. G. (1930). *J. Comp. Psychol.*, 10:221–23 (Upper limit of hearing in the cat).

594. Wimsatt, W. A. (1945). *J.M.*, 26:23–33 (Breeding behavior, pregnancy, and parturition of some vespertilionid bats).

595. Wimsatt, W. A., and Guerriere, A. (1962). *J.M.*, 43:17–27 (Food consumption of captive vampire bats).

596. Wood Jones, F. (1923–25). *The Mammals of South Australia.* Adelaide, Govt. Printer, 458 pp. Morphology (excellent), taxonomy, and some biology.

597. Wright, B. S. (1960). *J.W.M.*, 24:1–15 (Food habits of large African predators).

598. Wunder, W. (1937). *Ergebnisse der Biologie*, 14:280–348 (Nests and care of the young mammals. G).

599. Wüstehube, C. (1960). *Z.f.T.*, 17:579–613 (Innate feeding behavior of the polecat. G).

600. Wynne-Edwards, V. C. (1962). *Animal Dispersion in Relation to Social Behaviour.* Edinburgh and London, Oliver and Boyd, xi + 653 pp.

601. Yeh, J., and Davis, D. E. (1950). *Public Health Reports*, 65:337–42 (Seasonal changes in abundance of fleas on rats Baltimore).

602. Yerkes, R. M. (1942). *Chimpanzees: A Laboratory Colony.* New Haven, Yale University Press, xv + 321 pp.

603. Yerkes, R. M., and Learned, B. W. (1925). *Chimpanzee Intelligence and Its Vocal Expressions.* Baltimore, Williams and Wilkins, 157 pp.

604. Yerkes, R. M., and Yerkes, A. W. (1929). *The Great Apes: A Study of Anthropoid Life.* New Haven, Yale University Press, xix + 652 pp.

605. Young, W. C. (1941). *Quart. Rev. Biol.*, 16:135–56, 311–55 (Mating behavior in female mammals).

606. Zippelius, H. M. (1957). *Bonn Zool. Beitr.*, 8:81–85 (Formation of "caravans" by young *Crocidura leucoaon*. G).

607. Zippelius, H. M., and Goethe, F. (1951). *Z.f.T.*, 8:348–67 (Behavior of *Muscardinus avellanarius*).

Subject Index to Bibliographical References

GENERAL: 83, 128, 155, 233, 340.

Morphology: 128, 233, 589.

Physiology, endocrinology: 2, 3, 25, 31, 59, 60, 61, 68, 105, 109, 123, 124, 172, 189, 199, 200, 226, 230, 232, 235, 236, 239, 251, 293, 305, 306, 307, 308, 309, 310, 323, 326, 327, 338, 353, 361, 364, 375, 378, 384, 387, 388, 389, 402, 403, 413, 424, 449, 466, 472, 473, 475, 497, 498, 584, 592, 593.

Ecology: 131, 419, 600.

Genetics and evolution: 522, 570.

Behavior: 40, 248, 272, 273, 507, 600.

Classification: 128, 233, 589.

Techniques: 154, 400.

FAUNA:

Europe: 65, 190, 249, 279, 383, 420, 534, 534a, 536, 571.

Asia: 5, 34, 65, 122, 190, 279, 298, 420, 448, 534, 534a, 551.

Africa: 7, 18, 191, 376, 377, 502, 520, 575.

North America: 104, 113, 250, 422.

Neotropical fauna: 110, 111, 196, 250, 421, 430.

FAUNA (continued)

Australia, Indonesia, and the Pacific: 120, 122, 344, 379, 565, 596.

BIOLOGY OF THE MAIN TAXONOMIC GROUPS:

Monotremes and marsupials: 48, 101, 137, 209, 262, 264, 274, 275, 366, 379, 382, 392, 434.

Insectivores: 21, 139, 140, 141, 161, 227, 228, 265, 266, 282, 283, 338, 399, 426, 427, 428, 450, 453, 454, 479, 525, 583, 606.

Bats: 6, 29, 39, 54, 58, 64, 88, 89, 98, 121, 127, 129, 157, 168, 169, 183, 184, 185, 186, 187, 202, 231, 237, 238, 239, 240, 243, 263, 280, 313, 397, 412, 417, 446, 447, 457, 478, 530, 578, 581, 590, 594, 595.

Primates: 56, 69, 77, 114, 115, 116, 117, 118, 130, 164, 189, 229, 236, 247, 252, 256, 257, 258, 287, 299, 311, 312, 314a, 341, 371, 378, 387, 388, 416, 436, 437, 467, 487, 488, 503, 504, 505, 537a, 538, 569, 587, 588, 602, 603, 604.

Edentates: 84, 85, 337, 455, 546.

BIOLOGY OF THE MAIN TAXONOMIC GROUPS (continued)

Rodents and lagomorphs:
1, 3, 16, 22, 23, 30, 43, 44, 45, 47, 51, 52, 53, 55, 62, 66, 67, 68, 73, 79, 81, 86, 91, 99, 112, 138, 142, 143, 144, 145, 152, 153, 154, 156, 158, 159, 163, 165, 166, 167, 170, 172, 174, 175, 176, 179, 180, 193, 194, 195, 203, 206, 207, 208, 214, 216, 217, 218, 224, 225, 242, 254, 255, 259, 260, 261, 270, 281, 288, 292, 293, 294, 296, 301, 318, 319, 320, 321, 323, 329, 330, 331, 332, 334, 336, 343, 352, 355, 357, 359, 360, 362, 364, 369, 374, 384, 389, 395, 403, 410, 414, 415, 429, 431, 432, 438, 442, 456, 460, 464, 465, 470, 470a, 472, 475, 476, 481, 483, 493, 497, 512, 513, 514, 515, 516, 517, 519, 531, 533, 535, 537, 540, 541, 543, 544, 545, 560, 561, 562, 563, 568, 579, 592, 607.

Cetaceans: 28, 90, 126, 305, 306, 327, 339, 349, 367, 368, 425, 461, 521, 528, 552.

Pinnipeds: 41, 42, 46, 57, 119, 147, 150, 201, 253, 285, 305, 306, 308, 309, 310, 328, 345, 346, 347, 348, 350, 373, 380, 396, 459, 469, 489, 490, 524, 574.

Carnivores: 61, 80, 100, 109, 134, 173, 177, 195, 204, 205, 235, 278, 284, 286, 295, 302, 316, 325, 335,

BIOLOGY OF THE MAIN TAXONOMIC GROUPS (continued)

351, 356, 358, 361, 381, 386, 402, 404, 405, 406, 408, 411, 413, 435, 445, 492, 496, 506, 508, 509, 510, 518, 554, 555, 556, 558, 559, 573, 593, 597, 599.

Ungulates: 8, 9, 10, 11, 12, 13, 14, 15, 19, 20, 25, 26, 27, 31, 32, 33, 35, 36, 37, 38, 60, 70, 71, 76, 78, 82, 87, 92, 93, 94, 95, 97, 106, 107, 133, 135, 136, 146, 148, 149, 198, 215, 219, 220, 221, 222, 223, 244, 245, 246, 269, 273, 300, 303, 324, 333, 342, 372, 390, 401, 406, 407, 409, 433, 439, 440, 441, 443, 444, 452, 466, 471, 477, 484, 485, 495, 498, 499, 511, 529, 534, 542, 547, 548, 549, 550, 553, 564, 566, 572, 576, 577, 585, 586, 591.

MAJOR ECOLOGICAL AND ETHOLOGICAL TOPICS:

Locomotion: 28, 44, 45, 71, 183, 234, 286, 297, 304, 305, 306, 308, 425, 532.

Activity rhythms: 31, 92, 139, 156, 170, 201, 254, 300, 342, 480, 587.

Food and feeding habits:
64, 106, 112, 136, 161, 168, 169, 171, 177, 187, 202, 240, 252, 255, 265, 266, 277, 295, 302, 313, 399, 427, 436, 447, 454, 479, 501, 508, 516, 517, 525, 550, 561, 568, 572, 573, 590, 595, 597, 599.

MAJOR ECOLOGICAL AND ETHOLOGI-
CAL TOPICS (continued)

Home, territory, and home range: 39, 95, 100, 102, 103, 151, 155, 180, 181, 238, 254, 268, 271, 278, 294, 315, 328, 331, 465, 518, 531, 598.

Defense and protection: 55, 99, 143, 162, 163, 165, 259, 276, 290, 316, 364, 395, 418, 462, 514.

Sexual life and reproduction: 11, 17, 24, 48, 50, 51, 59, 60, 73, 89, 91, 117, 127, 132, 144, 167, 209, 243, 258, 260, 262, 263, 269, 285, 288, 294, 303, 312, 320, 351, 354, 368, 382, 424, 428, 437, 457, 463, 468, 499, 513, 515, 526, 527, 535, 552, 564, 574, 585, 586, 592, 594, 605.

Development and longevity: 3, 10, 40, 42, 43, 56, 73, 140, 152, 160, 173, 174, 199, 210, 211, 225, 256, 257, 285, 292, 312, 345, 358, 373, 392, 404, 415, 474, 503, 504, 510, 599, 606.

Hibernation and æstivation: 43, 47, 77, 85, 88, 96, 182, 188, 226, 280, 326, 365, 432.

Migrations and homing: 54, 98, 121, 157, 238, 241, 321, 322, 410, 477, 493, 543, 582.

Social life: 4, 8, 9, 10, 12, 16, 22, 23, 26, 27, 32, 41, 46,

MAJOR ECOLOGICAL AND ETHOLOGI-
CAL TOPICS (continued)

49, 74, 79, 90, 97, 106, 114, 115, 116, 118, 119, 130, 146, 149, 164, 178, 180, 221, 229, 252, 287, 299, 303, 314a, 324, 325, 328, 329, 341, 359, 360, 372, 385, 424, 436, 444, 445, 459, 467, 486, 487, 488, 492, 495, 505, 506, 512, 521, 537a, 540, 557, 558, 559, 560, 566, 569, 574, 585, 588, 602, 603.

Effects of environmental factors: 29, 30, 59, 66, 78, 105, 123, 125, 129, 158, 192, 193, 212, 213, 214, 242, 251, 259, 281, 289, 291, 301, 307, 314, 317, 319, 334, 364, 375, 391, 394, 430, 431, 437, 446, 451, 472, 497, 545, 562, 601.

Structure and dynamics of natural populations: 1, 13, 14, 15, 19, 32, 33, 52, 58, 62, 63, 67, 70, 72, 75, 76, 78, 81, 91, 102, 107, 108, 119, 124, 130, 135, 142 145, 148, 152, 153, 154, 160, 185, 194, 195, 197, 198, 217, 218, 224, 261, 267, 268, 318, 320, 321, 336, 347, 349, 350, 355, 357, 362, 363, 370, 371, 374, 390, 393, 401, 423, 434, 435, 442, 464, 467, 471, 474, 489, 491, 505, 511, 530, 533, 537, 539, 542, 544, 567, 581.

Index

aardvark, 50, 51, 72, 278
Acrobates, 27
Acynonyx jubatus, 165; see also cheetah
adaptive coloration, 122–37
addax, 69
age composition, 297–302
age determination, 289–93
agouti, 167, 172
Agouti paca, 323
Alcelaphine bovid, 156
Alces alces, 166
Allen's law, 256–7
Alouatta palliata, 294; seniculus, 164
altitude, 265–7
American pronghorn, 231, 245
angwantibo, 247
Anoa depressicornis, 201
Anomalurus, 17
anteater, 49; Australian spiny, 139–40, 195; giant, 50, 175, 179; marsupial banded, 145; three-toed, 16, 111
antelope, 38, 56, 57, 69, 156, 273, 276, 309; roan, 7, 153, 156; sable, 156; saiga, 245
antelope jackrabbit, 129, 173, 256
anthropoid, 9, 193
Antilope cervicapra, 166, 229
Aonyx capensis, 165
Aotus, 247, 323
ape, 246, 310, 327, 329

Apodemus, 120; sylvaticus, 165; see also mouse, long-tailed field
Arctocephalus, 165; australis, 165; pusillus, 165, 201
armadillo, 9, 74, 76, 112, 163, 254, 323; giant, 11; Texas, 21, 73, 76, 103, 163, 203
Artibeus, 42, 72–3
artiodactyls, 39, 279, 294
ass, 246; Indian wild, 7, 246; Mongolian wild, 172, 246; Nubian wild, 246; Somali wild, 246
Ateles ater, 164
atmospheric humidity, 259–60
Australian banded anteater, 50
Australopithecinæ, 11
autoeroticism, 161–2
autotomy of the tail, 120–1
Avahi, 247
aye-aye, 72, 247

baboon, 99, 109, 169, 234, 248–9, 310, 331; chacma, 194
badger (European), 48, 56, 59, 75, 76, 103, 163, 184, 185, 188, 198, 224, 263, 278
Balænoptera, 53; musculus, 201; physalus, 165, 201; see also whale, fin
banteng, 177
bat, 21, 30–6, 46, 51, 60, 70, 130, 149, 159, 162, 163, 166, 167, 169, 181, 190, 201, 212–13, 218–19, 255, 259,

bat (*continued*)
294, 302, 309, 314, 320, 328, 330, 335; big brown, 33, 34; Daubenton's, 21; fish-eating, 21, 49, 50; Florida free-tailed, 190; hoary, 214; Keen, 33, 163; large mouse-eared, 31, 212–13, 218; little brown, 32, 33, 159, 163; long-eared, 31, 35, 51; red, 181, 214; vampire, 55; whiskered, 35
Bathyergidæ, 322
Bathyergus maritimus, 74
bear, 17, 52, 62, 147, 163, 178–9, 197; black, 20, 52, 124; brown, 103, 172, 190; grizzly, 56, 103; polar, 59, 74–5, 124; sloth, 52
beaver, 90–5, 98, 159; American, 21, 22, 23, 25, 45, 65, 91–4, 151, 190, 225, 228, 236–7; European, 94–5, 237–8
Bergmann's law, 256
biotic factors, 269 ff., 318 ff.
birth rate, 303 ff.
bison, 169; American, 169, 175, 205, 245, 295, 303; European, 104, 169, 177
Bison bison, see bison, American; *bonasus, see* bison, European
black rhinoceros, 7, 162, 175, 191, 273
black-tailed prairie dog, 85–6, 224, 238, 322–3
blacktail jackrabbit, 173
Blarina brevicauda, 164, 201, 335; *see also* shrew, short-tailed
body temperatures, 195–6, 198, 252–5
bongo, 57
Bos gaurus, 166
Bovidæ, 40, 243, 245
Bovinæ, 148
brachiation, 18–20
Bradipus griseus, 164
brush wallaby, 145
buffalo, 7, 273, 278, 284, 295, 309
burrows, 72–88
bushbuck, 284

camel, 7, 56, 175
Camelidæ, 4
Camelus bactrianus, 166
Canidæ, 46, 147, 151, 177, 178, 229
Canis, 165, *see also* dog; *aureus*, 106, *see also* jackal; *latrans*, 165, *see also* coyote; *lupus*, 165, 201, *see also* wolf
cape buffalo, *see* buffalo
Capreolus capreolus, 166, 297; *see also* deer, roe
Caprinæ, 148
capybara, 176
"caravans," 182–3
care of the young, 177–83
caribou, 7, 45, 57, 104, 155, 156, 174–5, 204–5, 275–6, 300
carnivores, 20, 46, 57, 62, 74, 99, 158–9, 169, 175, 183, 186, 190, 197, 201, 260, 275, 284, 294, 309, 316–17, 319–20, 324, 325, 328, 330, 335
Castor, see beaver; *canadensis*, 164, 201, *see also* beaver, American
cat, 153, 175, 322, 324, 327, 335; fishing cat, 49; Pallas, 129
Cebus capucinus, 294, 310; *fatuellus*, 201
census methods, 282 ff.
Cephalophus maxwelli, 201
Cercocebus albigena, 204
Cercopithecidæ, 204
Cercopithecus, 104; *æthiops*, 201; *cephus*, 104, *see also* monkey, mustached white-nosed
Cervidæ, 40, 229, 289
Cervinæ, 147, 148
Cervulus muntjac, 226
Cervus, 166; *canadensis*, 166, *see also* elk; *elaphus*, 166, 297, *see also* deer, red; *unicolor*, 201
cetaceans, 23–7, 52, 67, 147, 159, 175, 176, 190, 201, 260, 328, 335
Chæropsis liberiensis, 201
chamois, 41, 69, 169, 172, 181, 191, 245, 289–90
cheetah, 6, 7

Cheirogaleus, 196; *major*, 201, 247, 335
chimpanzee, 11, 13, 21, 72, 161, 162, 168, 169, 186, 188, 191, 193, 201, 224, 234, 248, 322, 335
chipmunk, 45, 218, 220, 307
Chlamyphorus truncatus, 112–13
Chœronycteris, 46
Chœropsis liberiensis, 166; *see also* hippopotamus, pigmy
Cholæpus didactylus, 201
Chrotogale owstoni, 55
Citellus, see squirrel, ground; *columbianus*, 164; *tridecemlineatus*, 164, *see also* squirrel, thirteen-lined ground; *pygmæus*, 335
civet, 117, 228; Indo-Chinese, 55
Claviglis, 120
Clethrionomys gapperi, 164, *see also* vole, boreal red-backed; *rufocanus*, 305
climatic factors, 251–67
Colobus guereza, 248–9
common marmoset, 191, 226
communication, means of, 221–32
concealing coloration, 122–37
Conepatus inca, 49
Connochætes gnou, 202, see also wildebeest; *taurinus*, 273
copulation, 159 ff.
cow, 175, 277, 330
coyote, 7, 58, 59, 75, 183, 190, 278, 309
crest-tail pouched mouse, 46, 145
Cricetidæ, 147, 169
Cricetomys gambianus, see rat, African giant
Cricetus cricetus, 164; *see also* hamster
critical distance, 109
Crocidura russula, 201
Crocuta crocuta, 165; *see also* hyena, spotted
Cryptomys bigalkei, 74
Cryptotis floridana, 335; *parva*, 335
Ctenodactylus, 129

Ctenomys brasiliensis, 85
cutaneous glands, 117–20, 225–30
Cyclopes, 49
Cynocephalus volans, 30
Cynomys leucurus, 164; *ludovicianus*, 335

dam, 92–5
dama pademelon, 141
dance, 185
Dasycercus cristicauda, 129
Dasypus, 163, 164; *hybridus*, 163; *novemcinctus*, 164; *see also* armadillo, Texas
Dasyurinæ, 46
Dasyuroides byrnei, 129
death simulation, 116
deer, 6, 40, 44, 45, 103, 116, 243, 271, 297, 330; black-tailed, 245, 270, 297, 299; fallow, 44; mule, 205–6, 295–6; red, 44, 57, 103, 109–10, 161, 183, 244, 259, 264, 275, 295, 297, 324; roe, 44, 45, 69, 155, 163, 172, 176, 191, 297–9, 300, 331; white-tailed (Virginia), 69, 175, 269–70, 335
defensive attitudes, 108–20
delayed implantation, 163
"desert" coloration, 129–31
Desmodus, 55; *rotundus*, 335; *rufus*, 201
development, 170–95
Diæmus, 55
diet, 35–57, 269 ff.; carnivorous, 46–56; frugivorous, 42–3; granivorous, 43–4; hæmatophagous, 55; insectivorous, 49–51; mycophagous, 45–6; omnivorous, 55–6; vegetarian, 39–46
digging, 73–4, 80–5
Diphylla, 55
Dipodomys meriammi, 201
Diptera, 275
Dipus, 129
disease, 307 ff.
diving, 23–7

dog, 23, 57, 175, 176, 214, 253;
African wild, 58, 129, 324, 329;
see also black-tailed prairie dog
dolphin, bottlenosed, 24, 67, 156–7,
161, 162, 168, 175, 176, 183–4,
190, 224, 234
dormouse, 120, 197; common, 120,
188; fat, 43, 196, 199; forest, 120;
garden, 120, 121, 129, 196
dromedary, African, 335
Dryomys, 120
duiker, 156
dung pits, 103

Echidna, 139–40, 201, 254
"echo-sounding" in bats, 32–6; in
cetaceans, 225
ecology 250–320 *passim*, 321 ff
edaphic factors, 267
edentates, 175, 201; *see also* anteater
Eidolon helvum, 71, 214
eland, 60, 272
elephant, 21, 148, 162, 169, 243, 245,
273, 284, 331; African, 7, 38, 56–
7, 60, 69, 104, 271–2, 273, 314, 335;
Indian, 158, 161, 175, 191, 244
Elephas maximus, 165; *see also*
elephant, Indian
Eliomys, 120; *quercinus*, see dormouse, garden
elk, 205, 245
Ellobius, 80, 130, 322
emigration, 203
Eonycteris, 46
Epimys, 120
Epomorphus wahlbergi, 214
Eptesicus, 130; *fulvus*, 335; *isabellinus*, 130; *serotinus*, 130, *see also*
serotine
Equidæ, 148
Equus, 165, 202; *burchelli*, 201, *see
also* zebra, Burchell's; *zebra*, 166,
see also zebra, mountain
Eremodipus, 129
Erethizon dorsatum, 165; *see also*
porcupine, American

Erinaceus algirus, 201; *europæus*,
164; *see also* hedgehog
ermine, 20, 59, 123
Erophylla planifrons, 167
estivation, 196
Euphractus, 112; *villosus*, 201
Eutamias mœnus, 294

Falkland sea lion, 7, 8, 22, 54, 157–8,
240–1
fecundity, 164–6
feeding habits, *see* food
Felidæ, 46, 147, 148, 178
Felis, *see* cat, leopard, lion; *concolor*, 165; *leo*, 165, 201, 335, *see
also* lion; *lybica*, 165; *onca*, 165;
pardus, 165, *see also* leopard;
sylvetris, 165; *tigris*, 165, *see also*
tiger
ferret, 159
fetid secretions, 117–20
fisher, 190
flapping flight, 30–1
flight, 27–36
flying lemurs, 27, 30, 181
flying squirrel, 17, 27, 28; North
American, 27–8
food, 35–65; preferences, 47; storage, 61–5; *see also* diet
fox, 4, 48, 59, 62, 75, 184, 186, 257;
American red, 75, 99, 101–2, 105,
307, 325; Arctic, 106, 123, 124–5,
127, 253, 317; Bengal, 52; corsak,
75, 129; European red, 47, 75,
175, 177, 224–5, 278; northern
plains red, 46, 62
freezing behavior, 116
Fremont chickaree, 63

Galago crassicaudatus, 247; *garnetti*,
201
gallop, 5–6
gaur, 245
Gazella dorcas, 202
gazelle, 7; dama, 129; Grant's, 7;
Thomson's, 157, 245; Waller's,
9, 10

Geomyidæ, 80, 83-4, 148
gerbil, 87, 131; fat-tailed, 225; lesser Egyptian, 43; Wagner's, 154
Gerbillus, see gerbil; *dasyurus,* 165, *see also* gerbil, Wagner's; *gerbillus, see* gerbil, lesser Egyptian
gestation, 141-2, 162-7
giant forest hog, 284
giant panda, 40, 42
gibbon, 18, 169, 180, 247, 310; black, 12; lar, 9, 19, 21, 71, 151, 160-1, 168, 191, 224
Giraffa camelopardalis, 166, 201
giraffe, 4, 5, 7, 154-5, 156, 169, 172, 243, 245, 295, 324, 331
Giraffidæ, 4
Glaucomys volans, 165; *see also* flying squirrel, North American
gliding, 27-30, 31
Glis, 120; *Glis glis,* 201
Glossophaga, 46
Glossophaginæ, 46
golden hamster, 152, 158
golden potto, 71
gorilla, 11, 21, 72, 99, 169, 186, 224, 248-9
Graphiurus, 120
greater glider-possum, 29
ground squirrel, 45, 196; Barbary, 129; California, 64, 99, 197, 222-3, 224, 229, 230, 259, 262-3, 307, 322; thirteen-lined, 149
growth, 191-5
guanaco, 243
guinea pig, 162, 175, 230, 253, 278, 323, 328

hæmatophagia, 55
Halichoreus grypus, see seal, gray
hamster, 20, 63, 79, 159, 196, 296
Hapale jacchus, 164
hare, 5, 7, 20, 44, 70, 256, 260, 284; Arctic, 60, 122, 257, 260, 317; European, 70, 103, 167, 170-1, 173, 176; snowshoe, 122-3, 257, 275, 316; varying, 123, 127-8, 265

hearing, 327-8
hedgehog, 20, 48, 112-14, 182, 195, 323, 325
herbivores, 317, 319
Herpestes, 48; *smithii,* 201; *vitticollis,* 201, *see also* mongoose, striped-necked
Herpestidæ, 117
Heterocephalus glaber, 81
heteromyidæ, 44, 87, 147
hibernation, 195-9
Hippopotamidæ, 4
hippopotamus, 40, 107, 168, 175, 176, 181, 202, 243, 245, 277, 284, 291, 295, 335
Hippopotamus amphibius, 166, 201
Hipposideros fulvus, 70
home, 67-94
home range, 100-7
homing, 105-7, 214-19
homosexuality, 162
honey badger, 52, 117, 129, 277
horse, 44, 175, 246
horseshoe bat, 35; greater, 51, 166; lesser, 31
humans, 175, 202, 296, 322, 327-8
Hyæna hyæna, see hyena, striped
Hydrochœrus, see capybara; *isthmius,* 165
hyena, 46; spotted, 7, 48, 288; striped, 48, 117
Hylobates lar, 164, 201; *see also* gibbon, lar
hyrax, 243
Hystrix, see porcupine; *africæaustralis,* 165; *cristata,* 201

ibex, 41, 245, 289
Idiurus, 28-9
impala, 245, 295
inbreeding, 107
index of selection, 135
Indri indri, 164, 247
innate behavior, 186-90
insectivores, 51, 149, 158, 195, 201, 202, 260, 267, 294, 319-20, 335
insects, 275 ff.

isolation, 132, 261
Isthmian marmosa, 70

jackal, 7, 106, 117, 129
Jaculus jaculus, 201
jerboa, 14, 196; lesser Egyptian, 14, 225; northern three-toed, 14, 79, 86; thick-tailed three-toed, 80
jird, 130; Shaw's, 191–2, 225

kangaroo, 11, 40, 175; forester, 12; great gray, 141, 142, 143, 144; red, 110, 141, 143
kangaroo rat, 14, 43, 129, 258; giant, 64–5; Merriam, 14; Ord, 153
Kerivoula lanosa, 70; *nidicola*, 70
koala, 17, 41, 141, 144–5, 269
Kobus defassa, see waterbuck
kouprey, 7

lactation, 173–6
lagomorphs, 147, 175, 294, 301, 327
langurs, 180, 248–9
leaping, 11–15
learning processes, 186–90
lemming, 124, 203, 260, 317–18, 322; brown, 124; Greenland collared, 124, 125–6; Hudson Bay collared, 124; Norway, 124, 314–16
Lemmus lemmus, 136
lemur, 193, 226, 249; dwarf, 247, 288; mouse, 247, 288
Lemur, 164; *fulvus*, 201; *macao*, 164
leopard, 46, 62
Lepilemur, 247
Leptonychotes weddelli, 165; see also seal, Weddell's
Lepus, see hare; *europæus*, 164, see also hare, European; *americanus*, 164, see also hare, showshoe
lethal temperatures, 252–3
Libyan striped weasel, 129
light, 125–6, 261–5
lion, 7, 46, 47, 58, 59, 177, 224, 234, 283

litter size, 164–6
little mole rat, 82–3
little souslik, 78, 86, 274
llama, 266
locomotion: aerial, 27–36; aquatic, 20–7; arboreal, 15–20; terrestrial, 4–15
Lonchophylla, 46
longevity, 199
Lutra canadensis, 201; *lutra*, 165, see also otter, European
Lutreolina crassicaudata, 141
Lycaon pictus, 165, 201; see also dog, African wild
lynx, 275, 315–16
Lynx canadensis, 165; see also lynx

Macaca mulatta, 164, 201, 294; see also monkey, rhesus
macaque, 180, 224, 248–9, 324
Macroglossinæ, 46
Macropus, 323; *major*, 201
manatee, 23, 156, 169, 176, 261
Manis tricuspis, 114
marmot, 109, 196; Alpine, 86, 87, 109, 196, 238, 250; boback, 273, 335
Marmota marmota, 164, 201; see also marmot, Alpine
marsupial cat, 141, 143
marsupials, 140–6, 175, 179, 201, 254, 294, 323
marten, 163, 229
Martes, 165; *americana*, 165; *martes*, 165, 201; *pennanti*, 165, see also fisher
mating, 151–61
Megaderma lyra, 46, 49
Megaloglossus, 46
Mellivora ratel; see honey badger
Mephitis mephitis, 165; see also skunk, striped
Meriones lybicus, 335
Microcebus, 196, 247; *murinus*, 164, 335
microclimate, 87–8, 252

Micromys minutus, 165; *see also* mouse, harvest

Microtinæ, 40, 200, 316–7

Microtus agrestis, 335; *brandti,* 316; *pennsylvanicus,* 164, *see also* vole, meadow

migration, 203–19

milk, 173–6

Miniopterus, 166–7; *australis,* 167; *schreibersi,* 166, 294

mink, 20, 184, 295

mock fights, 184

mole, 73, 259, 260; Cape golden, 74; eastern, 51–2, 74; European, 20, 55, 60, 62–3, 74, 81–2, 149, 251, 256, 262, 267; golden, 322; marsupial, 322; star-nosed, 20

Molossidæ, 30, 196

mongoose, 48, 117, 229; crabeating, 117; striped-necked, 117

monkey, 17, 18, 21, 38, 42, 159–60, 178, 191, 193, 223, 246–9, 322, 325, 327, 329; capuchin, 322; mustached white-nosed, 42; owl, 247, 323; Panama howler, 71, 109, 160, 180, 223–4, 248–9, 310; red spider, 17, 18, 19, 42, 109, 248, 310; redtail, 248; rhesus, 21, 160, 162, 175, 322, 324; toque, 191

monogamy, 151, 235–7

monotremes, 201

moose, 169, 291

Mormoops megalophylla, 307

mortality rate, 297 ff., 307 ff.

mountain vizcacha, 109, 295

mountain zebra, 7, 246

mouse, 178, 192, 230, 253, 325; brush, 190; Cairo spiny, 192; deer, 102, 107, 129, 131, 133–7, 152, 177, 250, 294, 307, 311, 324, 333; field, 333; harvest, 88–9; house, 152, 162, 256, 305, 312–13; lemur, 333; lemming, 47; longtailed field, 120, 121, 267, 324–5; meadow jumping, 14, 87, 196;

mouse (*continued*) red tree, 42; white-footed, 215–17, 301; Wyoming pocket, 43; zebra, 152

mouse lemur, 196, 288

mud baths, 103

muntjac, 226

Muridæ, 20, 148, 152, 169

Mus, 120; *musculus,* 165, 305, *see also* mouse, house

Muscardinus, 120; *avallanarius,* 164, *see also* dormouse, common

musk glands, 117–20, 225–30

musk ox, 110, 124, 305

muskrat, 21, 23, 25, 90–1, 159, 295

Mustela, 165; *frenata,* 165, 335, *see also* weasel, long-tailed; *furo,* 165, *vison,* 165, *see also* mink

Mustelidæ, 20, 46, 59, 113, 117, 123, 147, 159, 163, 327

mycophagia, 45–6

Myocastor coypus, 165; *see also* nutria

Myospalax, 130

myotis, 30; gray, 163; Indiana, 163; small-footed, 159

Myotis daubentonii, 302; *emarginatus,* 294; *lucifugus,* 201, 294, 335; *myotis,* 164, *see also* bat, mouseeared; *mystacinus,* 294, 302, 314

Myrmecophaga tridactyla, 49, 50, 164, 201; *see also* anteater, giant

Mysticeti, 327

Nasua nasua, 165

Neotoma, 132; *albigula,* 132, *see also* rat, white-throated wood; *mexicana,* 132

"nests," 88–94

newborn, 170–3

Noctilio leporinus, 49

noctule, 30, 213, 218

Notoryctes, 80, 322

nutria, 190

Nyctalus noctula, 164; *see also* noctule

Nyctereutes procyonides, 106; *see also* raccoon dog
Nycticebus, 164, 247; *tardigradus,* 164

ocelot, 229
Odocoileus virginianus, 166; *see also* deer, white-tailed (Virginia)
okapi, 156, 331
olive colobus, 248
omnivores, 319
Ondatra zibethica, 164; *see also* muskrat
opossum, 322, 325; greater glider-, 29; murine, 145–6; pigmy, 195; silver-gray, 141; South American, 146; Virginia, 116–17, 140, 141–2, 143, 195, 294; woolly, 103, 195; *see also* marsupials
optimal temperatures, 252–4
orang-utan, 175, 249
orientation, 74, 214–19
Oryx, 156, 166, 202; *beisa,* 166
Otaria, 165; *flavescens,* 165
Otonycteris hemprichii, 130
otter, 21, 184; American, 184, 186, 189, 190, 290; European, 49, 159
oviparous mammals, 139–40
Ovis, see sheep; *canadensis,* 166; *see also* sheep, bighorn; *dalli,* 297, 299
owl, 310–11

Pachyuromys duprasi, 165; *see also* gerbil, fat-tailed
pangolin, 9, 50, 51, 112, 114, 179; Indian, 112; Sumatra, 179
Pan satyrus, 164, 201; *see also* chimpanzee
panther, 47
Papio, 164, 194; *hamadryas,* 164; *porcarius,* 194, 201, *see also* baboon, chacma
Paramelidæ, 146
parturition, 167–9
peccary, 119–20; collared, 175

Perodicticus, 247
Perognathus, 120, 132; *apache gypsi,* 132; *intermedius ater,* 132
Peromyscus, 133, 306; *maniculatus,* 164, 201; *nasutus,* 132; *polionotus* and subspecies, 133
Petaurista, 28; *alborufus,* 201
Petaurus, 27, 29
Phacochœrus æthiopicus, 166; *see also* wart hog
Phoca, 165; *sibirica,* 261; *vitulina,* 165, 261, *see also* seal, common
Phocæna phocæna, 165
Phyllostomus hastatus, 46
Physeter catodon, 165, 201; *see also* whale, sperm
pigmy hippopotamus, 159
pinnipeds, 7, 22, 24–7, 60, 68, 147, 173, 175, 190, 201, 210–11, 240–3, 294, 296
pipistrelle, 30; eastern, 33; European, 33, 163, 214, 218
Pipistrellus, 70, 130, 163; *abramus,* 163; *kuhlii,* 130; *nanus,* 70; *subflavus,* 335
Pizonyx vivesi, 49
platypus, 73, 139, 195, 201, 254
play, 183–6
playgrounds, 103
pocket gopher, 83, 274, 307; northern, 83–4; plains, 83–4; Sierra, 268
polecat, 20
polygamy, 150, 240–6
Pongo pygmæus, 201; *see also* orang-utan
population: dynamics, 302–3; growth and decline, 314 ff.
populations, natural, 281 ff.
porcupine, 44, 112; African, 114–15, 177; American, 115–16, 154, 158, 172, 185
porpoise, 35, 330, 331
Potos flavus, 201
potto, 247
predation, 275
Presbytis entellus, 249

primates, 17, 18, 21, 38, 42, 147, 159–60, 168, 169, 175, 191, 193, 201, 226, 247, 279, 294, 320, 325, 335
Proboscidea, 4
Procyon lotor, 165; *see also* raccoon
pronghorn, 231, 245
Propithelus, 247
prosimians, 323, 327
Psammonys obesus, 335
psychological factors, 250
Pteropidæ, 42, 149, 264
Pteropus, 201; *giganteus*, 201; *poliocephalus*, 214; *vampyrus*, 30
Pygerethmus, 129
pygmy hippopotamus, 105

rabbit, 305–6; cottontail, 102, 278, 279, 282; European wild, 7, 41, 76–7, 97–100, 105, 150, 151–2, 154, 170–1, 175, 176, 230, 231, 234–5, 239–40, 253, 255, 257, 294, 309, 335
raccoon, 256, 295
raccoon dog, 106
rack, 4
rat, 35, 77, 175, 178, 279, 301, 305, 330; African giant, 188; albino, 322; black, 278–80; brown, 55, 101, 102, 131, 152, 162, 278, 295, 300–1, 324, 333; dusky-footed wood, 90, 152, 225; giant forest, 263; hispid cotton, 190; kangaroo, 301, 328; Manipur, 55; spiny, 121; white, 23, 44, 152, 170, 192, 193, 223, 253; white-throated wood, 44, 85, 258
rat kangaroo, 141; dark, 146; Lesueur, 144; Tasmanian, 141
Ratufa indica, *see* squirrel, Indian giant
reedbuck, 156
refection, 41
regurgitation of food, 176
reindeer, *see* caribou
reproduction, 138–69, 272

reproductive seasons, 146–9
rhinoceros, black, 7, 162, 175, 191, 273
Rhinoceros, 165, 277; *bicornis*, 165; *unicornis*, 107, 175, 201
Rhinolophidæ, 35, 196
Rhinolophus hipposideros, 294
Rhynchiscus naso, 70
rodents, 13, 36, 43–4, 55, 63, 76, 80, 88, 132, 149, 152, 158, 162, 169, 171, 175, 176, 177, 178, 179, 193, 196, 201, 202, 235, 252, 254, 258, 260, 267, 273–4, 277, 294, 309, 311, 320, 322–3, 327–9, 335
roebuck, 177
roosts, 69–72
Roussettus leachi, 201
"rubbing posts," 103
Ruminantia, 6, 330
Rupicapra rupicapra, 166; *see also* chamois

sable, 153, 159, 190
salts, 56–7
Scalopus aquaticus, 164; *see also* mole, eastern
Schoinobates, 27
Sciuridæ, 147, 148
Sciurus, *see* squirrel; *carolinensis*, 164, 201; *vulgaris*, 164
seal, 7, 22, 24–7, 60, 68, 98, 190, 210–12, 240–3, 261, 323, 326, 331; bearded, 240; common, 23, 25, 190, 261; crab-eating, 7, 212, 309; elephant, 98, 100, 295, 300; fur, 98, 295, 314; gray, 9, 159, 189, 242–3; harp, 159, 173, 175, 176, 210–11; hooded, 175; leopard, 240; monk, 68, 295; ringed, 260; Ross, 240; Weddell's 8, 23, 68, 173
sea otter, 22, 53, 67–8, 159, 168, 181
seasonal color change, 122–8
security devices of burrows, 85–7
Senegal bush baby, 148, 224, 247
serotine, 163, 166
sex ratio, 293 ff.

sexual life, 138–62
sexual maturity, 190–1
sexual periodicity, 146–9
sexual promiscuity, 149–50, 239, 242
sheep, 7, 267, 330; Barbary, 69, 233–4; bighorn, 69, 99, 191, 245; dall, 205, 297–8, 299–300; short-tailed wallaby, 143; wild, 156
shrew, 61, 182, 301, 307, 331–2; bicolor white-toothed, 182; common, 41, 182, 294, 302, 333; European water, 60; short-tailed, 61, 63, 153, 158, 162, 230
sifaka, 247
Sigmodon hispidus, 164; *see also* rat, hispid cotton
signals, 221–32; acoustic, 221–5; olfactory, 225–30; visual, 230–2
"sign language," 230–2
skunk, 48, 75, 117–19; Andean, 49; hooded, 85; prairie spotted, 99; striped, 118, 159
sleeping habits, 67–94
sliding, 184, 186
sloth, 17, 180, 255; three-toed, 180, 254–5; two-toed, 159
snow, 260–1
social hierarchy, 232–5
social life, 220–49
Sorex araneus, 164, 335; *see also* shrew, common
Soricidæ, 147
southern elephant seal, 7, 22, 54, 241–2
Spalacidæ, 322
Spallax, 80
speed: on land, 6–7, 8, 12; in water, 23
Spilogale gracilis, 119
springbok, 7
spring haas, 13
squirrel, 16, 17, 18, 63, 88, 325; American gray, 264; American red, 63–4, 90, 98, 218; eastern fox, 90, 190; European red, 27, 44, 45, 88, 53, 187, 251; Indian giant, 90;

squirrel (*continued*)
tree, 306; *see also* ground squirrel, California
stink glands, 117–20
stoat, 190
storage, *see* food storage
Stylodipus telum, 80
submersion, 23–7
sugar glider, 29
Suncus etruscus, 335
sunning-grounds, 103
superfetation, 167
Sus scrofa, 166, 201; *see also* wild boar
swimming, 20–7
Syncerus caffer, 335; *see also* buffalo

Tadarida cynocephala, 164; *see also* bat, Florida free-tailed
Talpa europæa, 164, 335; *see also* mole, European
Tamandua tetradactyla, 49; *see also* chipmunk, eastern
Tamiasciurus, 45
Tapirus, 166; *americanus,* 202; *indicus,* 166
tarsier, 15, 16, 17, 247
Tarsius, 201
Tasmanian wolf, 46
Taurotragus oryx, 166; *see also* eland
temporary shelters, 69–72
tenrec, 87, 196
territory, 94–100, 105–7, 228–30, 270 ff.
Tetraceros quadricornis, 227
thar, Himalayan, 245
thermic optimum, 253
Thos adustus, 165
Thylacinus cynocephalus, 46
tiger, 46, 47, 58
Tolypeutes conurus, 112–13
topi, 48, 245, 273, 284, 295
Tragelaphine bovid, 156
transportation of young, 178–83
Trichechus manatus, 165

Trichosurus vulpecula, 201
trot, 5
tuco tuco, 84–5, 278
Tursiops truncatus, 165, 335; *see also* dolphin, bottlenosed
Tylonycteris pachypus, 70

Uganda kob, 98–9, 245, 284, 295
ultrasonic vibrations, 32–6, 225
ungulates, 20, 39, 56–7, 69, 167, 172, 175, 177, 181, 183, 191, 201, 204, 243–5, 258, 260, 275, 276–7, 279, 283, 289, 296, 297, 303, 309, 311, 319, 325, 327, 335
Uroderma bilobatum, 72
Urogale everetti, 164
Ursidæ, 4, 147
Ursus, see bear; *americanus*, 165, *see also* bear, black; *arctos*, 165, 201, *see also* bear, brown

venomous mammals, 61
Vespertilionidæ, 35, 196
vicuna, 97–8, 243, 245, 266; territories, 106
vision, 321 ff.
Viverra, 117, *see also* civet; *civetta*, 201, *see also* civet, West African; *zibetha*, 228
Viverricula, 117
Viverridæ, 117, 327
vizcacha, 172, 238–9, 266
voice, 221–5
vole, 44, 260, 305; boreal red-backed, 152; common, 63, 79, 84, 99, 179, 264, 268, 301; common red-backed, 179, 217, 325; field, 44, 148, 303, 307, 333; Levant,

vole (*continued*) 304, 310, 316; meadow, 190, 217, 294, 306–7, 313–14; snow, 84; water, 44
Vombatus ursinus, 201
Vulpes, see fox; *fulva*, 165, *see also* fox, American red; *vulpes*, 165, *see also* fox, European red

walk: bipedal, 9–11; quadrupedal, 4
wallows, 103
walrus, 54, 69, 173, 181, 191
wart hog, 7, 72, 284
water, 43–4, 257–61
waterbuck, 156, 245, 284, 295
weasel, 123, 182; Bonaparte, 265; long-tailed, 163, 265
whale, 23–7, 52, 67, 169, 174–6, 190, 206–9, 225, 293; baleen, 327; blue, 23, 52, 175, 207–8, 335; bottlenose, 23, 327 ff.; fin, 23, 52, 175, 190, 207–8, 300; finback, 190; gray, 206; Greenland right, 23; humpback, 52, 207–9; sei, 335; sperm, 23, 24, 327, 331; white, 190
wild boar, 20, 71, 129, 168, 261
wildebeest, 7, 273, 295, 311, 314
wild goat, 156
wolf, 7, 62, 103, 151, 186, 231–2, 309
wolverine, 59, 124
woodchuck, 190

yak, 177

Zalophus californianus, 201
zebra, 175, 181, 246, 289; Burchell's, 246; Grevy's, 246; mountain, 246

A Note on the Type

The text of this book was set on the Linotype in Janson, a recutting made direct from the type cast from matrices (now in possession of the Stempel foundry, Frankfurt am Main) made by Anton Janson some time between 1660 and 1687.

Of Janson's origin nothing is known. He may have been a relative of Justus Janson, a printer of Danish birth who practiced in Leipzig from 1614 to 1635. Some time between 1657 and 1668 Anton Janson, a punch-cutter and type-founder, bought from the Leipzig printer Johann Erich Hahn the type-foundry that had formerly been a part of the printing house of M. Friedrich Lankisch. Janson's types were first shown in a specimen sheet issued at Leipzig about 1675. Janson's successor, and perhaps his son-in-law, Johann Karl Edling, issued a specimen sheet of Janson types in 1689. His heirs sold the Janson matrices in Holland to Wolffgang Dietrich Erhardt of Leipzig.

Designed by HARRY FORD.

This book was printed and bound by Kingsport Press, Incorporated, Kingsport, Tennessee.